D0679254

THREADING MY WAY

THREADING MY WAY

AN AUTOBIOGRAPHY

BY

ROBERT DALE OWEN

[1874]

REPRINTS OF ECONOMIC CLASSICS

AUGUSTUS M. KELLEY · PUBLISHERS
NEW YORK · 1967

First Edition 1874

(New York: G. W. Carleton & Co., *Publishers*, 1874)

Reprinted 1967 by

AUGUSTUS M. KELLEY · PUBLISHERS

LIBRARY OF CONGRESS CATALOGUE CARD NUMBER

67 - 18582

PRINTED IN THE UNITED STATES OF AMERICA
by SENTRY PRESS, NEW YORK, N. Y. 10019

Twenty-seven Years of Autobiography.

THREADING MY WAY.

BY

ROBERT DALE OWEN,

AUTHOR OF

"THE DEBATABLE LAND BETWEEN THIS WORLD AND THE NEXT,"

AND OF

"FOOTFALLS ON THE BOUNDARY OF ANOTHER WORLD."

"Que faites-vous là, seul et rêveur?"—
"Je m'entretiens avec moi-même."—
"Ah! prenez garde du péril extrême
De causer avec un flatteur."

NEW YORK:

G. W. Carleton & Co., Publishers.

LONDON: TRUBNER & CO.

M.DCCC.LXXIV.

TO

A DEAR FRIEND,

AT WHOSE PLEASANT HOME ON LAKE GEORGE PART OF THESE
PAGES WERE WRITTEN,

MISS LOTTIE WALTON KELLOGG,

THEY ARE

INSCRIBED.

A WORD TO THE READER.

IT was at the suggestion of my friend, Mr. W. D. Howells, to whose able leadership the Atlantic Monthly owes much of its well-earned popularity, that these papers were written as a serial for his Magazine. I owe to him many pleasant, and I hope profitable hours, since a calm retrospect, at an advanced age, of past hopes, labors, errors, experiences, can never be without its use.

If the public, passing these in review, finds itself under similar obligation to Mr. Howells, I shall be glad that I was invited to a task which, till he incited, I had not thought of undertaking.

R. D. O.

TABLE OF CONTENTS.

————•••————

of over-zealous teachings.—A confession.—The old enigma.—
Become a Universalist.

PAGE

fencing-master and his visitor.—Our annual Excursions on foot
throughout Switzerland and into Italy.—The Simplon.—Lakes
Maggiore, Lugano, Como.—Carlo Borromeo : ascension into the
head of his colossal statue,—Charm of these excursions.—Met
our quondam Master of the Goats in Naples.—I owe to my life
at Hofwyl an abiding faith in human virtue and social progress.

PART 6.—A GERMAN BARON AND ENGLISH REFORMERS......... 176

Departure from Hofwyl and a pleasant reminiscence from my College
life.—Down the Rhine.—Dannecker's studio and colossal statue
of Christ.—Luxury of lazily floating past scenery which, with its
romantic accessories, is hardly equalled in the world.—Desolation
caused by French rule.—Spires, Mannheim, Coblentz.—Visit to
Baron von Münchhausen.—His charming daughters.—A family
banquet " unter den Linden."—The Baron's patriarchal kindness to dependants.—Hamburg.—A Scotchman mistaken for a
Hanoverian.—Dangers of a tempestuous voyage.—Robert Owen's
waning popularity.—His early successes and later mistakes.—
Meetings at the City of London Tavern.—Sweeping denunciation
of all religions.—Loses caste with the upper classes, but retains
his influence over the people.—My first book.—It procures me an
introduction to Jeremy Bentham.—Invitation to his *symposium*.—
A utilitarian philosopher at seventy-eight.—John Neal and Henry
Brougham.—William Godwin at seventy.—Portrait of Mary
Wollstonecraft.—Left manager at New Lanark.

PAPER 7.—EDUCATING A WIFE............................. 210

Society at Braxfield.—Two dashing Milesians.—Lord Edward Fitz-
gerald and his daughters.—Sir Guy Campbell falls in love.—Jessie.
—Her beauty and grace.—What made me a regular church-goer.—
Anne Owen.—Her letter to my father favorably answered.—
Jessie's progress at Braxfield.—I narrowly escape detection.—
To love or to be loved, which is best?—Sequel to my experiment.
A mother's counsel followed, and with what result.—A marriage
and a meeting in after years.—Parting.—Two Irish love stories.—
Mr. Becher and Miss O'Neill.—Love no respecter of ages.

PAPER 8.—THE SOCIAL EXPERIMENT AT NEW HARMONY....... 239

George Rapp and associates.—Their pecuniary success.—Robert
Owen purchases from them New Harmony.—The village as he

needs intermeddle, in the way of Reform.—But here ends the First
Portion of my life ; its tentative Years, in which I was threading
my way.—Much important moral and spiritual Knowledge, underlying human Civilization, then a sealed book to me.—My future
life destined to be a public one, active and stirring.

INDEX.

——:o:——

THREADING MY WAY.

"Que faites-vous là, seul et rêveur?" —
"Je m'entretiens avec moi-même."—
"Ah! prenez garde du péril extrême
De causer avec un flatteur."

PAPER I.

MY ANCESTORS.

IN the winter of 1858–59 I was threading the streets of Glasgow, Scotland, seeking the residence of an old friend, formerly my father's confidential clerk, and who still, though an octogenarian, rejoiced in the name of John Wright, Junior.

It was a portion of the city that had grown up many years after I had known anything of Glasgow. Uncertain of my way, and having for some time scrutinized the countenances of the passers-by, as is my wont before accosting any one in the street, I met a face that pleased me: hale, ruddy, the shadow of some sixty years resting lightly and cheerfully upon it, despite the snow on head and beard: a benignant face, of leisure, that did not look as if it would grudge five minutes to a stranger. It lit up kindly when I asked how I should find the street I sought.

"I am going in that direction, and shall be glad to walk with you." Then, after a pause: "You'll be a stranger in Glasgow?" The well-known accent and the turn of phrase brought all my youth back to me; and, in reply to my smile, he added: "Or are you a Scotchman yourself, may be?"

"I scarcely know," I replied, "whether to call myself a stranger or not. It is more than thirty years since I have seen your city, yet Glasgow is my native place."

"Ah! In what part of the city were you born?"

"In Charlotte Street."

"Were you? But in which house was it?"

"In the last house on the right hand, next to the Green; close to the iron gates that used to close the street."

"Why, man! That was David Dale's house! How in the world did you happen to be born there?"

"Very naturally. I am his grandson."

"An Owen, then?"

"Yes."

He stretched out his hand; and the firm, Scottish grip made my fingers tingle.

David Dale was a remarkable man; and he lived and labored through a busy and prosperous life, during a remarkable period of time. He witnessed, and did his part in aiding, the world's first Titanic steps in Industrial Science.

Born in Ayrshire and in the year 1738, in humble circumstances; educated, as all children of reputable parents throughout Scotland even then were, in a strictly disciplined public school; he evinced, even while at work as a journeyman weaver, what became afterwards his chief characteristic,—expending regularly a portion of his scanty wages in relieving his poorer neighbors. With the steady perseverance of his country he gradually won his way to riches and position ; so that, ere he had much passed middle age, he was already a wealthy merchant and bank director.

When nearly forty he won the hand of Miss Ann Caroline Campbell, daughter of John Campbell, who, having been, during the rebellion of 1745, Cashier of the Royal Bank of Scotland, got together a body of still loyal troops, conveyed the specie belonging to his bank to the castle of Edinburgh which held out against the Pretender ; and so, saved to the government a large amount of funds. This John Campbell came of a noted family and had a romantic history : his grandfather being a Scotch earl.

John Campbell of Glenorchy, born 1635, and created first Earl of Breadalbane in 1681, was (according to Nisbet) a man of sagacity, judgment, and penetration.* He aided King Charles II., and sought to induce Monk to declare for a free Parliament. He served in Parliament for the shire of Argyll, and was privy councillor under James II.

When King William had unsuccessfully endeavored to reduce the Highlands, Breadalbane undertook it singly with twelve thousand pounds ; and " effected it in such a manner as to obtain the thanks of James for saving his people whom he could not succor." †

Being accused of complicity in the massacre of Glencoe, the Parliament, in 1695, instituted a process of high treason against him; he was committed prisoner to

* Douglas, Peerage of Scotland, p. 238.　† Ibid, p. 230.

Edinburgh castle, but afterwards released without trial ;
it is said because no evidence was found against him.

Macky, a contemporary, says of him, probably not
without reason : " It is odds, if he lives long enough, but
he is a duke : he is of a fair complexion, and has the
gravity of a Spaniard, is as cunning as a fox, wise as
a serpent, and slippery as an eel." *

He died in 1716; and had, by his wife, the Lady Mary
Rich, daughter of the first Earl of Holland,—

1. Duncan, Lord Ormelie.
2. John, second Earl of Breadalbane.
3. The Honorable Colin Campbell, of Ardmaddie.

For this Colin Campbell, who was my great-great-
grandfather, I have a far greater respect—with ample
reason, I think—than I could ever entertain for that
cold-blooded father of his, even if the complicity of the
latter in the shocking affair of Glencoe had never been
surmised.   The son, who was an officer in the Life
Guards, seems, indeed, neither to have had the gravity
nor the cunning nor the worldly wisdom of his ancestor ;
but to have possessed instead, inherited perhaps from
his mother, the richer qualities of the heart.

At all events this Colin, true to his pastoral name,
fell desperately in love with a Miss Fisher, the handsome daughter of a respectable farmer living on his
father's estate.   If he had seduced and deserted her, it
would no doubt have been passed over, as a mere pec-
cadillo, to be expected in the career of any young noble of that day.   But he committed that unpardonable
sin, for which we have no appropriate word—not having yet learned (thank God !) to consider it a sin—but

* Macky's Memoirs, p. 199.

which the French call a *mésalliance*.   So far as one can, judge of the facts at this distance of time, he was irregularly, but, according to Scottish law, legally married to one whom the old father no doubt contemptuously set down as " a peasant hussy."   And the culprit the son of one Earl and grandson of another !   Very shocking, of course !

The young officer tried to obtain the recognition of his bride by his parents ; and when his request was met by a haughty refusal, he left his native country ; residing, when off duty, in a French seaport ; and continuing to live with his wife until his death, which occurred (at the age of twenty-nine) in 1708.   He left one child only, whom its parents named after the grandfather, who persisted in ignoring its existence.   Breadalbane died eight years after he lost his youngest son ; but whether he ever repented driving that son into exile to gratify family pride, does not appear.

At a later period the widow and her son brought suit to procure the acknowledgment of the marriage and the recovery of her husband's property.   The terms upon which this suit was finally compromised sufficiently indicate the light in which the Breadalbanes regarded the matter.   The family paid over to the claimants thirty thousand pounds ; a sum which, taking into account the difference in the value of money now, and then, is to-day the equivalent of three or four hundred thousand dollars.   But neither the mother's name nor the son's appears in the British Peerage ; and it may probably have been a condition of the compromise that this point should not be pressed.   A wise woman, that peasant ancestress of mine !   She accepted the substantial ; and refrained from insisting on reception by a family who imagined they had a right to look down upon her.

John Campbell—the Cashier, not the Earl—did well in the world. He married Lady Stirling of Glorit; and when she died without issue, contracted a second marriage with Miss Campbell of Tofts, by whom he had five children. Of these, General Colin Campbell, afterwards Lieutenant-Governor of Gibraltar, was one, and my grandmother, Ann Caroline Campbell, another. Upon her seem to have descended the charms which may have led captive the Life Guardsman; for my grandmother Campbell was noted throughout Scotland as one of the most beautiful women of her day; though she failed, unfortunately, to transmit her fair looks to her grandchildren of the Owen branch.

David Dale's marriage with this lady was, as I have always heard, a most harmonious union; and, in every respect save its comparatively brief duration, a happy one. She died when her eldest child, my mother, was about twelve years old; and upon that child devolved thenceforth the care of a widowed father and four younger sisters; a charge the duties of which she fulfilled with a devotion and prudence beyond her years.

But David Dale himself, and his connection with the marvellous events of his time, are better worth writing about than his wife's relatives or their fortunes.

George III. succeeded to the British throne in 1760, and it was the lot of that weak sovereign to witness, during his sixty years' rule, a succession of inventions and discoveries such as was never before crowded into the reign of earthly monarch. They revolutionized the producing powers of man.

Though the expansive force of steam was understood, and even mechanical effects were produced by its agency, before the Christian era, yet when George became king, the steam-engine proper was unknown. Watt was at work upon it in 1765, and patented his invention in 1768–69.

So, again, when George ascended the throne, the foundation of all textile fabrics—that is, thread, whether woollen, cotton, linen, or silk—was spun on the single wheel ; the same of which the hum is still to be heard in some of the cabins of the West : * the spinner, with utmost exertion, producing but a few hanks by a day's labor. Ere he died that same king, had he passed through his British dominions, might have found nearly half a million engaged, in vast factories, in spinning and manufacturing cotton ; each spindle turning out, on the average, some three hundred times as much yarn as before.

In 1771 the first cotton-mill—a small one, worked by horse-power—was built. Eleven years later Arkwright had four or five thousand persons employed in various mills, though his patents were still contested. He sought partnerships with capitalists ; they furnishing

---

* The ancient emblems of female industry, the distaff and spindle, have been in use certainly more than three thousand years. At what period these were superseded in India by the spinning-wheel is not on record : but four hundred years ago the spinning-wheel was unknown in Europe, having first been used by English workmen in the reign of Henry VIII. For thirty centuries (and how many more we know not) the invention of the world found nothing better wherewith to manufacture thread than a small wooden wheel impelled by the foot on a treadle, and giving motion by a cord or belt to a single spindle. And now ! A century since it would have required the manual labor of one third the population of the world to supply as much cotton yarn as is turned out to-day by the cotton-mills of Great Britain alone.

the money and he contributing his right to use his cot-
ton-machinery. In 1782 my grandfather and he had entered into such a partnership ; the waters of the Clyde,*
about thirty miles above Glasgow, to be used as motive
power.

In 1784 a village and several large cotton-mills were
completed. The site was a strip of valley land adjoining the river, about a mile from the ancient town of
Lanark : and the entire waters of the Clyde, brought
through a rock-tunnel a thousand feet long, formed the
mill-race.

Then, for the first time, Arkwright (not yet Sir
Richard) came to Scotland, to visit the new manufac-
tory. Taking a post-chaise from Glasgow, Mr. Dale
and he reached the summit of a hill which commanded
a view of the village, and on the gentle slopes of which
were laid out small garden spots, separated by gravel
paths. It was a fine summer evening. Getting out of
the carriage, Mr. Dale led his partner to a favorable
point, whence could be seen not only the entire establishment, including the vast factory buildings, the mechanics' shops, the school-house, and the rows of stone
dwellings for the work-people, but also the picturesque
river winding its way below the mills between abrupt
walls of shrub-covered rocks, the landscape bounded
by a beautiful champaign country stretching out on the
other bank. Well do I remember the scene !

"How does it suit you ? " my grandfather asked at
length.

Arkwright scanned the whole with a critical business

---

* The most important river of Scotland, passing by Lanark, Hamilton,
Bothwell, and Glasgow; and terminating at Greenock, in the great est-
uary known as the Frith of Clyde.

eye for some time before he answered : " Capital ! That site was selected with great judgment."

" You like the way the streets are laid out and the mill buildings placed ? "

" Very well—couldn't be better."

" Each family in the village has one of these garden patches."

" A very good idea."

" We had to tunnel the rock for a long distance at a heavy expense ; but we gained a fall of twenty-six or twenty-eight feet."

" It's a spot in a thousand," cried Arkwright. " Might have been made on purpose."

" I'm glad you like it."

" I do, very much." Then, after another long look over the village and all its surroundings, he added, pointing to a wooden cupola within which the factory bell was hung : " But that ugly steeple—or whatever it is— what made you put it off at the end of the building ? "

" Why, where would you have it ? "

" Over the middle of the mill, of course."

" I don't see any ' of course ' about it. It's just right where it is."

" You think so ? " asked Arkwright.

" To be sure I do, or I wouldn't have put it there."

" Well, you've a curious idea of things. I'd like to hear a single good reason for having the thing stuck on to the end of that mill, the way you've got it."

" If a man's so blind he can't see that was the proper place, it is na worth while finding him reasons for it."

" Blind ! A man with half an eye might have seen better. I don't care to argue with a man that hasn't more common-sense."

This was too much for my grandfather. " Arkwright," said he, "*I* don't care to have a man for a partner who would get stirred up anent such a trifle, and talk such nonsense about it too."

" Neither do I.   So there's one thing we do agree about.   I'm ready to sell out to you to-night."

" Good !   Let's get into the carriage and I'll show you all over the place.   Then we'll go back to the auld town " (so Lanark was usually called), " get something to eat and a glass of toddy,"—(my grandfather was a strictly temperate man, but no Scotchman in those days thought an occasional glass of Highland whiskey toddy an offence against temperance),—" and I dare say we can hit it off atween us."

That evening Richard Arkwright and David Dale dissolved partnership, the latter remaining sole proprietor of the village and mills of New Lanark.*

If such an issue in so important a matter seem strange, it was yet natural enough in the case of men born and circumstanced as these men had been.   Successful strugglers both, through difficulty and opposition up to great success, accustomed as both had been, from their youth, to take their own way and to find that way the fortunate one, they had become unused to contradiction.   Men of strong, untrained energy, they had grown to be self-willed even in petty things.

Their success in life, however, was not wholly due to character and abilities.   The lines had fallen to them in wondrous places.   They were pioneer workers in the

* This anecdote, which I have heard many times from my father's lips, was confirmed to me, in all its essential particulars, by Mr. John Wright, during the visit to him referred to at the commencement of this chapter.

richest mine ever opened to human enterprise. It had not entered into the heart of man to conceive the physical results that were to follow a contrivance simple almost to commonplace : consisting, substantially, in the substitution of rollers, driven by machinery, for the human hand. That invention determined the fate of nations. Coupled with the modern application of steam, it was mainly instrumental in deciding the giant struggle between England and the first Napoleon.

The soft fleece of the cotton-plant is peculiar in character. When freed from seeds and impurities, its fine, strong fibres slip past each other readily, and can, with facility, be arranged so as to lie in parallel lines. In the earliest days the Hindoo, holding in his left hand a staff around one end of which was wrapped a portion of the vegetable fleece, drew out, with forefinger and thumb moist and delicate, and then deftly twisted, the thread. After tens of centuries Arkwright substituted, for human forefinger and thumb, two sets of rollers, revolving with unequal velocity : the lower roller of each pair fluted longitudinally, the upper covered with leather. This gave them a sufficient hold of the cotton as it passed between them.

The space between the two pairs of rollers was made somewhat greater than the length of the cotton fibre. The back pair, which received the cotton in the form of a band or ribbon, revolved much more slowly than the front pair which delivered it. The effect was that, at the moment when this cotton ribbon was released from the grasp of the back pair of rollers, the front pair, because of their greater velocity, exerted upon it a slight, steady pull. The result of this was twofold: first to straighten out the fibres left crooked or double in the carding ;

secondly, to elongate the line of cotton presented to the
action of these rollers, and thus diminish its calibre. In
other words, the front pair of rollers drew the cotton out,
as the finger and thumb, pulling on the contents of the
distaff, had done ; but with far more rapidity and regularity than human fingers ever attained. This process
was repeated through three machines, and the cotton
band was thus reduced in thickness by successive atten-
uations, and was then loosely twisted in long, cylindrical
revolving cans (made into *rovings*, the mill phrase was).
By the front rollers of the last of these machines, usually
called a *throstle-frame*, the cotton-cord was drawn out
to the calibre or fineness of the thread to be produced ;
and underneath these rollers were stationary spindles
(revolving with much greater velocity than the spindle of
the cottager's wheel had done) on which the hard-twisted
thread was finally wound.*

In this way, by an expedient so simple that a child
may, at a glance, comprehend its operation, each set of
four rollers, thus arranged in pairs, took the place of a

---

* It need hardly be said, except to those who have never entered a cotton
factory or read the details of its operations, that, by an antecedent process,
the raw cotton, after being cleansed and having its matted locks loosened
and opened, and after being passed over cylindrical cards, whence it came
out a thin broad sheet, was drawn together, converging into the continuous,
soft, untwisted cord, or rather thick ribbon, of which I have above
spoken.

Because the yarn made on the throstle-frame had a much harder twist
than it had been possible to give it by the treadle of the old spinning-
wheel, it was found that it could be fitly used for warp, for which, up to
Arkwright's time, the weaver had been compelled to employ linen thread
alone. This was a great advance.

I pass over the question whether thread-making by two sets of rollers
was, originally, Arkwright's invention. We know that it was he who first
brought that wonderful adaptation into practical operation.

human being; the metallic fingers, however, working much faster than those of flesh had done. The inanimate spinner, set in his frame, with a hundred other similar workmen ranged in rank beside him, turned out in a day several times the length of thread which the most diligent house-wife, toiling at her solitary spinning-wheel from morning till night, had been able to produce.

And each company of these *automata* had, for its leader or captain, not an adult, female or male, but a child, perhaps ten or twelve years old. The urchin learned to direct the ranks of his subordinates with unfailing skill. He noted their shortcomings, corrected their blunders, supplied their deficiencies. If some thick, rough portion of yarn escaped the iron lips, he caught and excluded it. If one of his *automata* suffered a thread to break, the child's quick eye detected it, and his deft fingers mended it (*pieced* it, as the mill phrase was) on the instant.

Thus a tiny superintendent, boy or girl, took the place of a multitude of adult work-people. Myself at the age of twenty-three superintending a manufacturing establishment where some fifteen hundred operatives were employed, I had a thousand opportunities to witness the skill and fidelity with which these child-rulers acquitted themselves. I found that each one of them, aided by the magical rollers, was even then producing as much, in any given time, as two hundred cottage spinners had done before Arkwright's day.

It need hardly be said that, during the first years of such an industrial revolution, the profits, in large establishments, after making allowance for imperfect machinery and other accidents incident to every new scheme, were very great. The prices then obtained seem to us now incredible. Yarn, of a quality which in 1815 was sold for three shillings a pound, brought, in the infancy of the manufacture, as high as thirty shillings. The " British mulled muslins" which, when first manufactured, were eagerly bought up by the rich at two dollars and a half a yard, are now offered to the poor—of less durable quality, however—for six cents a yard !

The population of New Lanark in 1784 was upwards of seventeen hundred, of whom several hundred were orphan children, from seven to twelve years of age; these being procured from the poor-houses of various parishes. It was, I believe, the largest cotton-spinning establishment at that time in Great Britain; employing about a thousand work-people. The orphan children were comfortably cared for, and but moderately worked; and they attended evening-school after the labor of the day was over.

My grandfather remained sole proprietor for thirteen years; that is, until 1797. He sought to make money, of course, as all business men do; but, according to the testimony of his contemporaries, he was not willing to do so at expense of the comfort of his work-people. Many of the manufacturers of that day, urged by the dazzling prospects of fabulous profits, became cruel taskmasters; demanding from children exertions which even from adults ought never to have been exacted. But David Dale was not one of those who, for gain, lay upon their fellows burdens grievous and heavy to be borne. A tourist, visiting New Lanark in 1796, thus describes its condition :—

" Mr. Dale deserves well of his country, dispensing happiness and comfort to many of his fellow-creatures by his attention not only to their health, but to their

morals; training them up in habits of industry, instruct-
ing them in the necessary branches of education, and
instilling into their minds a knowledge of the important
truths of Christianity. Four hundred children are entirely fed, clothed, and instructed at the expense of this
venerable philanthropist. The rest live with their
parents in neat comfortable habitations, receiving wages
for their labor. The health and happiness depicted
on the countenances of these children show that the
proprietor of the Lanark Mills has remembered mercy in
the midst of gain. The regulations here to preserve
health of body and mind present a striking contrast to
those of most large manufactories in this kingdom, the
very hotbeds of disease and contagion. It is a truth
that ought to be engraved in letters of gold, to the eternal honor of the founder of New Lanark, that out of
nearly three thousand children who have been at work
in these mills throughout a period of twelve years, only
fourteen have died and not one has suffered criminal
punishment." *

The character of the man is well illustrated by an
incident which occurred I know not at what precise
date, but some years after the New Lanark mills were
in full operation, and when their owner already
saw what a large fortune he was reaping from Arkwright's patent. One of the principal factory buildings
was destroyed by fire, throwing some two hundred and
fifty persons out of employment. As soon as the news
reached Mr. Dale at Glasgow where he then was, he
hastened to the spot and found the work-people lamenting their hard fate, and expecting to be turned adrift

* Life of Robert Owen. Philadelphia, 1866; pp. 61, 62.

at once.   He caused them to assemble in the principal
school-room, and when he rose to speak many of them
shed tears.   After pausing to control his own emotion,
he said,—the Scottish idiom mixing in, as it always did
in familiar talk with his own countrymen, especially
when much moved,—

"Dinna greet, my children.   You've helped me
to muckle siller by your labor ; and I can weel afford
to spend some of it in taking care of you till that mill's
built up and started.   You shall bide where you are
till then.   I'll employ as many of you as I can in clear-
ing off the rubbish and other jobs.   But I'll pay you all
the same wages you've had till now.   And be gude
bairns till ye can go to work again.   The Deil finds
mischief, ye ken, for idle hands to do."

It was long ere the mill was rebuilt and refitted ; for
the construction of the new machinery, in those days,
was a very tedious process, the demand exceeding the
supply.   Between twenty and thirty thousand dollars
were expended before the people were again at work.
I can well understand how the villagers, even in my
day, had preserved the memory of my grandfather's
very words, and were wont to speak of " gude David
Dale " as the best man the sun ever shone upon.

From my father's autobiography we learn that Mr.
Dale was very religious, being at the head of a sect of
"Independents" ; that he had charge of about forty
churches in different parts of Scotland, and preached
every Sunday to his congregation in Glasgow.*   These
Independents were an order of Presbyterians, who,
conscientiously believing that the Word of God should

---

* Life of Robert Owen, written by himself.   London, 1857 ; p. 71.

be taught to men without money and without price, gave their pastors no salary nor other remuneration. Their preachers, in consequence, followed secular occupations; some, like my grandfather, being merchants or manufacturers; some, members of various professions; while others, in humbler position, labored, like Paul, with their hands. But after my grandfather's death the sect over which he had presided fell off; the doctrine embodied in a well-known text prevailing in spiritual matters; namely, that " the laborer is worthy of his hire."

Strict Presbyterianism was my grandfather's belief, to the day of his death. But the abundant geniality of the man saved him from the intolerance, and the harshness towards offenders, which often ally themselves with such a creed. My father, who knew him intimately for years, and who was himself, even then, outspoken in his heresies, testifies to his father-in-law's unfailing good temper. He says: " Mr. Dale was one of the most liberal, conscientious, benevolent, and kind-hearted men I ever met with through my life: one universally respected for his simplicity and straightforward honesty of character. . . . From my marriage to his death he and I never exchanged one unpleasant expression or unkind word. Yet our religious opinions were widely different, and we distinctly knew this difference." * My father mentions, also, that Mr. Dale was wont to close their frequent discussions kindly and affectionately, with some such expression as "Thou needest be very right, for thou art very positive," which was doubtless quite true.

A trifling tradition, current in the family, illustrates

* Autobiography, pp. 71, 72.

his good-natured mode of dealing with sinners. Passing down the garden behind his house in Charlotte Street, early one morning, he discovered, crouched behind a large gooseberry-bush, a man with a bag evidently half filled with what in that country is a favorite fruit. Mr. Dale stepped quietly up to him, laid his hand on his shoulder, and—adopting a friendly Scottish mode of address toward one of inferior rank—asked : " Honest man, what are ye aboot there ? " The culprit, confounded, stammered out some apology about his being very hungry, to which my grandfather replied : " Aweel, tak the berries and gang yer way ; but think o' yer soul, man, and steal nae mair." A lad, who chanced to be in the vicinity, overheard and repeated this conversation ; and when the story got wind, David Dale's notion of an " *honest* man " excited many a smile among the friends who loved him.

Like most of his countrymen he had a quick sense of the ludicrous, and keenly enjoyed a joke, even at his own expense. One fine winter morning—being then advanced in years and having become quite corpulent, especially around the waist—he appeared in his business office in St. Andrew's Square, his clothes bespattered with snow.

" Hae the bairns been snowballing ye, Mr. Dale ? " laughingly asked an old friend who had been awaiting his arrival.

" Hoot no," replied my grandfather ; " but it's slippery, and I just fell doon on the sma' " (small) " of my back."

" Weel, that's news to me, auld friend," rejoined the other ; " I never kenned afore that ye *had* a sma' to yer back."

When my grandfather came home to the family dinner that day, he repeated the jest with great glee.

He was generous to the poor, almost to a fault; "giving away," my father says, "large sums, often in mistaken charities." * My mother estimated that he must have expended for benevolent purposes, in the course of his life, more than a hundred thousand dollars.

Such a man—rich but open-handed, determined yet tender, sturdily upright but merciful to those who went astray, eminently religious yet feeling kindly toward those who differed from him in opinion, simple, humorous, familiar with all, high and low—was just the character to be appreciated by his countrymen. There were more distinguished men in Scotland, toward the close of the last century, than David Dale; but not one, perhaps, more generally loved. His townsmen mourned his death, which occurred in 1806, as a public calamity; and every shop in Glasgow was closed on the day of his funeral.

That funeral is, of all my childish recollections, one of the earliest and most distinct. I was then between four and five years old, for I was born November 7, 1801; and, as usually happens as to events dating from such an age, things important and unimportant retain their places with equal persistence. The coming from the tailor's of a suit of black, the unprecedented fact that I was hurriedly dressed in it the moment it arrived; the stream of visitors, the unexampled stir in the house and the vast assemblage around it; the show, the carriages, and the interminable procession; the long

---

* Autobiography, p. 71.

walk, with my hand in my father's, just behind the
hearse ; the crowds along every street as we passed on
—all remain vividly stamped on my memory, as if of
yesterday.   A more dim reminiscence is of my grandfather himself; his gold-headed cane ; his portly form
filling the large easy chair ; then the hand on my head
and the face lighted up with kindness—the nicest face, I
thought, in the world—that always welcomed me when
I was brought to see him and talk with him in the parlor after dinner.

The next event that comes in lifelike traits before me,
dating about a year later, is a visit to Rosebank, my
grandfather's country-seat on the banks of the Clyde,
some four miles above Glasgow.   It was occupied, at
that time, by four maiden aunts, who vied with each
other in efforts to spoil their eldest nephew—not without success.

The sky-born charm that hallows certain familiar
spots is a current phrase, not always meaning much.
But the strange glamour under which my young eyes
regarded what then seemed veritable fairy-land—the
quaint, old-fashioned mansion, with its honeysuckle-
shaded porch, its pointed gables, its dormer-windows,
the sunk area that surrounded it like a moat, its unexpected nooks and corners, and its perfume of migno-
nette from boxes set in window-sills ; then the marvellous garden in front, with its succession of terraces, its
gigantic evergreen hedges, its enigmatical sun-dial, its
wonderful bowling green, and its wilderness of roses,
with a thousand unknown flowers beside ; again, off to
the left, the long, dim, pleached avenue of venerable
beeches, with a ha-ha stone fence on one side, whence
a spacious lawn swept down to the river-bank ; then,

farther off beyond the garden, a mysteriously shaded winding road that led down, through a dark valley, to another part of the Clyde—the inexplicable glamour, I say, which invested all this, made the place, for me, an abode of bliss apart from the real world : its trees, its flowers, its mystical paths, all its accessories and its surroundings, like none other upon earth ; instinct with vague fancies, feelings, obscure emotions, the like of which I may realize in the next world, but have never found since in this.

There was, too, an element of wonder, rising to awe, that intervened among gentler excitements. A mile or more distant and on the opposite side of the river loomed up the " Clyde Iron Works," a large establishment with extensive foundries and rolling-mills. Its fires never went out ; and the red flames that shot from its tall chimneys lit up, with lurid glare, the night landscape. I had never seen or heard of anything like it ; I had no distinct idea what was going on there ; and, when I gazed on it through the darkness, the scene called up the pictures which my good mother had deemed it her duty to set before me, of a burning hell. Fancy peopled its mysterious regions of fire and smoke with grim, swart, unearthly figures, like the demons I had been told of, as inhabiting the Brimstone Lake.

But these visions vanished when day dawned on my fairy-world. All was rose-hued then.

What influence a brief episode in my life at Rosebank may have had in coloring its day-dreams I cannot tell ; nor whether the incident itself was due to impulses inherited, in somewhat precocious phrase, from my ancestor, the Life Guardsman. I had wandered off alone, one sunny day, into the shady Beach Walk, some dis-

tance from the house.   There I met a certain little maid,
a stray from a neighboring farm-house (five past, she
told me, her last birthday), very neatly dressed in tartan, and, to my thinking, the prettiest creature my eyes
had ever seen.   We were soon well acquainted, walking
up and down the ancient avenue, as older lovers no
doubt had done before us.   After a time it occurred to
us that we might be intruded on in so public a place.
Just back of the Beach Walk was a tall, thick hawthorn
hedge, in which we found a gap large enough for a
Newfoundland dog to creep through.   This admitted
us to a meadow in which the grass was nearly as high
as our heads, and there we found a charming resting-
place, where, day after day, we used to spend hours together; terribly afraid, at first, of being found out;
but finally gaining confidence in the verdant screen that
sheltered us.

If we had been readers of Campbell, we might have
called to mind that description of his (carped at by
Byron in one of his cynical moods) touching a seques-
tered spot " where transport and security entwine ; "
but I am not sure whether, at that time, the lines were
written.   My little love was somewhat coy at first ; but
after we had faithfully promised each other that we would
be married as soon as we " grew big," we came to an
excellent understanding, and had long talks about the
sort of house we were to have built, and the nice time
we were to have in it together when it was finished.

Our nest was never discovered ; and the birds singing
in the fragrant hedge near by were not more blithe-
hearted than we.   Our love was warm and honest, and
so were the tears we shed when at last, after a few weeks
—altogether too short weeks they were—our prospects

of domestic happiness were broken in upon, and I had to leave my land of enchantment for the workaday world at New Lanark—or rather at Braxfield, for that was then my father's residence.

Robert Owen, born in Newtown, North Wales, in 1771, was, like my grandfather, a self-made man. His specific plans, as a Social Reformer, proved, on the whole and for the time, a failure ; and this, for lack of cultivated judgment and critical research, and of accurate knowledge touching what men had thought and done before his time ; also because he strangely overrated the ratio of human progress ; but more especially, perhaps, because, until late in life, he ignored the spiritual element in man as the great lever of civilized advancement. Yet with such earnestness, such vigor, such indomitable perseverance, and such devotion and love for his race did he press, throughout half a century, these plans on the public, and so much practical truth was there, mixed with visionary expectation, that his name became known, and the influence of his teachings has been more or less felt, over the civilized world. A failure in gross has been attended by sterling incidental successes ; and toward the great idea of co-operation— quite impracticable, for the present at least, in the form he conceived it—there have been, even since his death, very considerable advances made, and generally recognized by earnest men as eminently useful and important.

His father, also named Robert Owen, seems originally to have been what used to be called a man of substance ; but having lost in a lawsuit—as he believed through bribery of the lawyer he employed—an estate worth five hundred pounds a year,* he afterwards made

* The probable equivalent, in our day, of five thousand dollars' rental.

a modest living in the saddlery and ironmongery business. Of his ancestors I know nothing save what my father has vaguely left on record in his Autobiography. He tells us that, at the age of nine, he was the daily companion of a young gentleman, ten years older than himself, Mr. James Donne, then studying at Oxford or Cambridge, for the church. The theological student afterwards became Dr. Donne of Oswestry, well known and highly respected for his learning and research. In 1817, when all England was stirred up by my father's public speeches to thousands at the City of London Tavern, Dr. Donne wrote to him stating that, in the course of his genealogical studies, he had traced my father's pedigree in regular descent, from the native princes of North Wales, and offering to send him particulars.* My father, at that time engrossed by the

---

* I fear the line may have run back to a certain truculent hero, sung by Gray (translating from Gwalchmai, the son of Melir) in the ode beginning :—

> " Owen's praise demands my song,
> Owen swift and Owen strong ;
> Fairest flower of Roderick's stem,
> Gwyneth's shield and Britain's gem,
> Lord of every regal art,
> Liberal hand and open heart."

The drawback is that this " dragon-son of Mona " was chiefly famed for his " wide-wasting sword " ; as the succeeding lines (describing a famous battle gained by him, in 1157, over the combined forces of Iceland, Denmark and Norway) indicate :—

> " Checked by the torrent-tide of blood,
> Backward Meinai rolls his flood ;
> While heaped, his master's feet around,
> Prostrate warriors gnaw the ground."

And, in the original, the concluding sentiment is : " And the glory of our Prince's wide-wasting sword shall be celebrated in a hundred languages, to give him praise."

Gwyneth is the ancient name for North Wales. Owen succeeded his father, Griffith ap Cynan, in the principality of North Wales, A.D. 1137.

exciting delusion that he was about suddenly to revolutionize society and reform the world, ' cared," Gallio-like, '' for none of these things," and overlooked the friendly offer. If the Doctor ever sent him a chart of the family tree, the matter has not come to my knowledge.

At the age of ten, his travelling expenses paid and ten dollars in his pocket, Robert Owen found himself in London, whither he had been sent, to the care of an elder brother, to '' push his fortune." Six weeks afterwards he obtained a situation as shopboy with an honest, kind Scotchman, Mr. James McGuffog, a linen-draper of Stamford, Lincolnshire, where he remained four years : the first year for board and lodging only ; afterwards with a salary added, of eight pounds the second year and a gradual increase thereafter,—an independence for the child, who thenceforth maintained himself. The labor was moderate, averaging eight hours a day. McGuffog was childless ; but he adopted a niece, two years younger than his Welsh apprentice ; and between the two children there grew up a warm friendship. When my father finally decided, at fourteen years of age, to return to London, he and the family parted with mutual regrets.

He then became salesman in the long-established haberdashery house of Flint and Palmer, on Old London Bridge. There he had twenty-five pounds a year, with board and lodging ; but he was occupied often till one or two o'clock in the morning, arranging and replacing goods, so that he was scarcely able to crawl, by aid of the balusters, up to bed. The details of the morning toilet I give in his own words : '' We were up, had breakfast, and were dressed to receive customers at eight; and dressing then was no slight affair. Boy as I was, I had to wait my turn for the hairdresser to powder and pomatum and curl my hair, —two large curls on each side and a stiff pigtail,—and until all this was nicely done, no one thought of presenting himself behind the counter." *

He endured this ceremonious slavery for half a year; then found another, easier situation, and a larger salary, with Mr. Satterfield, in Manchester, which he kept for four years and until he was between eighteen and nineteen.

His life, so far, had been passed entirely in subordinate positions; in which, however, he acquired habits of regulated industry, strict order, and persistent attention to business.

For a few months after this he was in partnership with a Mr. Jones, manufacturing cotton machinery. While. thus engaged, he received a cordial letter from his former master, McGuffog, now become old and wealthy, with a proposal, if Owen would join him in business, to supply all the capital and give him half the profits at once; and with the further intimation that he would surrender the entire establishment to him in a few years. It appears that the niece had conceived a childish attachment to her playmate, though the object of her affection did not discover that she had, till many years afterwards; and, perhaps, a knowledge of this may have influenced the uncle. " If I had accepted," says my father in his Autobiography, "I should most likely have married the niece, and lived and died a rich Stamford linen-draper." Why, then only nineteen years old, he refused an offer in every way so eligible,

* Autobiography, p. 19.

does not appear. If, as is probable, he then expected large profits from his present enterprise, he soon discovered his mistake ; separating from his partner, in whom he had lost confidence, after a few months, and taking, as his share of stock, three mule-machines only.

With these, however, he did well ; engaging three men to work them and superintending the business himself. He bought *rovings* at twelve shillings a pound and sold them, spun into thread, for twenty-two shillings ; thus gaining two dollars on each pound of yarn he turned out. At these rates the profits soon ran up to thirty dollars a week; a fact which lets one into the secret of the enormous fortunes then made in this business.

Some months passed, when one Monday morning he read an advertisement by a Mr. Drinkwater, a wealthy merchant and manufacturer, for a factory manager. A sudden impulse induced him to present himself, an applicant for the place.

" You are too young," was Mr. Drinkwater's curt objection.

" They used to object to me," said my father, " on that score four or five years ago ; but I did not expect to have it brought up now."

" Why, what age are you ? "

" I shall be twenty in May next."

" How often do you get drunk in the week ? "

My father blushed scarlet. " I never," he said indignantly, " was drunk in my life."

This seemed to produce a good impression. The next question was : " What salary do you ask ? "

" Three hundred a year" (that is, three hundred

pounds; as much as from two to three thousand dollars to-day).

" Three hundred a year ! Why, I've had I don't know how many after the place here, this morning ; and all their askings together wouldn't come up to what you want."

" Whatever others may ask, I cannot take less. I am making three hundred a year by my own business."

" Can you prove that to me ? "

" Certainly.   My books will show."

" I'll go with you, and you shall let me see them."

He inspected them, was so far satisfied ; and then my father referred him to Satterfield, McGuffog, and Flint and Palmer.

Ten days later Robert Owen was installed manager of what went by the name of the " Bank Top Mill." A raw youth, whose entire experience in the operations of cotton-spinning was limited to the running of three mules,—who had never entered a large factory in his life,—found himself suddenly at the head of five hundred work-people.   It might conceal his first blunders, but in reality it added to the difficulty of the position, that Mr. Lee, the working partner and a practical cotton-spinner, had just formed another business connection and deserted Mr. Drinkwater, who, though an experienced fustian manufacturer and a successful importing merchant, knew nothing practically of the new manufacture then coming into vogue.

It was the turning-point in my father's fortunes. There is not, probably, one young man in a thousand, coming suddenly to a charge so arduous and for which no previous training had fitted him, who would not have miscarried, and been dismissed ere a month had passed.

But Robert Owen had received from nature rare administrative capacity, large human sympathy, and a winning way with those he employed. For six weeks, he tells us, he went about the factory, looking grave ; saying little, but silently inspecting everything ; answering requests for instructions as laconically as possible, and giving no direct order in all that time ; at night studying Mr. Lee's notes and drawings of machinery. Then he took the reins, and so managed matters that in six months there was not, in Manchester, a more orderly or better-disciplined factory. He had gained the goodwill of employer and work-people ; and had greatly improved the quality and reputation of the Bank Top yarn. He had also become an excellent judge of cotton ; and, early in 1791, he bought, from a Mr. Robert Spear, the two first bags of American Sea Island cotton ever imported into England.

Then, one day, Mr. Drinkwater sent for him to his country residence. He describes his feelings when he received the unexpected invitation. "An ill-educated, awkward youth," he calls himself ; "alive to his defects of education ; speaking ungrammatically a sort of Welsh-English ; sensitive among strangers and dissatisfied with his own speaking and acting when in company : then also painfully subject to blushing, which no effort of his could prevent." * (His eldest son, Robert Dale, inherited in full both bashfulness and ungovernable blushing ; but I have bravely got over the first ; and though I have not lost the habit of blushing, it is in moderation and no longer with painful consciousness.)

Mr. Drinkwater had an offer to make to his young manager,—a salary of four hundred pounds for the sec-

* Autobiography, p. 31.

ond year, five hundred for the third ; after that, a partnership with himself and his two sons, with a fourth of
the profits.   It was gratefully accepted, and the contract
signed ere they parted.

It was during the period of this contract that my
father, boarding in Brazen Nose Street, Manchester, at
the same house as Robert Fulton, of steamboat celebrity, became intimate with that inventor, then much
straightened for means.   He advanced to Fulton, at various times, to aid the " project of running boats independent of locks," the sum of a hundred and seventy
pounds.   Of this the other repaid him sixty pounds in
1797 ; but was never able to acquit the remainder of the
debt.

The contract with Drinkwater was never fulfilled.
Before the third year closed there was a new son-in-law,
who wished to take my father's place as partner.   Mr.
Drinkwater offered any salary that my father might
name as manager, if the partnership was waived.   In
reply, my father, who had his contract with him, thrust
it into the fire, saying : " I desire no partnership in any
case where it is unwelcome ; but I decline to continue
manager."   And all Mr. Drinkwater could obtain from
him was a promise to remain till some one else could be
found to fill his place.

But by this time my father's name was up as one of
the best fine-cotton spinners in England, and offers of
partnership flowed in upon him.   He finally connected
himself, in the spring of 1797, with two rich and long-
established firms, Borrodaile and Atkinson of London
and the Bartons of Manchester, under the name of the
" Chorlton Twist Company."   Soon after, business took
him to Scotland ; and there, both as regards his domes-

tic life and his future career, public and private, he met
his fate.

A sister of the Robert Spear above mentioned happened, at that time, to be on a visit to my grandfather;
and my father, walking near the Cross of Glasgow one
day, met and recognized her. She introduced him to a
young lady who was with her, Miss Ann Caroline Dale,
David Dale's eldest daughter; and, turning, he walked
with the ladies some distance. Miss Dale and the young
cotton-spinner seem to have been mutually attracted
from the first. She offered him an introduction to her
uncle, then manager of her father's establishment at
New Lanark; suggesting, at the same time, that the
Falls of Clyde, a mile or two beyond the mill, were well
worth seeing. The offer was eagerly accepted, and the
lady then added that, when he had made the trip, she
would be glad to hear from him how he liked it.

Of course he called, on his return to Glasgow, to render thanks for her kindness. Fortune favored the young
people. Mr. Dale was absent; the morning was fine;
a walk in the "Green" (the park of Glasgow) was proposed, and my father accompanied Miss Dale and her
sisters to the banks of the Clyde. The young lady
dropped a hint—not quite as broad as Desdemona's—
that they would probably be walking there early next
day.

But "on this hint" my father, less adventurous than
Othello, spake not. He joined the party, indeed; but
the day after he returned to his snug bachelor quarters
at a country-house called Greenheys, near Manchester.

The standing and reputation of David Dale dismayed
him: not alone his wealth, his eminence as a manufacturer, his prominence as a popular preacher and boun-

teous philanthropist, his position as chief of the two
directors, in the Glasgow branch of the Royal Bank of
Scotland ; but, more than these, his former station as
one of the magistrates of Glasgow.

We of America are unfavorably situated, at this day,
to appreciate the exalted respect with which the magistrates of Scotland's chief cities were then regarded ;
and which, to a great extent, they have retained till
now.   During a week which I spent, in 1859, with
Robert Chambers, the well-known author and publisher,
at his Edinburgh residence, I questioned him closely as
to the manner in which the municipal affairs of the city
were conducted.   His replies surprised me.   " I have
never," he said, " heard even a suspicion whispered, af-
fecting the unblemished integrity of our city magistrates.
There is not a man who would dare approach one of
them with any offer or suggestion touching official action inconsistent with the strictest honor.   He would
know that, if he did, he might expect to have a servant
rung for, and bidden to show him into the street."

" And the contracts," I asked, " by the City Coun-
cils, as for building, street alterations, and the like,—
how are they managed ? "

" With better judgment, and more economy, it is
generally admitted, than the average of contracts by
private individuals."

" Who are these incorruptible men ?   What are their
antecedents ? "

" Usually gentlemen who have made large fortunes
here; eminent merchants or manufacturers, or others
who have retired, perhaps, from active business, and
who consider it the crowning glory of their lives to take
place among the magistracy of Edinburgh."

I must have smiled sadly, I suppose, for Chambers asked : " You are thinking of New York and some others of your own cities, with their universal suffrage ? "

" Yes."

But my father was thinking of a Glasgow magistrate, such as held office toward the close of the last century ; and he despaired of winning the great man's daughter. Nor is it likely that he would have seriously attempted the citadel, had it not been betrayed by the sympathetic imprudence of one of its fair allies.

Miss Spear, probably taking compassion on my father's lonely condition, told tales out of school.

" I could let you into a secret worth knowing," she said to him one day ; " I don't think I ought to tell it, but it would make you very happy."

Of course my father earnestly begged to be made happy, and solemnly promised to make no improper use of what might be revealed.

Then it came out that, when my father, the first time he walked with Miss Spear and her Scotch friend, had parted from them, Miss Dale had made special inquiry as to who and what that Englishman was ; and that, when her curiosity was satisfied, she had confessed to her friend, after a pause : " Well, I don't know how it is ; but, it seems to me, if I ever marry, that is to be the man."

This breach of confidence by Miss Spear caused a third visit to Glasgow, and more walks on the Green. After a while the younger sisters—discreet girls !—got into the way of straying off, and giving my father a chance. The great life-question was put, and the lady answered, like a dutiful child : " You must get my father's consent, or you can never have mine ; " adding, however, like a dear, frank girl as she was : " I dare say he won't agree ; and if he doesn't, I do not intend to marry at all."

I should be ashamed of my father, had he not found some way out of the difficulty. But he was equal to the occasion. He had heard a vague report about the Lanark mills being for sale, and he resolved to make that a pretext for calling on the old gentleman. When he asked Mr. Dale's terms, the reply was : " Why, *you* don't want to buy them. You're too young."

" But I'm in partnership with older men who have capital enough. We are cotton-spinners ourselves."

" Have you seen New Lanark ? "

My father said he had taken a cursory view of it.

" Well, have a good look at it ; see your partners, and bring them to me if they want to buy."

My father thought this was a put off ; but as Mr. Dale gave him a letter authorizing him to examine every part of the works, he posted to New Lanark at once, went over the mills and work-shops thoroughly, and came to the conclusion (perhaps thinking of Miss Dale the while) that the property was a desirable purchase.

On his return to Manchester, he brought over his partners to his views, and persuaded two of them to return with him to Glasgow. After brief negotiation, they purchased the entire establishment for sixty thousand pounds. This was in the summer of 1797.

The outworks were carried, but still the garrison held out. Miss Ann had spoken to her father of the suitor who had won her heart. But David Dale, like many of his countrymen, had his prejudices against the English (shared by his grandson Robert in the nursery,

and for years after) as the oppressors of their northern
neighbors and the murderers of William Wallace.   He
felt disposed to resent the attempt of a *land louper*
(foreign interloper) to carry off one of his daughters.
So the lady wrote to her lover saying that he would
have to resign her, and advising him to look for a better wife in England.   Later, when they met at New
Lanark, she repeated to him the assurance that, as her
father held out against their union, she should never
marry.

But my father, as might be expected in a character
so strongly stamped as his with perseverance, had no
idea of condemning his ladye-love to a life of celibacy.
Two years brought great changes.   A Mr. Scott Mon-
crief, co-director with my grandfather in the Royal
Bank, and his wife, were won over by the young couple
to their interests.   The lover had frequently to meet
Mr. Dale on business, and took pains to please him ;
the young lady adhered to her resolution, refusing several eligible offers ; and the father was indulgent, calling to mind what a faithful little housekeeper his
daughter had been to him.   And so it was brought about
that, on the 30th of September, 1799, Miss Dale became Mrs. Robert Owen.

The Rev. Mr. Balfour, of the Scottish kirk, offi-
ciated.   He bade the bride and bridegroom stand up,
and asked them, respectively, if they took each other
as husband and wife.   They nodded assent, and he
added : " Then you're married ; you may take your
seats."   When my father expressed his surprise, Mr.
Balfour replied : " I usually explain to the young
couple the duties of married life ; but with Mr. Dale
present, and to his children, I could not presume to do

what he doubtless has already and much better done."
Surely a modest and sensible speech.

For a few months my father remained manager of the
Chorlton Mills. Then his partners wished him to take
charge of New Lanark ; which he did, at the commencement of the present century—about the first of
January, 1800.

At first, the newly married couple spent their winters
in Charlotte Street, and their summers in a cottage,
with garden attached, near the centre of New Lanark.
But, after a few years, my father took a long lease of
Braxfield, a country-seat about a quarter of a mile from
the village, belonging to Lord Braxfield, a judge of the
Supreme Court of Scotland.

And thus it happened that it was to Braxfield House
I returned, when I had taken leave of my indulgent
aunts and of that charming little country maiden, at
Rosebank.

PAPER II.

BOY-LIFE IN A SCOTTISH COUNTRY-SEAT.

I MUST have been, from my earliest years, a very self-willed youngster. I recollect my mother telling me of some of her troubles, dating from the time when I was still unable to walk; the old story of the baby screaming persistently, if refused anything he had set his little heart on. Very gentle though she was, the doctrine of innate depravity, in which she had been bred, urged her to slap me into quiet. But my father —an advocate of system, and an undoubting believer in his favorite tenet that "man's character is formed for him, not by him"—stoutly opposed that. Yet the screams, whenever my mother objected to having her lace collar torn, or a teacup, of some old china-set, snatched from the table and flung to the floor, remained a stubborn reality which no theory could get over; and it seriously disturbed my father as well as the rest of the house. Something must be done.

"When the child screams from temper, my dear Caroline" (my father thought my mother's middle name more romantic than the plain Ann; but I think I should have called her *Annie*),—"when the child screams, set him in the middle of the nursery floor, and be sure you don't take him up till he stops crying."

"But, my dear, he'll go on crying by the hour."

"Then let him cry."

" It may hurt his little lungs, and perhaps throw him into spasms."

" I think not.   At all events it will hurt him more if he grows up an ungovernable boy.   Man is the creature of circumstances."

My mother, who had been a dutiful daughter, was also an obedient wife, and she had great respect for my father's judgment—in temporal matters.   So the next time I insisted on trying innocent experiments on tea-cup or collar, I was carried off to the nursery and set down, screaming lustily, on mid-floor.

My mother must have suffered dreadfully for the next hour ; but soon after that the fury of disappointment wore itself out, and I dropped asleep on the pillow behind me.

This punishment had to be repeated five or six times. My mother was beginning to despair, when she found, one day, to her great relief, that baby could be crossed in his wishes, and made to give up, with just a little fretting.   After a time even the fretting ceased.   The infant culprit had learned a great lesson in life,—submission to the inevitable.

This was all very well : but the temper remained, and culminated, six or seven years after the nursery experiments, in a fit of indignant rage, after this wise.

Braxfield House was situated about half way between the village of New Lanark and the ancient shire-town of Lanark.   The latter is famed in Scottish history ; and on " the Moor " near to it *wappin-schaws* used to be held in the olden time.   There was no post-office in the village, and one of the supplementary workmen there, a certain James Dunn, an old spinner who had lost an arm by an accident in the mills, was our letter-carrier,—the bearer of a handsome leather bag with gay brass padlock, which gave him a sort of official dignity in the eyes of the rising generation ; and by this time there were some three or four young vine-shoots growing up around the Owen family table.

If James Dunn had lost one arm, he made excellent use of the other ; constructing bows and arrows and fifty other nice things, for our delectation, and thus coming into distinguished favor. One day he gave me a clay pipe, showed me how to mix soap-water in due proportion, and then, for the first time in our lives, we children witnessed the marvellous rise, from the pipe-bowl, of the brightly variegated bubble ; its slow, graceful ascent into upper air ; and, alas ! its sudden disappearance, at the very climax of our wonder. My delight was beyond all bounds; and so was my gratitude to the one-armed magician. I take credit for this last sentiment, in extenuation of the crime which was to follow.

We had in the house a sort of odd-job boy, who ran errands, helped occasionally in the stables, carried coals to the fires, and whose early-morning duty it was to clean the boots and shoes of the household. His parents had named him, at the fount, after the Macedonian conqueror ; but their son, unlike King Philip's, suffered nicknaming, or at least contraction of his baptismal title into Sandy.

Sandy, according to my recollection of him, was the worst of bad boys. His chief pleasure seemed to consist in inventing modes of vexing and enraging us ; and he was quite ingenious in his tricks of petty torture. Add to this that he was most unreasonably jealous of James Dunn's popularity ; especially when we told him, as we often did, that we hated *him.*

One day my brother William, a year younger than myself, and I had been out blowing soap-bubbles (" all by ourselves," as we were wont to boast, in proof of our proficiency), and had returned triumphant. In the courtyard we met Sandy, to whom, forgetting, for the moment, by-gone squabbles, we joyfully related our exploits, and broke out into praises of the pipe-giver as the nicest man that ever was. That nettled the young scamp, and he began to abuse our well-beloved post-carrier as a "lazy loun that hadna' but yin arm, and could do naething with the tither but cowp letters into the post-office and make up bairns' trashtrie."

This incensed me, and I suppose I must have made some bitter reply; whereupon Sandy snatched the richly prized pipe from my hand, deliberately broke off its stem close to the bowl, and threw the fragments into what we used to call the " shoe-hole : " that contemptuous appellation designating a small outhouse, hard by, where our tormentor discharged his duties as shoe-black.

Unwilling to be set down as tell-tales, we said not a word about this to father or mother. But when, an hour later, I burst into tears at the sight of James Dunn, I had to tell him our story. He made light of it, wisely remarking that there were more pipes in the world; and, shouldering his post-bag, went off to the " auld town." If my readers can look back far enough into their early years, they may imagine my joyful surprise when, on his return, he presented me with another pipe.

I took it up to an attic room of which I had the run when I wished to be alone; locked the door, with a vague feeling as if Sandy were at my heels; sat down and gazed on the regenerated treasure. The very ditto of the pipe I had tearfully mourned! brand new, just from the shop. But the delight its first sight had given me faded when I thought of the sacrifices that dear, good man had been making for my sake. It was so generous of him to give me the first pipe! I had no idea whatever of its money value; to me it was beyond price. Then here his generosity had been taxed a second time. Again he had been spending for me out of his wages, which I supposed must be small, since he had only one arm to work with. And who had been the cause of all this woful self-immolation? That vile, cruel, rascally Sandy! To him it was due that James Dunn had felt compelled to make a second purchase,—to the stinting, perhaps, of his poor wife and children! And—who could tell?—the same malignant ill-turn might be repeated again and again. Ah! then my indignation rose, till I could hear the heart-beats.

I remember distinctly that no plans of revenge had arisen in my mind caused by the destruction of my first pipe, however enraged I was at the perpetrator of that outrage. It was only when I found one of my dearest friends thus plundered, on my account, that my wrath, roused to white heat, gave forth vapors of vengeance.

I brooded over the matter all day, so that I must needs plead guilty to malice aforethought. Toward evening my plans took shape; and, ere I slept, which was long after I went to bed, every detail had been arranged. My adversary was a large, stout, lubberly fellow, more than twice my age; and I had to make up in stratagem for my great inferiority in strength.

Next morning, before the nursery-maid awoke, I crept furtively from bed, dressed in silence, descended to the courtyard, and armed myself with a broom : not one of your light, modern, broom-corn affairs, but a downright heavy implement, with a stout handle and heavy wooden cross-head attached, set with bristles. It was as much as I could do to wield it.

Then I reconnoitred the enemy's camp. No Sandy yet in the " shoe-hole " ! I went in, set the door ajar, and took post, with uplifted weapon, behind it.

I had long to wait, Sandy being late that morning ; but my wrath only boiled the more hotly for the delay. At last there was a step, and the door moved. Down with all the might of concentrated rage came the broom —the hard end of the cross-piece foremost—on the devoted head that entered. The foe sank on the ground. I sprang forward—but what was this ? The head I had struck had on a faultlessly white lace cap ! It flashed on me in a moment. Not the abhorred Sandy, but our worthy housekeeper, Miss Wilson !

Miss Wilson was one of a class common in Great Britain, but rare in this country,—a notable, orderly, painstaking, neatly dressed maiden of thirty-five or forty summers ; deeply read in all the mysteries of householdcraft; but kindly withal, and much disposed to make pets of the children around her. With the exception of James Dunn, she was one of our greatest favorites. I am afraid one element in our affection for this good woman was of a selfish nature. She had obtained from my mother permission to have us all to tea with her every Sunday evening, on condition of a two-thirds dilution with warm water, but without any sumptuary regulation as to the contingent of sugar.

Now, in that country and in those days, young folks, both gentle and simple, were restricted to very frugal fare. For breakfast, porridge * and milk; for supper, bread and milk only. At dinner we were helped once sparingly to animal food and once only to pie or pudding; but we had vegetables and oatmeal cake *ad libitum*. Scottish children under the age of fourteen were rarely allowed either tea or coffee; and such was the rule in our house. Till we were eight or ten years old we were not admitted to the evening meal in the parlor.

Miss Wilson's tea-table furnished the only peep we had of the Chinese luxury.

Thus the Sunday evening in the housekeeper's parlor (for Miss Wilson had her own nicely appointed parlor between the kitchen and the servants' dining hall) was something to which we looked eagerly forward. On that occasion we had toast as well as tea; and the banquet sometimes culminated with a well-filled plate of sugar-biscuit, a luxury doubly prized because its visits were rare as those of angels.

These hebdomadal symposia gave rise among us to a peculiar definition of the first day of the week. We took this, not from the sermons we heard, or the catechism we learned, on that day, but from the delicacies on Miss Wilson's table, somewhat irreverently calling

---

* It may or may not be necessary here to say that porridge is a sort of mush, or hasty-pudding, made by gradually dropping oatmeal into boiling water, seasoned with salt. The cake spoken of was composed of oatmeal and water, rolled out thin, and browned before the fire.

In the Scottish dialect oatmeal porridge is called *parritch;* and there is a story illustrating the ridiculous extent to which early promotion, even of mere children, in the British army is, or was, obtained by family influence; and marking also the customary breakfast fare in the nursery. A gentleman, visiting a family of distinction in the Highlands and coming downstairs in the morning, heard a loud bawling. Meeting a servant, he asked him what was the matter. "O sir," said the man, "it's naething but the Major, greetin for his parritch."

Sunday the *toast-biscuit-tea-day*. I am not certain
whether this juvenile paraphrase ever reached my
mother's ears ; for Miss Wilson was too discreet to retail
the confidential jokes which we permitted ourselves in
the privacy of her *petits soupers*.

Under the circumstances one may judge of my horror
when I saw on whom the broom-head had fallen. The
sight stunned me almost as much as my blow had
stunned the poor woman who lay before me. I have a
dim recollection of people, called in by my screams,
raising Miss Wilson and helping her to her room ; and
then I remember nothing more till I found myself, many
hours later, in the library ; my mother standing by with
her eyes red, and my father looking at me more in sorrow than in anger.

" Wouldn't you be very sorry, Robert," he said at
last, " if you were blind ? "

I assented, as well as my sobs would allow.

" Well, when a boy or man is in such a rage as you
were, he is little better than blind or half mad. He
doesn't stop to think or to look at anything. You
didn't know Miss Wilson from Sandy."

My conscience told me that was true. I had struck
without waiting to look.

" You may be very thankful," my father went on,
"that it wasn't Sandy. You might have killed the
boy."

I thought it would have been no great harm if I had,
but I didn't say so.

" Are you sorry for what you have done ? "

I said that I was very, *very* sorry that I had hurt Miss
Wilson ; and that I wanted to tell her so. My father
rang the bell and sent to inquire how she was.

" I am going to take you to ask her pardon. But it's of no use to be sorry unless you do better. Remember this ! *I have never struck you. You must never strike anybody.*"

It was true. I cannot call to mind that I ever, either before or since that time, received a blow from any human being ; most thankful am I that I have been spared the knowledge of how one feels under such an insult. Nor, from that day forth, so far as I remember, did I ever myself give a blow in anger again.

The servant returned. " She has a sair head yet, sir ; but she's muckle better. She's sittin' up in her chair, and would be fain to see the bairn." Then, in an undertone, looking at me : " It was a fell crunt,* yon. I didna think the bit callan could hit sae snell."

When I saw Miss Wilson in her arm-chair, with pale cheeks and bandaged head, I could not say a single word. She held out her arms ; I flung mine round her neck, kissed her again and again, and then fell to crying long and bitterly. The good soul's eyes were wet as she took me on her knee and soothed me. When my father offered to take me away I clung to her so closely that she begged to have me stay.

I think the next half hour, in her arms, had crowded into it more sincere repentance and more good resolves for the future than any other in my life. Then, at last, my sobs subsided, so that I could pour into her patient ear the whole story of my grievous wrongs: Sandy's unexampled wickedness in breaking the first pipe ; James Dunn's unheard-of generosity in buying the sec-

---

* *Crunt,* to be interpreted in English, must be paraphrased. It means a blow on the head with a cudgel.

ond ; the little chance I had if I didn't take the broom
to such a big boy ; and then—

"But, Miss Wilson," I said, when I came to that
point, "what made *you* come to the shoe-hole, and not
Sandy ?"

"I wanted to .see if the boy was attending to his
work."

I then told her I would love her as long as she lived,
and that she mustn't be angry with me ; and when she
had promised to love me too, we parted.

It only remains to be said, that about a month afterwards, Sandy was quietly dismissed. We all breathed
more freely when he was gone.

If I deserved more punishment for this outbreak than
my father's reproof and the sight of Miss Wilson's sufferings, I came very near receiving it, in a fatal shape,
a few months afterwards.

The estate of Braxfield is beautifully situated on the
banks of the Clyde. The house stands on a bit of undulating table-land, then set in blue-grass, containing
some thirty or forty acres ; and the slope thence to the
river was covered with thick woods, through which
gravel-paths wound back and forth till they reached the
Clyde, a quarter of a mile below the mills. What
charming nutting we used to have there !

At low-water there was a foot-path under the rocks,
by which these woods could be reached from the village ; and, of course, there was great temptation on
Sundays for the young people—pairs of lovers especially—to encroach on this forbidden ground ; to say
nothing of the hazel-nut temptation, when autumn came.
Nothing could be more romantic and inviting.

Of course, it would not have done to give two thousand people the range of the woods : so trespassing therein was strictly forbidden. Yet I remember, one Sunday afternoon, when my father had taken me out to walk, seeing, through the underwood in a path below us, and to which our road led, a lad and lass evidently so intent in conversation that they were not alive to anything else : if they had known who was near they would have taken to flight at once. My father stopped and looked at them, calling to mind, I dare say, his own walks in the Green with Miss Ann Caroline. " They don't see us," he said to me ; " let us turn back. If I meet them, I must order them off the place ; and they have so few pleasures and so much work ! It's hard." So we took another path ; and the lovers pursued their way, unconscious of the danger that had approached them.

Besides this wooded " brae" in front of the mansion, there was, on one side, a steep declivity into a deep, bushy dingle, with large, old trees interspersed, and, rising on the other side, a precipitous bank of similar character, on the summit of which was perched the house of our next neighbor. This could not be reached by vehicle without making a circuit of a mile and a half; but a slanting foot-path led from our stable-yard down into the glen, and a rough, scrambling way ascended thence the opposite bank, conducting the pedestrian, by a short cut, to the old town. This rude pass was known far and near by the euphonious name of *Gullietoodelum.*

All this afforded good cover for foxes ; and one of these midnight prowlers had carried off certain fowls and ducks belonging to James Shaw, a burly farmer who tilled the arable portion of the Braxfield estate, and whose cottage we were wont to frequent, attracted by the excellent mashed potatoes, prepared with milk, with which Mrs. Shaw secretly treated us. They turned a penny by supplying our family, from time to time, with poultry; and now the "gudeman" took arms in defence of his live stock. Having loaded a fowling-piece heavily with slugs, he deposited it in a dark corner of the coach-house, which, with stables attached, stood on the edge of the wooded dingle where Reynard had been seen.

There, during a morning ramble, my brother William and I came upon the gun. It was a flint-lock, of course, for the days of percussion-caps were yet afar off. Having brought it out to the light for inspection, my brother amused himself by pointing it at me, and attempting to draw the trigger. I reminded him that our mother had forbidden us ever to point guns at one another.

"But it's not loaded," remonstrated William.

"I know that," was my reply (though how I came to that hasty conclusion I am quite unable to explain), "I know it isn't loaded, but mamma said we were never to pretend to shoot one another, whether the gun was loaded or not."

Whereupon he submitted, and I further informed him that the flint of a gun could not be snapped without drawing back the cock, which I showed him how to do, having once snapped a gun before. With my aid he then hugged the stock of the weapon under his right arm, pointing the barrel in the air, and pulled the trigger; this time so effectually that the recoil threw him flat on his back.

He struggled to his feet and we looked at each other. Not a word was spoken. I seized the gun, flung it

back into the coach-house, not quite certain whether
that was the end of the explosion, and, by a common
impulse, we both took to our heels, fled down the glen-
path, nor stopped till at the foot of Gullietoodelum.
There we paused to take breath.

"I do believe, Robert," my brother ejaculated at
last—"I do believe that gun was loaded!"

I had gradually been coming to the same conclusion;
so I did not dispute the point. Slowly and silently we
reascended from that dark glen to the upper world
again, sadder and wiser boys.

I have often thought since how Young America would
have laughed us to scorn as Molly-caudles, for our green
ignorance, at seven or eight, touching fire-arms, and
their use. Half a year later, however, I obtained leave
to go on a shooting expedition with a young man who
had a salary from the New Lanark Company as surgeon
of the village, and who attended the sick there gratuitously. We proceeded to a neighboring rookery where
sportsmen were admitted on certain conditions. I carried a light fowling-piece, and was then and there initiated into the mysteries of loading and firing. Though
at heart mortally afraid I stood stoutly to my gun, and
brought down two confiding young crows who were yet
inexperienced in the wiles and murderous propensities
of men and boys.

As we were returning home in the dusk I overheard
a brief conversation, not intended for my ears, between
the surgeon and a comrade of his who had accompanied
us. They had been pleased, it seems, with the spirit I
had shown; and the mention of my name attracted
me.

"He's a fine, manly boy, that," said the comrade.

" He's a noble little fellow," rejoined the surgeon.

Most children, I think, accustomed to hear themselves commended, would have forgotten the words within twenty-four hours ; but they sunk into my heart, and I could swear, to-day, that I have textually repeated them here. This wineglassful of praise intoxicated me ; for I think it was the first I had ever tasted. My father's creed was that " man is not the proper subject of praise or blame ; " being but what circumstances, acting on his original organization, make him. So his approval, when I deserved approval, was testified only by a pleased smile or a caress.

The words haunted me all the way home and for days afterwards. Their effect was similar to that sometimes produced during the excitement of such camp-meetings as I have witnessed in our western forests. They woke in me what, in revival-language, is called " a change of heart." I solemnly resolved that I would *be* what these men had said I was.

Next morning, accordingly, I not only myself submitted, with exemplary forbearance, to the various matutinal inflictions of cold bathing, scrubbing, hair-combing and the like, but I exhorted my younger brother and sisters to similar good conduct. The nursery-maid was amazed, not knowing what to make of it ; no doubt I had been rebellious enough in the past.

" What's come over the bairn ? " she exclaimed. " Where has he been ? I think he must hae gotten religion." Then, looking at my sober face, she asked me, " Were you at the kirk yestreen, Robert ? "

" No," said I, " I was shooting crows."

" Shootin craws ! " I remember to this day that look of

blank perplexity. The girl was actually alarmed when she missed my wonted wilfulness. " It passes me," she said at last ; " the callan must hae gane daft. He's no the same bairn ava."

This fit of meekness lasted, in its extreme phase, so far as I remember, about ten days. Yet—strange if it seem—I think it left·its impress on my character for years.

The powerful influence which seeming trifles exerted over my conduct in those days—now stirring to revenge, now prompting to reformation—may in part be traced to the recluse lives we led in that isolated country-seat ; a seclusion the more complete because of the unquestioning obedience to the strictest rules (especially as to metes and bounds) in which we were trained. The Clyde, though the largest river in Scotland, was not, at its usual stage and where we were wont to bathe, over thirty or forty yards wide ; and we were pretty good swimmers. The enterprise of any urchin, ten years old, in our own day and country, would undoubtedly have suggested the construction of a small raft on which to convey our clothes across, and then an exploration of the unknown regions beyond. But we were forbidden to trespass there ; and it did not enter into our heads to break bounds.

There was a bridge over the river, but little more than a mile below our house ; but, during the first decade, my mother was unwilling to trust us so far from home, and we had never crossed this bridge except in our carriage and on the turnpike road. I had passed my tenth birthday when my father told William and myself, one day, that he was going to take us a walk across the bridge and on the other side of the river. Our blissful anticipations of this remote expedition were enhanced by knowing that there was to be found, close to the bridge, a far-famed baker's shop, of which the *parleys* (that is thin, crisp ginger-cakes) were celebrated all over the county; and when my mother put into our pockets sixpence apiece, to be there expended as we pleased, our joy was full.

The parleys were purchased to be eaten by and by as luncheon; and my father conducted us, by a winding country-road, up the opposite bank of the river. It was a bright summer day, and the sunshine was the more welcome, because, in Scotland, it is somewhat grudgingly dispensed. Suddenly we came upon a view which at once arrested us, calling out our youthful admiration. Across the river appeared a large house, standing in beautiful grounds, but not very distinctly seen, through trees. There was a spacious garden surrounded by high walls, covered with espaliers; and at one end a large green-house peeped forth. Beyond this was a meadow, with sheep-pasturing; and, crowning that again, we saw an eminence with a dark grove of firs.

"Oh, what a beautiful place, papa!" I exclaimed. "Wouldn't you like to live there, William? What a nice time we would have!"

My father smiled, and a sudden idea came to me: "*Are* we going to live there, papa?"

"Yes, my son."

"Oh, I am so glad. I'm sure there must be plenty of nuts in the woods."

"You never saw that house before?" asked my father.

"Of course not. We never were here before."

"That's true ; but take a good look at the grounds, Robert."

I did ; but the only conclusion I came to was that their garden was larger than ours.

"My child," said my father, at last, "you're doing now what older and wiser people have often done before you. You are looking from a distance at a beautiful place, with the envious eyes of a neighbor. It *is* a very pretty place, as you say ; but that's Braxfield !"

I did not understand the moral of this at the time. But I never forgot the words ; and their full meaning came to me, years afterward.

But if, as regards pedestrian excursions, we were held under strict rule, in other matters we were free and privileged. We had the unrestricted range of my father's library, which was a pretty extensive one.

I have no recollection as to when and how I learned my letters. All I remember is that, at seven or eight years of age, I was an omnivorous reader. "Robinson Crusoe," pored over with implicit faith, made the first deep impression. Then, one after another in succession, came Miss Edgeworth's winning stories—household words they were in our family. "Sandford and Merton" came next into favor ; succeeded by "Thaddeus of Warsaw" and the "Arabian Nights." After these I devoured Miss Porter's "Scottish Chiefs" ; not a doubt obtruding itself as to whether the gallant and romantic military gentleman—the courteous Knight of Ellerslie, whom the lady's pencil has depicted in rosy colors—was the veritable champion of Scotland— the same hot-blooded and doughty warrior, sung by Blind Harry, who, while yet a stripling, stabbed, in a

Scottish castle, the son of its governor, in requital of a few insulting words. My indignation, originally roused by nursery legends, was rekindled, and my national prejudices confirmed, by this more modern version of Monteith's treachery and his noble victim's cruel fate. These feelings were intensified during a visit to Cartland Crags (or *Craigs*, as we pronounced the word), a deep, narrow gulch a little way beyond the town of Lanark, walled by precipitous rocks some two hundred feet high, and forming the water-course of a small stream called the Mouse. From the bed of that stream we climbed thirty or forty feet up the face of the rock to a deep cleft known to all Scotland as "Wallace's Cave," and to which, when in peril of his life, that sturdy chieftain was wont to retreat. No Fourth-of-July oration, no visit to Plymouth Rock, ever produced, on young scion of Puritan, a deeper impression than did the sight of this narrow, secluded cell upon me— its pavement worn by the feet of patriotic pilgrims. I think, if I had but been stirred by a Hamilcar of a father prompting me, I might have sworn, then and there, eternal enmity against the English. But, in my case, the paternal sentiment was, "Love to the whole human race;" so that, outgrowing hate-bearing prejudices in the genial atmosphere of home, I have reformed, and can say, as Webster said of himself on a well-known occasion, "I am very little like Hannibal;" having come to eschew strife of all kinds, and devoutly believing that "love is the fulfilling of the law."

In those early days, however, martial deeds had their usual fascination. My brother and I used to pore over Pope's Homer for hours; the episode of the combat between Ajax and Hector so working on our imaginations that we resolved to get up, for the benefit of a younger sister, a mimic representation of the fight.

The shield of Ajax was our chief difficulty.

> " Huge was its orb, with seven thick folds o'ercast
> Of tough bull-hides ; of solid brass the last."

We had no Tychius, "excelling in arts of armory," to aid us, to say nothing of the weight of hide and metal ; but we did our best. We found, in the depths of that bushy dingle where Reynard had sought refuge, certain large, thick leaves,—plantain or flag, perhaps, but my botany is at fault here,—at all events eight or ten inches long ; and these we contrived to fasten in front of a buckler of thick pasteboard, stained yellow. Two ash saplings supplied our lances ; but, my mother fearing for our eyes and objecting to a combat at *outrance*, we had somewhat blunted their points. Nevertheless, after two or three devious throws, the great object of my ambition was attained. A more fortunate cast of my javelin caused it to penetrate the seven vegetable bull-hides and remain sticking in the brazen-hued disc beyond. I had outdone Hector, whose spear never reached the brass.

> " Through six bull-hides the furious weapon drove,
> Till in the seventh it fixed."

And my sister's shouts of applause, at sight of this exploit, completed my exultation.

But the time was approaching when child's play was to give place to a matter of serious importance that has gravely influenced all my after years : for one's opinions on great life-subjects essentially determine well-doing and well-being, here and hereafter.

My mother, a devout Presbyterian, though too gentle

to be bigoted, was thoroughly imbued with the belief
that the most orthodox form of Protestantism is essential
to happiness, if not to virtue.   Upon this conviction she
acted with persistent conscientiousness.   It colored her
daily conduct.   Was any one among us sick ?   She sat,
hour after hour, by his bedside ; and administered, by
turns, temporal comforts and spiritual consolation.   Had
we lost a pious friend ?   His death was spoken of as a
translation to a world of bliss.   Did any of us ask for a
pretty story ?   It was selected out of the Scriptural
pages.   We were told of the place above for good boys
and girls, and of the fire below for the wicked ; and
when we asked who were good and who were wicked,
we were taught that all boys and girls and men and
women were wicked unless they believed, in the first
place, that Jesus Christ was the only son of God, and,
in the second place, that nobody could escape from hell
except by vicarious atonement through his death and
sufferings.   My mother added that all who believed
that, and who read the Bible every morning, and said
prayers every night, and went to church twice every
Sunday, became good people, and would be saved and
go to heaven ; while all who disbelieved it were lost
souls, who would be punished forever with the Devil
and his angels.

My father, a Deist, or free-thinking Unitarian, was
tender of my mother's religious sentiments, and did not,
in those days, interfere with her instructions or seek to
undermine our belief.   I recollect, one day when he
had been explaining to me how seeds produced plants
and trees, that I asked him where the very, *very* first
seeds came from, and that his answer did not go to shake
my faith in the Mosaic account of the creation.   I re-

member, too, that on another occasion, fresh from my mother's lesson on the almighty and all-pervading power of the Creator, who made the sun to shine and all things to live and grow, I inquired of my father whether God went under the roots of the trees and pushed them up. But my father, in reply, only smiled, and said he did not know how it was done.

Thus left to orthodox teaching, I soon became an apt and zealous scholar ; often prejudiced, I was never indifferent ; still more often mistaken, I was sincere in my errors, and I always sought to act out what I believed.

Very peculiar was my state of mind in those early years. Breathing an orthodox atmosphere, I never doubted that it extended over the whole earth. I had just heard of pagans and Romanists and infidels; but I thought of all such dissenters from the creed I had learned as a handful of blinded wretches, to be met with in some small remote corner of this vast world,—a world that bowed to Christ alone as its God and Saviour. To set up my own opinion against all the pious—that is, against all good men, or rather against all men except a few who were desperately wicked—was an acme of arrogance that did not once cross my thoughts.

My good mother—more amiable than logical—did not perceive the perilous insecurity of a creed so narrow in a character like that of her eldest son. In a chart given to me, in the year 1827, by Spurzheim, causality and conscientiousness are marked as predominant organs, and self-esteem as a large one. If that diagnostic may be trusted, the danger to my orthodoxy was the greater. The first doubts as to the religious belief of my infancy were suggested when I was about eleven years old.

By this time the New Lanark establishment had ob-

tained considerable celebrity, and was frequented by
visitors of some distinction.   Among these a bishop of
the Anglican Church, having brought a letter of introduction to my father, was invited to his table, and I sat
next to him.   During dinner conversation turned on the
original depravity of man, which, to my utter astonishment, my father called in question; the bishop, of
course, stoutly affirming it.   I listened, with greedy ears,
to the discussion; and, during a pause, I put in my
word.

"Papa," said I, "I think you'd find it a very difficult
thing to make a bad heart a good one."

The bishop, amused and astonished to find so youthful an auxiliary, patted me, laughingly, on the back,
and said, "You're in the right, my little fellow.   God
only can do that."   Then he encouraged me to proceed, to the no small increase of my vanity and self-
importance.   My father, instead of checking me,
replied patiently to my argument; and his replies left
me much to think about.

Next day I had a lecture from my mother on the sin
of self-sufficiency, and was told that little boys must
listen, and not join in grown people's conversation.
But this did not quiet me.   When I pressed my mother
closely about my father's opinions, she confessed, to my
horror, her doubts whether he firmly believed that Christ
was the son of God.

I remember, to this day, the terrible shock this was
to me, and the utter confusion of ideas that ensued.
My state of mind was pitiable.   I knew there were
wicked unbelievers among the Hottentots and New-
Zealanders whom I had read about; and my mother
had once confessed to me that, even in England and

Scotland, there were a few low, ignorant people who read the books of an infidel called Tom Paine : but my own father ! kind, indulgent to us all, and loved and respected by everybody,—was *he* wicked ? was *he* as bad as the pagans ? I took to watching his benevolent face ; but he talked and smiled as usual. There was no cloven foot to be seen, nor any sinister inference to be drawn from his quiet, pleasant demeanor.

In fear and trembling I laid my perplexities before my mother. Excellent woman ! I know well now in what a strait she must have found herself, between her creed as a Calvinist and her love as a wife. Somewhat at expense of conscience, perhaps, she compromised matters. Swayed by her great affection for my father, and doubtless also by her fears that the disclosure of his heresies might weaken the paternal authority, she sought to soften their enormity by declaring that, but for these, he was everything that was good and estimable. " Pray to God, my child," she would say, "that he will turn your dear father's heart from the error of his way and make him pious like your grandfather." Then, with tears in her eyes, " O, if he could only be converted, he would be everything my heart could desire ; and when we die he would be in heaven with us all."

" If he could only be converted ! " These words sank deep. " My father is too good a man," I said to myself, " to sin on purpose. Perhaps nobody ever explained holy things to him as my mother did to me. If I could only save his soul ! "

The more I pondered upon this, the more it seemed possible, probable, at last unquestionable. I called to mind some texts my mother had read to us about the

mouths of sucklings, and what they might do ; also what
Jesus Christ had said about little children as being of the
kingdom of Heaven.   I did not, indeed, conceal from
myself that my father was a wise and prudent man ; I
saw that men listened to him with respect and treated
him, on all occasions, with consideration.   But my
mother, whose habit it was to read a chapter from the
Bible to us every evening, happened, about that time, to
select one from the Gospel of Matthew, in which Christ
returns thanks to God that things hidden from the wise
and prudent are revealed to babes.   It occurred to me
that perhaps God had caused my mother to read that
chapter for my especial encouragement.

Then, again, I had great faith in the efficacy of
prayer.   Several years before, while we were staying,
for a time, in my grandfather's town-house, I had been
shooting with bow and arrow in the same garden where
David Dale found that *honest* man.   I had lost my best
arrow, and sought for it a long time in vain.   Then, instead of following Bassanio's plan,—

> " When I had lost one shaft,
> I shot his fellow of the self-same flight
> The self-same way, with more advised watch,
> To find the other forth,"—

I dropped on my knees behind a gooseberry-bush and
prayed to God that he would show me where my missing arrow was.   Rising and turning round, lo ! there it
stood, deep sunk in the ground close to another bush.
My mother, when I told her of this, had, indeed, expressed doubt as to the propriety of prayer for a thing
so trifling ; but I retained the conviction that God had
answered my supplication : and every night, on my
knees, I prayed, as fervently, I think, as any young

creature ever did, that he would help me also to convert my father.

But, as commonly happens to propagandists, more selfish motives supervened, to enkindle my zeal. We learn from history that Louis XIV. was prompted to repeal that charter of religious freedom, the edict of Nantes, by the desire to save an abject soul, loaded down with the debaucheries of a lifetime, from perdition. And though the class of sins to which I was prone differed somewhat from those of the French monarch, they weighed heavily upon me, nevertheless. A hundred times my mother had told me that I was a miserable sinner ; and conscience brought up before me many proofs of this.

My activity being great, and my spirits of a restless order, the breach of the fourth commandment was my besetting sin. Though I had successfully resisted a great temptation to play at foot-ball on Sundays, yet when James Dunn, one Saturday evening, brought me a new hoop of his own manufacture, I hid it in the woods, stole away in the afternoon of the next day, and "broke the Sabbath" by trundling it for an hour, stung with compunction the while. Then there was that conspiracy against Sandy, with its awful result ! Add to this that I was terribly given to yawning in church, and that, on two different occasions, I had fallen sound asleep during evening prayers. Worse still, there was a romance (entitled "Anne of Brittany," I remember) in which, when I was summoned to bed one Saturday evening, I had left the heroine in a most interesting and perilous situation, and next morning, when my mother came quietly into the library to tell me it was time to prepare for church, so absorbed

was I in Anne's imminent danger, that I was detected—
flagrante delicto—in the very act of reading a novel on
the Lord's day !   Could there be a doubt as to my innate depravity ?   And was it strange that, while Louis
sought salvation by coercing millions of Huguenots to
flee or to embrace Catholicism, I should strive to have
my father's redemption placed to my credit on that
great book that was to be opened oh the Day of Judgment ?

But aside from religious convictions and the desire to
atone for my sins urging me on, there was that organ of
self-esteem, hereditary perhaps, the size of which in my
brain the great phrenologist had detected.   Under its
influence I could not get away from the resolve to convert my father.   I say the resolve to *convert him*, not
to *attempt his conversion;* for so I put it to myself,
nothing doubting.

I don't think I had any clear conception what a mission is.   Yet I had a vague idea that God had chosen
me to be the instrument of my father's salvation, so
that he might not be sent to hell when he died.

I was mightily pleased with myself when this idea
suggested itself, and I set about preparing for the task
before me.   Summoning to my recollection all my
mother's strongest arguments, I arranged them in the
order in which I proposed to bring them forward.   Then
I imagined my father's replies ; already anticipating my
own triumph and my mother's joy when I should have
brought my father to confess his errors and repent.
But I said not a word of my intentions to her or to any
one.   The joyful surprise was to be complete.

I recollect, to this day, the spot on which I commenced my long-projected undertaking.   It was on a path

which skirted, on the farther side, the lawn in front of our house and led to the garden.   I could point out the very tree we were passing when—with some misgivings, now that it was to be put to the test—I sounded my father by first asking him what he thought about Jesus Christ.   His reply was to the effect that I would do well to heed his teachings, especially those relating to charity and to our loving one another.

This was well enough, as far it went ; but it did not at all satisfy me.   So, with some trepidation, I put the question direct, whether my father disbelieved that Christ was the Son of God ?

He looked a little surprised and did not answer immediately.   " Why do you ask that question, my son ? " he said at last.

" Because I am sure—" I began eagerly.

" That he *is* God's Son ? " asked my father, smiling.

" Yes, I am."

" Did you ever hear of the Mahometans ? " said my father, while I had paused to collect my proofs.

I replied that I had heard of such a people who lived somewhere, far off.

" Do you know what their religion is ? "

" No."

" They believe that Christ is not the Son of God, but that another person, called Mahomet, was God's chosen prophet."

" Do they not believe the Bible ? " asked I, somewhat aghast.

" No.   Mahomet wrote a book called the Koran ; and Mahometans believe it to be the word of God. That book tells them that God sent Mahomet to preach the gospel to them, and to save their souls."

Wonders crowded fast upon me. A rival Bible and a rival Saviour! Could it be? I asked, "Are you *quite* sure this is true, papa?"

" Yes, my dear, I am quite sure."

" But I suppose there are very few Mahometans : not near—*near* so many of them as of Christians."

" Do you call Catholics Christians, Robert?"

" O no, papa. The Pope is Antichrist."

My father smiled. " Then by Christians you mean Protestants?"

" Yes."

" Well, there are many more Mahometans than Protestants in the world : about a hundred and forty million Mahometans, and less than a hundred million Protestants."

" I thought almost everybody believed in Christ, as mamma does."

" There are probably twelve hundred millions of people in the world. So, out of every twelve persons only one is a Protestant. Are you *quite* sure that the one is right and the eleven wrong?"

My creed, based on authority, was toppling. I had no answer ready. During the rest of the walk I remained almost silent, engrossed with new ideas, and replying chiefly in monosyllables when spoken to.

And so ended this notable scheme of mine for my father's conversion.

My mother had claimed too much. Over-zealous, she had not given her own opinions fair play. Even taking the most favorable view of the Calvinistic creed, still what she had taught me was prejudice only. For if, looking to the etymology of that word, we interpret it to mean a judgment formed before examination, then must we regard as prejudices his opinions, however true, who has neglected to weigh them against their opposites, however false. Thus even a just prejudice is always vulnerable.

Had my mother been satisfied to teach me that the Old Testament was a most interesting and valuable contribution to ancient history, filled with important lessons ; had she encouraged me to compare the ethical and spiritual teachings of Christ with those of the Koran, or of Seneca, or Socrates, or Confucius (all of which were to be found in our library) ; and had she bid me observe how immeasurably superior they were in spirit and civilizing tendency to all that had gone before—she would, I think, have saved me from sundry extreme opinions that lasted through middle life.

But she was not content without setting up the Bible, as Caliph Omar did the Koran, not only as the infallible, but also as the solitary source of all religious knowledge whatever. The days of Max Müller were not yet. My mother had no doubt heard of comparative anatomy, but never of comparative religion. Lowell's lines had not then been written :—

> " Each form of worship that hath swayed
> The life of man and given it to grasp
> The master-key of knowledge, reverence,
> Enfolds some germs of goodness and of right."

The immediate effect, however, of my mishap in the attempt to make a Calvinist of my father was good. My failure served as a practical lesson in humility. I listened and thought and doubted more than had been my wont, and I spoke less.

Nor did I give up the creed of my childhood without a long and painful struggle.

I daily searched the Scriptures as diligently, I think I may say, as any child of my age could be expected to do ; coming upon many seeming incongruities and contradictions, which were sad stumbling-blocks. The frequent discussions between my father and his visitors, to which I eagerly listened, still increased my doubts. After a time I lost faith in my mother's favorite doctrine of the infallible. The axe had been laid at the root of my orthodoxy.

For more than a year, however, I listened with exemplary patience—even with more attention, indeed, than formerly—to my mother's pious homilies, and was seldom deficient when called up to repeat my catechism task. I did not say anything, during all that time, to betray my growing scepticism ; but neither did I, as I formerly had done, profess zeal for religion, or implicit faith in the Bible. I do not recollect ever to have deceived a human being on a matter of conscience ; and this I owe to my parents.

On one point the teachings of my father and mother strictly harmonized. My father sought to impress upon me that I could never become a gentleman unless I spoke, on all occasions, the exact truth; while my mother's teaching on that subject was that the Devil is the father of lies ; and that, if I told falsehoods, God would reckon me among the Devil's children. The organ of conscientiousness, if Spurzheim had made no mistake, may have aided these lessons. At all events, I grew up to regard a lie as of all sins the most heinous.

To this sentiment it was due that, in the end, my

conscience sharply reproached me for a deceptive silence, and I determined to tell my mother that my faith was changed. Once or twice I had resolved to do so after our evening devotions; but her sad face—for she had begun to surmise that all was not right—deterred me. Finally I stated the facts, plainly and succinctly, in a letter which I intrusted, one evening just before going to bed, to an aunt who was staying with us.

Had I known the effect my missive was to produce, I do not think I should have sent it. My mother did not appear next morning at breakfast, and I afterwards found out that she had spent the night in tears. She had always considered me, as she told me afterwards, the most devout among her children—the most careful for the future welfare of my soul, the most earnest in my zeal for the things of another world, her most attentive listener, too; and her disappointment, when she found me a backslider, was the greater because of the hopes she had cherished.

Unwilling to add to her sorrow by engaging with her in any religious debate, I fell back, for a solution of some of my difficulties, on a good-natured private tutor, named Manson, who, for a year or two, had been doing his best to teach my brother and myself Greek and Latin, after the tedious, old-fashioned manner. He had studied to qualify himself as a minister of the Scottish Kirk, was orthodox, but mild and tolerant also, and did not meddle with my spiritual education.

The old, old enigma, unsolved through past ages, and but dimly guessed at to-day, came up, of course—the enigma of evil and its punishment.

" Mr. Manson," I said one day, " does God send all

unbelievers to hell, and are they tormented there in the flames forever ? "

" Certainly.　Haven't you read that in the Bible ? "

" Yes.　Does not God love all men, and wish them to be happy ? "

" He surely does.　His tender mercies are over all His works."

" Yes ; I know the Bible says that too.　Then I don't understand about the unbelievers.　God need not have created them, unless he chose ; and he must have known, before they were born, that they would sin and that they would soon have to be burned to all eternity."

" But you know that God puts it in our power to save ourselves ; and if we neglect to do so, it is our fault, not His."

" But yet," persisted I, " God was not obliged to create a man that was sure to be an unbeliever.　Nobody said he must.　He might have prevented him from being born, and that would have prevented him from being wicked, and prevented him from going to hell.　Wouldn't it have been much better for such men not to be born, than to live a few years here, and then be tormented forever and ever ? "

I took my tutor's silent hesitation for consent, and added, " Well, then, if it would have been better, why didn't God do it ? "

" I cannot tell you," Mr. Manson said at last ; " and I advise you not to think of such things as these.　It *seems* better to our human reason ; but it cannot *be* better, or else God would have done so."

As may be supposed, this putting aside of the question was unsatisfactory ; and from that day I became a Universalist.

PAPER III.

I AM very desirous to estimate at its just value, and no more, the character of that remarkable man, my father.

Perhaps no one has been more favorably situated than I to judge him fairly and dispassionately. His child, but not (except during my youth) a believer in his specific plans for regenerating the world,—or to use his own favorite phrase, his "disciple,"—the partiality of a son is so far corrected by the scruples of a dissenter, that I hope to avoid alike the weakness of eulogy and the error of extenuation.

Robert Owen's ruling passion was the love of his kind, individually and collectively. An old friend of his said to me, jestingly, one day, when I had reached manhood, "If your good father had seven thousand children, instead of seven, I am sure he would love them devotedly." But the inference thence to be drawn is unfounded. If we *were* only seven, he was, to every one of us, a most affectionate, even indulgent, parent. His organ of adhesiveness could not have been less than that of benevolence; while the organs of hope and self-esteem were equally predominant. I think that these four sentiments, together with very large order and firmness, chiefly governed his life and shaped his destiny.

My father enabled his children to obtain many weapons which he himself never possessed. He had none of the advantages of regulated study. He did, indeed, between the ages of eight and ten, devour a good many volumes ; among them he himself enumerates Robinson Crusoe, Quarles (including no doubt his Emblems and his History of Samson), Pilgrim's Progress, Paradise Lost, Richardson's novels, Harvey's Meditations, Young's Night Thoughts, and many other religious books, chiefly Methodist ; but these works, justly famed as some of them are, must have made a strange jumble in an infant mind, left to digest their contents unguided even by a suggestion, and, as he tells us, " believing every word of them to be true."

When I first remember him, he read a good deal ; but it was chiefly one or two London dailies, with other periodicals as they came out. He was not, in any true sense of the word, a student. One who made his own way in life, unheeded by a single dollar, from the age of ten, could not well be. I never found, in his extensive library, a book with a marginal note, or even a pencil-mark of his, on a single page. He usually glanced over books, without mastering them ; often dismissing them with some such curt remark as that " the radical errors shared by all men made books of comparatively little value." Except statistical works, of which his favorite was " Colquhoun's Resources of the British Empire," I never remember to have seen him occupied in taking notes from any book whatever.

In this way he worked out his problems for human improvement to great disadvantage, missing a thousand things that great minds had thought and said before his time, and often mistaking ideas, that were truly his own, for novelties that no human being had heretofore given to the world.

Thus it happened that, while bringing prominently forward principles of vast practical importance that had been too much neglected both by governments and individuals, he forfeited, in a measure, the confidence of cultivated men by evident lack of familiarity with precedent authorities on the same subjects, and from inability to assign to a few favorite axioms their fitting place and just relative importance in a system of reformatory philosophy.

But to counterbalance these disadvantages he had eminent mental qualities that worked for him, with telling effect, whenever he came into contact with the masses, either as employer, in the early days of which I am now writing, or, later in life, as a public teacher. The earnestness of his convictions—all the stronger for imagining old ideas to be original—amounted to enthusiasm. I do not think that Napoleon was more untiring in his perseverance, or that Swedenborg had a more implicit confidence in himself; and to this was joined a temperament so sanguine that he was unable,—no matter what rebuffs he met with,—unable, even as an octogenarian, to conceive the possibility of ultimate failure in his plans. During the afternoon immediately preceding his death he was arranging, with the rector of the parish, for a series of public meetings (at which he promised to speak), looking to an organization that should secure to every child, in and near his native town, the best education which modern lights and knowledge could supply.

But I am speaking now of a period more than half a century past, when he was in the vigor of early manhood. At that time his two leading ideas of reform were temperance and popular instruction.

In those days Scotland would have been a rich field for Father Matthew's labors. Habits of drunkenness were common alike to rich and poor. They were associated with good-fellowship, and were tenderly dealt with, even by the Church. The orgies of Osbaldistone Hall, graphically described in Rob Roy, found their counterpart in many a Scottish manor. The old bacchanalian rhyme,

> " He who goes to bed, goes to bed sober,
> Falls as the leaves do, and dies in October ;
> But he that goes to bed, goes to bed mellow,
> Lives a long, jolly life, and dies an honest fellow—"

was quoted, half in earnest, as apology for the excesses which wealthy and respectable hosts, under the guise of hospitality, literally forced upon their guests, when the cloth was drawn and the ladies had abandoned the dinner-table to their riotous lords and masters.

I have heard my father, more than once, relate what happened on such an occasion, when he was one of the actors. He had been dining, with a party of eight or ten gentlemen and a few ladies, at the luxurious country-seat of a friend who had shown him much kindness. When the ladies withdrew, the host, having caused the butler to set out on the table two dozen bottles of port, sherry, and claret, locked the door, put the key in his pocket, and said to his guests, " Gentlemen, no shirking to-night ! Not a man leaves this room till these bottles are emptied."

No remark was made in reply, and the wine passed round. My father drank three glasses,—the utmost limit to which I have ever known him to go, though he habitually took a glass or two of sherry after dinner. At the fourth round he passed the bottles without filling. His host remonstrated, at first in jest, then in a half-angry tone, when the recusant persisted. Thereupon my father, approaching a front window which opened on the lawn, only a few feet below it, threw up the sash and leaped out, followed by three or four other guests.

This enraged their host. As the fugitives looked back they saw him upset the dinner-table with a violent kick, smashing bottles and glasses, and declaring, with an oath, that, if they didn't choose to drink that wine, nobody else should.

The deserters joined the ladies in the drawing-room, but the host did not reappear ; and my father, as leading conspirator, lost, and never regained, his friendship.

Under my grandfather's mild and easy rule, the vice which embittered poor Burns's life, and which blemishes some of his inimitable verses, had been very imperfectly checked. No grogshops, indeed, were permitted in the village, but liquor was obtained in the old town. Robert Owen, acting on his belief in the efficacy of circumstances, soon wrought a radical change. He had village watchmen, who patrolled the streets at night, and who were instructed to take down the name of every man found drunk. The inebriate was fined so much for the first offence, a larger sum for the second, the fines being deducted from his wages ; and the third offence resulted in dismissal, sometimes postponed if he showed sincere repentance. Then the people were so justly and kindly treated, their wages were so liberal, and their hours of labor so much shorter than the average factory-hours throughout Great Britain, that dismissal was felt to be a misfortune not to be lightly incurred.

The degree to which, after eight or ten years of such discipline, intemperance was weeded out in New Lanark may be judged by the following incident.

I was in the habit of going to " The Mills," as we called them, almost daily. One day, in my twelfth year, when I had accompanied my father on his usual morning visit, and we had reached a sidewalk which conducted from our porter's lodge to the main street of the village, I observed, at a little distance on the path before us, a man who stopped, at intervals, in his walk, and staggered from side to side.

" Papa," said I, " look at that man. He must have been taken suddenly ill."

" What do you suppose is the matter with him, Robert ? "

" I don't know. I never saw any man act so. Is he subject to fits ? Do you know him, papa ? "

" Yes, my dear, I know him, He is not subject to fits, but he is a very unfortunate man."

" What kind of illness has he ? "

My father stopped, looked first at the man before us, and then at me. " Thank God, my son," he said, at last, " that you have never before seen a drunken man."

Robert Owen's predominant love of order brought about another important reform. Elizabeth Hamilton, who spent several years as governess in a Scottish nobleman's family, has well described, in her Cottagers of Glenburnie, the careless untidiness and slatternly habits which, at the commencement of the present century, characterized the peasantry of Scotland. " I canna' be fashed," was the usual reply, if any one suggested that cleanliness, among the virtues, should rank next to godliness.

A writer, whose parents settled as workers in the New Lanark mills as early as 1803, states that, in those days, each family had but a single apartment, the houses being of one story only; and that before each door it was not unusual to find a dunghill. He tells us, also, that one of Robert Owen's first reforms was to add an additional story to every house, giving two rooms to most of the families; and that the dunghills were carried off to an adjoining farm, and a renewal of the nuisance was imperatively forbidden. *

As I recollect the village, its streets, daily swept at the expense of the company, were kept scrupulously clean; and its tidy appearance in every respect was the admiration of strangers.

A reform of a more delicate character, upon which my father ventured, met serious opposition. After each family became possessed of adequate accommodations, most of them still maintained, in their interior, disorder and uncleanliness. My father's earnest recommendations on the subject passed unheeded. He then called the work-people together, and gave several lectures upon order and cleanliness as among the Christian virtues. His audience heard, applauded, and went home content " to do as weel as their forbears, and no to heed English clavers."

Thereupon my father went a step further. He called a general meeting of the villagers; and, at his suggestion, a committee from among themselves was appointed, whose duty it was to visit each family weekly, and report in writing upon the condition of the

---

* Robert Owen at New Lanark, with a Variety of Interesting Anecdotes. By a former teacher at New Lanark; p. 4. Manchester and London, 1839.

house. This, according to the statement of the author last quoted, while grumblingly acquiesced in by the men, was received " with a storm of rage and opposition by the women." * They had paid their rent, and did no harm to the house ; and it was nobody's business but their own whether it was clean or dirty. If they had read Romeo and Juliet. which is not likely, I dare say they would have greeted the intruders as the Nurse did her prying master,—

> " Go, you cot-quean, go ;
> Get you to bed ! "

As it was, while a few, fresh from mop and scrubbing-brush, received the committee civilly, a large majority either locked their doors or met the inquisitors with abuse, calling them " bug-hunters " and other equally flattering names.

My father took it quietly ; showed no anger toward the dissenters ; encouraged the committee to persevere, but instructed them to ask admittance as a favor only ; and allowed the small minority, who had welcomed these domiciliary visits, to have a few plants each from his greenhouse. This gratuity worked wonders ; conciliation of manner gradually overcame the first jealousy of intrusion ; and a few friendly visits by my mother, quietly paid to those who were especially tidy in their households, still further quelled the opposition. Gradually the weekly reports of the committee became more full and more favorable.

Within the mills everything was punctiliously kept. Whenever I visited them with my father, I observed that he picked up the smallest flocks of cotton from the

* Work quoted, p. 5.

floor, handing them to some child near by, to be put in his waste-bag.

"Papa," said I one day, "what *does* it signify,—such a little speck of cotton?"

"The value of the cotton," he replied, "is nothing, but the example is much. It is very important that these people should acquire strict habits of order and economy."

In working out these and other reforms, my father, a scrupulous respecter of the rights of conscience and of entire freedom of opinion, never exercised, except in the case of habitual drunkards, the power of dismissal which his office as sole manager placed in his hands. The writer already quoted, who spent his youth and early manhood at New Lanark, bears testimony to this. "I never knew," he says, "of a single instance in which Mr. Owen dismissed a worker for having manfully and conscientiously objected to his measures." *

Even when necessary rules were violated, he was quick to soften and ready to forgive. The same writer tells us that during his childhood, he and another boy had slyly entered Braxfield woods to cut *shinties* (hockies, I believe, we generally call them) needed for a favorite sport. They proceeded in fear and trembling. "If Mr. Owen sees us, won't we catch it!" said the one to the other, as they found two prime ash-rods, with the requisite crook, and proceeded to use their knives upon them. Scarcely were the words pronounced and the trespassers busy at work, when Mr. Owen's hand was laid on one of their shoulders. They knew they were recognized, hung their heads, dropped

* Robert Owen at New Lanark, p. 5.

their knives, and remained silent and self-convicted. My father stood looking at them for some time, sorry, I dare say; that he had come upon them. Then he said, " Perhaps you don't know that what you are doing is wrong. It *is* wrong ; and if your parents never told you so they neglected their duty. Take the shinties you have cut for this time ; but if you should want more some other day, don't steal them : thieves never come to any good. Come to me, and I will give you permission ; then you can take them without doing any wrong."

The culprits slunk away ; and one of them says that when he went, seventeen years afterward, to hear Robert Owen lecture at " Bywater's Room," this act of clemency came back to his mind at the first sight of the benignant face, as freshly as the day it happened.*

This same boy, when past middle age, relates another reminiscence of his youth. At the age of seventeen he obtained a situation as teacher in the New Lanark schools, contracting to remain a year and a half. But after six months, prompted by an ambition not uncommon among the poorer classes in Scotland, he took a fancy to go to college. Ashamed, however, thus to break faith with his employer, he gave him no hint of his intention, and left abruptly, without even taking leave of him. When the college session closed, his funds being probably exhausted, he returned to New Lanark; and there one day, almost as unexpectedly as in the Braxfield woods, he met Robert Owen. He wished himself, he tells us, " a hundred miles off." But to his surprise and joy, his former employer came up to him at once, took him kindly by the hand, and, without alluding at all to the violated contract, asked him how

* Robert Owen at New Lanark, p. 8.

he liked college life in Glasgow ; adding an inquiry as to what he intended to do during the summer, and telling him he could have his former place again, if he wished it. " This," adds the narrator, who was a member of the Scottish Kirk, " this was genuine, practical Christianity." *

The New Lanark schools, and the cause of popular education generally, were the subjects which, at this period of my father's life, chiefly engrossed his attention. His first appearance as a speaker was as president at a public dinner, given in the city of Glasgow in 1812, to Joseph Lancaster, the well-known educational reformer. In the character of this gentleman, a Quaker, there was a strange mixture of honest, self-sacrificing zeal, and imprudent, self-indulgent ostentation. As early as 1789 he labored stoutly among the poor of Southwark, teaching a school of three hundred outcast children for years almost gratuitously. When his system finally attracted attention, and subscriptions poured in upon him, prosperity called forth weaknesses, and he squandered the money given for better purposes. I recollect that he drove up one afternoon, on invitation of my father, to Braxfield House, with four horses to his post-chaise,†—a luxury in which I never knew my father to indulge.

* Robert Owen at New Lanark, pp. 7, 8.

† The *post-chaise* of those days, partly crowded out now by the first-class railway carriages, was a strong, light vehicle, corresponding to our *coupé*, and seating comfortably two persons, though more could be crowded in, as in " John Gilpin's " case :—

> " My sister and my sister's child,
>   Myself and children three,
> Will fill the chaise ; so you must ride
>   On horseback, after we."

It was a pleasant, even luxurious mode of travelling; relays of horses

When, somewhat later, my father gave five thousand dollars to aid in the general introduction of the Lancastrian system of instruction, I remember that my mother, adverting to the four horses, demurred to the wisdom of so munificent a subscription. And I think that, in view of Lancaster's prodigality, she was in the right.

This Lancastrian system—one of mutual instruction, with *monitors*, selected from the pupils, as sub-teachers —was equally economical and superficial. It had its good points, however, and could be maintained where the funds were insufficient for anything better. My father, enthusiastic at first in its favor, gradually changed it for something more thorough and effective.

In the speech which Robert Owen made at the Lancaster dinner, the views which he afterwards elaborated touching the formation of character first peeped out. " General differences," he said, " bodily and mental, between inhabitants of various regions, are not inherent in our nature, nor do they arise from the respective soils on which we are born ; they are wholly and solely the effect of education." While it is difficult to exaggerate the importance of education, in the extended sense of the term, this proposition is clearly extravagant, ignoring as it does the influences, often dominant, of race, climate, soil, whether fertile or barren, and hereditary qualities transmitted through successive generations.

---

being obtained at intervals of about ten miles, and at the cost of thirty-five cents a mile for a single pair, the usual speed being from eight to ten miles an hour. Only the nobility and wealthy gentry indulged in four horses. The cheery, dashing mail-coach, with its red-coated guard and many-caped coachman—a cheaper and equally speedy conveyance—is now almost a thing of the past.

But the speech was applauded to the echo, and called
forth from a certain Kirkman Finlay—then the great
man of Glasgow—a laudatory letter.

" This induced me," says my father in his Autobiography, " to write my four Essays on the Formation of
Character." Of these hereafter.

As early as 1809 my father had laid the foundations of
a large building, afterwards called " The New Institution," designed to accommodate all the children of the
village. But the estimated cost, upwards of twenty
thousand dollars, alarmed his partners, who finally vetoed
the enterprise. Thereupon my father offered to give or
take for the establishment four hundred and twenty
thousand dollars, and at that rate they agreed to sell out
to him.

A new partnership was formed, the two principal
partners being sons-in-law of a Mr. Campbell, usually
called Campbell of Jura, being the proprietor of a small
island of that name, one of the Hebrides. Others
eagerly joined when it was shown, from the books of the
late partnership, that the net annual profits, on the average of the ten years it lasted, were fifteen per cent.

This second partnership continued three years only.
Campbell of Jura, a relative of my mother, had entrusted
to my father, for safe-keeping on interest, a hundred
thousand dollars. This he did unknown to his sons-in-
law, for family reasons. Finally it came to their ears,
and greatly exasperated them. Either from jealousy or
desire for large profits, they objected to the new school-
building, and carried a partnership vote against it ;
taking the ground that they were cotton-spinners, doing
business for profit, and had nothing to do with educating children: other manufacturers never troubled them-

selves about such matters. They took exception, also, to the salaries and wages paid, as being too high.

By this time, my father says, he was " completely tired of partners who cared for nothing but to buy cheap and sell dear." So he sought others, this time among philanthropists. Jeremy Bentham, the utilitarian philosopher, was one ; William Allen of London, a noted Quaker, was another ; Michael Gibbs, afterwards Lord Mayor of London, a third. There were three others, equally benevolent, but not noted names. Of these three one was a gentleman of leisure, who had never before been in business. I afterwards became well acquainted with him and his amiable family. My father, who highly esteemed him, and ultimately won his entire confidence, told me one day certain particulars of his life—a remarkable story that I never forgot. I think its lesson influenced, more or less, my whole life.

A man of letters, educated to every classical attainment, and the inheritor of a princely fortune, this gentleman had been able to gratify, at a wish, his cultivated tastes. His marriage was fortunate, and his children grew up around him with the fairest promise. He had a handsome town house in a fashionable square in London, and a country-seat six or eight miles off in the midst of one of those magnificent English parks,— the ideal of stately rural elegance,—with its trimly kept lawn and its wide-spreading chase, dotted over with clumps of noble old trees, where the deer sought refuge from the noonday heat, and a lair at nightfall.

Its owner had travelled over Europe and brought back, as mementos of his journey, paintings and statuary by some of the best masters, ancient and modern, with which to adorn his favorite retreat. The house itself, in

which I spent some happy days, with its rich marble
columns and balustrades, was a fine specimen of the
purest Palladian marble, where all that luxurious refinement could devise had been unsparingly lavished.

There my father—during a brief interval in his own
public life of incessant bustle—found his friend, with no
occupation more pressing than to pore over the treas-
ures of his library, and no graver care than to superin-
tend the riches of a conservatory where wealth had
brought together, from half the world, its choicest
plants and flowers. They spent some days of undisturbed quiet : not an incident beyond the conversation
of a sedate and intellectual family circle and the arrival
and departure of a friend or two to break the complete
repose.

Delightful my father thought it, in contrast with the
busy turmoil he had left ; and one day he said to his
host, " I've been thinking that if I ever met a man who
has nothing to desire, you must be he. You have health,
cultivation, a charming family. You have gathered
round you every comfort wealth can give, the choicest
of all that nature and art can supply. Are you not
completely happy ? "

Never, my father said to me, would he forget the sad,
unexpected reply : "Happy ! Ah, Mr. Owen, I committed one fatal error in my youth, and dearly have I
paid for it ! I started in life without an object, almost
without an ambition. My temperament disposed me to
ease, and I indulged it. I said to myself, ' I have all
that I see others contending for ; why should I struggle ? ' I knew not the curse that lights on those who
have never to struggle for anything. I ought to have
created for myself some definite pursuit, literary, scien-

tific, artistic, political, no matter what, so there was something to labor for and to overcome. Then I might have been happy."

My father suggested that he was scarcely past the prime of life, and that in a hundred ways he might still benefit others, while occupying himself. " Come and spend a month or two with me at Braxfield," he added. " You have a larger share in the Lanark mills than any of my partners. See for yourself what has been done for the work-people there and for their children ; and give me the benefit of your suggestions and your aid."

" It is too late," was the reply. " The power is gone. Habits are become chains. You can work and do good ; but for me,—in all the profitless years gone by I seek vainly for something to remember with pride, or even to dwell on with satisfaction. I have thrown away a life. I feel, sometimes, as if there were nothing remaining to me worth living for."

And neither then, nor at any future time, did this strange martyr to leisure visit the establishment in which he had invested a hundred and fifty thousand dollars.

But in this I anticipate. It was in the year 1813 that my father, then in London and engaged in publishing the first two of his Essays on the Formation of Charac-ter, made the acquaintance of his new partners ; and he submitted to them these Essays as embodying the prin-ciples on which he proposed to manage the New Lanark establishment. They were briefly :—

1. Man does not form his own character : it is formed for him by the circumstances that surround him.

2. Man is not a fit subject of praise or blame.

3. Any general character, good or bad, may be given

to the world, by applying means which are, to a great extent, under the control of human governments.

Important propositions, doubtless, with great underlying truths; but not, as the author claimed in his title, A New View of Society.

Paul had already said: " What hast thou that thou didst not receive ? Now if thou didst receive it, why dost thou glory as if thou hadst not received it ? "

Both Calvin and Luther had gone further, denying to man free-will.

Hobbes, about the year 1654, had said: " Liberty and necessity are consistent. . . . . God, that seeth and disposeth all things, seeth also that the liberty of man, in doing what he will, is accompanied with the necessity of doing that which God will, and no more nor less.*

Priestley, more than a hundred years later, had written: " There is some fixed law of nature respecting the will, ... which is never determined without some motive of choice." †

And this last writer, at least, seems to have estimated as highly as Robert Owen the doctrine of which he is a chief advocate ; for he says : " I the less wonder at the general hesitation to admit the doctrine of necessity in its full extent, when I consider that there is not, I believe, in the whole compass of human speculation, an instance in which the indisputable consequences of any simple proposition are so numerous and important ; " and as to these consequences he adds : " Great and glorious as they are, it requires so much strength of mind to comprehend them that (I wish to say it with the least offence possible) I cannot help considering

---

* Leviathan, p. 108.   † Philosophical Necessity, Sec. I.

the doctrine as that which will always distinguish the real moral philosopher from the rest of the world." *

But here the difference in the minds of Joseph Priestley and Robert Owen shows itself; for Priestley sagaciously adds: " Like all other great and practical truths, even those of Christianity itself, its actual influence will not always be so great as, from theory, it might be expected to be ; " while Owen, advocating a phase of the same principle, declares: " No human power can now impede its rapid progress. Silence will not retard its course, and opposition will give increased celerity to its movements. The commencement of the work will, in fact, insure its accomplishment. Henceforth all the irritating angry passions, arising from ignorance of the true cause of bodily and mental character, will gradually subside, and be replaced by the most frank and conciliating confidence and good-will."

My father, after his own fashion, was a believer in the speedy advent of the millennium. It has always seemed to me a strange thing that a man who had so much practical knowledge of the world should have made the mistake of imagining that when one has set before human beings the means of being wise and happy, one has insured the certain and speedy adoption of these means, by the individual and by the government. If that were so there would be no drunkards ; for the veriest sot will not, in his lucid intervals, deny the blessings of temperance. My father, carried away by zeal and hope to benefit his race, failed to note the cogent fact that our civilization of to-day has not reached that point of progress when present self-indulgence shall no longer rule the majority of mankind.

* Preface to Philosophical Necessity, p. xxi.

Then his propositions lost part of their force because they were too sweeping and insufficiently guarded; for example, when he asserted that praise, even of the best man, is irrational. Eulogy, laudation,—self-laudation especially,—is irrational; but if we are just, we approve, we commend the conduct of the good; if we are warm-hearted, we like, we love them for their goodness. In strictness it may be that they cannot help doing good actions. Then, if not for the actions, at least for the disposition of mind which impels to them, they are entitled to commendation, they are worthy of love. So of the wicked. We cannot help disapproving a propensity to vicious indulgence; we cannot help disliking him who indulges such a propensity. The true point is, that we ought not to hate him; and that all punishments should be reformatory, not vindictive. We know the evil deed; we can never, as Burns reminds us, know the temptations resisted, that may have preceded it.

So of the third proposition, looking to governments as the chief agents of human regeneration. Goldsmith had said :—

> " How small, of all that human hearts endure,
> That part which laws or kings can cause or cure."

He and Robert Owen ran equally into extremes. But Robert Owen had this apology, that he regarded it as the legitimate province of government to provide for and educate all the children of the land. In New Lanark, however, he merely proposed to give a good common-school education to all the children of his work-people ; and to this end he obtained the assent of his proposed partners.

He showed them that the net profits of the concern, for the last four years, *had exceeded fifty per cent* on the capital invested (eighty-four thousand pounds); but he did not conceal from them that the reforms he had in view would materially diminish these.

His old partners refused to let him fix a sum which he would give or take for the property, insisted on putting it up at auction, and set to work to decry its value; busily spreading the report that the mills, under the management of a visionary like Owen, were not worth more than forty thousand pounds. But my father, meanwhile, quietly obtained permission from his philanthropic associates to bid three times that amount, if necessary.

The day of sale was one of great excitement in Glasgow; and the large hall in which it took place was crowded to the doors. The bidding was protracted; the former partners, who bid in person, retiring several times for consultation, while my father's solicitor, who had his instructions once for all, bid up, to the utter astonishment of his opponents and the public, to a hundred and fourteen thousand one hundred pounds; at which sum the property was knocked down to him.*

The defeated party, anticipating success as a certainty, had incautiously invited their friends and well-wishers, in advance, to a public congratulatory dinner. Crestfallen as they were, they had to play the hosts; and their mortification reached its climax, when a certain Colonel Hunter, a leading newspaper editor and a wag, rose to propose the health of the favorites of fortune

* The equivalent of five hundred and seventy thousand dollars; but as money rates, now and then, equal to more than three quarters of a million to-day.

who had just sold for a hundred and fourteen thousand pounds a property which they valued at forty. " A bumper, gentlemen," he cried, " to a victory so unexampled ! " The Colonel had his jest against the Campbells and their friends ; but it was the last time he sat at their dinner-table.

Their disappointment was to receive an additional aggravation. William Allen, with two others of the new partners, Quakers like himself, had come on to Glasgow to await the issue of the sale, and they accompanied my father to view their purchase. The author from whose pamphlet I have already extracted gives an account of their reception.* And my father, in his Autobiography, supplies additional particulars.†

The Scotch, though a warm-hearted people, are not usually demonstrative . But I remember the deep anxiety our work-people showed for weeks before the sale, and the enthusiasm with which they hailed my father's success.

The writer alluded to says : " Never will the inhabitants of New Lanark forget the afternoon of that day on which the sale of the mills to Mr. Owen took place. A horseman had been despatched, at speed, to make known the result. It was now in vain to check the sincere and unbounded joy of the workers. The managers saw and felt it ; the people having unanimously

* Robert Owen at New Lanark, pp. 15, 16. The author says of himself: " Brought up in the Church of Scotland, having never received a farthing from Mr. Owen but what I rendered equivalent service for, being in no way dependent upon any one connected with the ' Social System,' it may be reasonably inferred that any statements made by me which tend to reflect credit on Mr. Owen could neither have been dictated by love to his principles nor published from selfish motives."

† Autobiography, pp. 97, 98.

resolved to testify their feelings by an act of public rejoicing. The mills were stopped. Bands of music
played merrily through the village, and the windows
were illuminated, as for some great national triumph.
The next day the work-people, with hundreds from the
borough town and surrounding country, met Mr. Owen
and his new partners three miles from New Lanark and
proceeded to ungear the horses from the carriage. It
was in vain that Mr. Owen warmly remonstrated,
reminding the crowd that the workingman had too long
already been treated as the brute. Accompanied with
bands of music and the acclamations of some thousands,
the people bore their benefactor triumphantly to Braxfield ; where, to the dense and happy multitude, he delivered an impressive address."

My father states that when his Quaker friends first
saw the crowd rushing to the carriage and calling to the
postilions to stop, they were seriously alarmed ; but
when they heard the cheers, and saw the men relieving
each other at intervals, and found the cavalcade gradually increasing, and then, the procession passing first
through the old town and afterwards through the village,
the people everywhere filling the windows or crowding
out of their houses to witness it, and testifying by the
liveliest demonstrations their gratitude and delight, the
amazement of these sober disciples of George Fox, unused to such scenes, was equalled by their gratification ;
and they wrote, in glowing terms, an account of their
reception to the other London partners.

The management of the mills and schools pleased
them much, except in one particular ; dancing had been
introduced by my father as one of the school exercises.
But Barclay, in his Apology, had taught : " Games and

sports, plays, dancing, consist not with the gravity and godly fear which the Gospel calls for ; " and William Allen, especially, held strictly to all the rules set forth in that text-book of early Quakerism, as I well remember. For one day, a year or two later, dining with him at his London residence, in Plough Court, Lombard Street, I had a lesson, not easily forgotten, teaching me how to walk in the strait way.

I was sitting next to a gentleman in whose conversation I was interested. We had roast beef for dinner ; and when I had exhausted the quantity first sent me, my host asked, " Will thee have more roast beef ? "

" Thank you, no more," I replied, mechanically, engrossed in something my neighbor had just said. By and by I bethought me that I was still hungry ; and, begging leave to change my mind, asked for a further supply.

" Robert, thee has already refused," was all the answer I got, in solemn tones of reproof. Had I not said I would take no more ? I must not be suffered to tell a lie.* It was better to let me eke out my dinner with vegetables.

To such a man, not dancing only, but music also, was a " sinful divertisement." † But the more liberal sentiments of the majority of the partners overruled him

---

* The definition, here implied, of a falsehood, reminds me of a story which I have somewhere read. A Quaker, walking near London, on a road leading to that city, met a youth who asked his way, thus wording his question : " This is not the road to London, is it ? "

" Friend," was the stern reply, " I understand thee not. Thou first tellest me a lie, and then askest me a question."

† " As to their artificial music, either by organs or other instruments or voice, we have neither example nor precept for it in the New Testament." —Barclay's Apology, p. 442.

in this matter ; so that, under protest of himself and one or two of his rigid friends, the reels, Highland fling, and country dances still went on.

The villagers were almost all Presbyterians ; but (in those days at least) dancing, a favorite national amusement in Scotland from the earliest times, was not forbidden by the Kirk. My mother had strong scruples about our walking on Sunday, except to church and back again ; but she sent us to dancing-school while we lived in Glasgow ; and when at Braxfield, the village dancing-master came twice a week to give us lessons.

This artist, whose name was Dodge, had "graduated," as he was wont to tell us, in Edinburgh ; whence he returned with exalted ideas of his profession. No Pundit, skilled in Sanscrit lore, no Doctor of Divinity in the Middle Ages, could have indulged in manner more stately or diction more pompous. After a year or two's instruction in the various Scottish dances and the cotillon, as the quadrille was then called, he announced to us his intention of going a step further ; not to teach us the waltz, for that was spoken of in Scotland then as we speak of the *can-can* now ; nor the *German*, for that was an unknown term ; but something very different.

He came, one day, more elaborately dressed than usual, and, after he had called us up on the floor, paused, kit in hand, before the lesson began. "Young ladies and gentlemen," he said at length ; "I have had the honor of teaching you, so far, a few of those simpler exercises in the polite art of dancing which no person moving in good society can possibly dispense with ; and, on the whole, I am not dissatisfied with your progress. I shall now proceed to induct you into the mys-

teries of a higher order of motion. I propose to give
you some idea of the inimitable Minuet de la Cour, and
the Gavotte, which is, as it were, its appropriate pero-
ration. I use the term, 'give you an idea,' advisedly ;
for I can do no more than that. A man's life is too
short to learn to walk a minuet properly."

The earnest gravity and emphasis with which he pronounced the closing axiom, and the graceful wave of
his bow as he declaimed, impressed us with mingled
awe and curiosity; and I have a hundred times since
recalled the incident with a smile. I am not sure but
that the minuet (if it *be* old-fashioned) might still be
taught with advantage ; not for public exhibition on the
ball-room floor, as in Sir Charles Grandison's day, but
as a useful exercise tending to easy grace of motion and
elegance of carriage.

In the main, my father was now free to carry out his
plans of education. He gradually completed and fitted
up, at a cost of between thirty and forty thousand dollars, the spacious school-house, the building of which
his former partners had arrested. It had five large
rooms or halls, besides smaller apartments, and a bath-
room on an extensive scale, sufficing for the accommodation of from four to five hundred children. No
charge whatever was made ; and not only all the children of the work-people, but also children of all families living within a mile of the village, were thus gratuitously instructed.

In this institution a novel feature was introduced.
Pestalozzi and Oberlin have each been spoken of as
originating the infant-school system ; but my father
seems to have been its true founder. I have found no
proof whatever that either of them even thought of

doing what he carried out.   He brought together upwards of a hundred children, from *one* to six years of
age, under two guardians, James Buchanan and Mary
Young.   No attempt was made to teach them reading
or writing, not even their letters ; nor had they any set
lessons at all.   Much of their time was spent in a spacious play-ground.   They were trained to habits of order and cleanliness ; they were taught to abstain from
quarrels, to be kind to each other.   They were amused
with childish games and with stories suited to their
capacity.   Two large, airy rooms were set apart, one
for those under four years and one for those from four
to six.   This last room was furnished with paintings,
chiefly of animals, and a few maps.   It was also supplied with natural objects from the gardens, fields, and
woods.   These suggested themes for conversation, or
brief, familiar lectures ; but there was nothing formal,
no tasks to be learned, no readings from books.
" When the best means of instruction are known and
adopted," says my father in his Autobiography, " I
doubt whether books will be used until children attain
their tenth year."   But this he could not carry out at
New Lanark, as the children were admitted to the mills
and were usually sent thither by their parents at twelve
years of age.

No corporal punishment, nor threat, nor violent language was permitted on the part of the teachers.   They
were required to treat the children with the same kindness which they exacted from them toward each other.

Some years later an attempt was made by a London
association, headed by the Marquis of Lansdowne and
Lord Brougham, to introduce infant-schools into the
British metropolis.   They obtained a teacher from New

Lanark. But they undertook to do too much, and so failed in their object. They had lessons, tasks, study. Not satisfied with moral training and instructive amusement, as at New Lanark, they sought prematurely to develop the intellectual powers. The tender brain of the infant was over-excited ; more harm than good was done ; and the system fell, in a measure, into disrepute, until Frœbel, in his *Kindergartens*, brought things back to a more rational way.

I visited our village infant-school almost daily for years ; and I have never, either before or since, seen such a collection of bright, clean, good-tempered, happy little faces.

PAPER IV.

I WAS somewhat precocious in my literary preten-
sions. My father's habit, during my early youth, was
to move from the country, for the three winter months,
into that garden-surrounded cottage in the heart of our
village where he and my mother had spent some of
their earliest married days ; I think he did so that his
work-people and he might become better acquainted.
One of these removes gave rise to my first effort in
authorship. I still remember its pathetic exordium :—

" Farewell, Braxfield,—a long farewell to all thy
beauties ! No longer shall our jocund footsteps trace
thy winding walks, nor our joyous voices sound through
thy delightful groves. We now bid adieu to thee "—
And a good deal more in the Araminta-Sophonisba
vein.

Neither my father nor my mother was critical in literary matters, and my aunts, who were living with us,
were blinded by partiality. The result was to lay the
foundation, in the boy of eleven unduly commended for
a trivial rhapsody, of a false estimate of his own abilities ; which, similarly fed, grew for years, and required
many years more to chasten it.

About this time—the great struggle with Napoleon
being then at its height—several French officers, prison-
ers of war on parole, were quartered in the old town of
Lanark. From one of these, Monsieur Levasseur, a

handsome young fellow, my brother William and I had
our first lessons in French; and my father, now and
then, invited him to our table, with a result, no doubt,
little expected. I observed that Monsieur gradually
became more spruce and showy in his dress and appointments, carrying a gold (?)-headed cane; and that
from his dark, sleek, carefully brushed and curled hair
came the odor of some perfumed oil. On Christmas
eve he handed me, with a flourish, a letter addressed to
my Aunt Mary. It was not closed, and he told me I
might read it, which of course I did. It began by saying that, at this season of *fêtes*, when cherished friends
were invoking blessings on those who were well beloved, the heart had pushed him to imitate that mode,
and to offer her his profound congratulations. Then it
ran off into various sentimental effusions which were not
very intelligible to me,—making no direct offer of marriage, but speaking (in very touching terms, I thought)
about the " solace, very soft, of the friendship of heart,
and the charms inexpressible of the life domestic."
That seemed to me all right, and I duly delivered the
missive. Great was my surprise at the effect it produced!

My Aunt Mary, who is still living, was then about
twenty-one years old; a belle, rather tall and pretty, a
good musician and a graceful dancer; stylish, too,
having returned a year or two before from a fashionable
boarding-school. Her three sisters and herself, all unmarried and considered very good matches, made our
house their home.

She and her elder sister, Jane, a little beauty with a
charming figure, had both had sundry very eligible
offers of marriage, among others from officers of rank

in the British Army ; and, as they had rejected these, it may be imagined with what feelings the rich belle perused the overtures of an obscure foreigner, of whom nothing was known except that he had held a lieutenant's commission in an enemy's ranks.

" Just to think of it ! " she exclaimed ; " as if I had ever given the man the least little scrap of encouragement ! He must be downright crazy." Then to me : " It was very wrong of you indeed, Robert, to bring me any such letter as that."

" Why, how could I tell, Aunt, whether you would like it or not ? It's very polite."

" Like it ! polite ! The most impudent— " There she checked herself, remembering no doubt that he was my teacher ; then enclosed the tabooed letter in a blank envelope, and bade me return it to the writer the very first opportunity.

" And what shall I say to him, Aunt Mary ? "

" That if he ever repeats the offence—no, say nothing, except that I have forbidden you ever to receive such a letter again."

I was very sorry for poor Monsieur, who wore for a week the air of a martyr, and went to no further expense, I think, for the sweet-scented oil.

My father was informed by his sister-in-law of this piece of presumption, for which she wished the Frenchman to be dismissed at once. But taking pity, probably, on the poor fellow, he continued him as our teacher so long as the war lasted. I was glad of this, for he was very good-natured, and I made progress under his tuition, especially during long walks with him, when only French was spoken. But I observed that he did not appear at our dinner-table again,—a concession, I imagine, to the offended dignity of my sensitive aunt.

We had many interesting visitors at Braxfield, some of whom remained with us for a day or two ; among them one of the Edgeworths, brother of that Maria to whose labors for young people we children were indebted for so much pleasure. He was a bright, cheery youth, who sank considerably in my father's estimation by preferring, to long disquisitions with him on the formation of character, a good romp with us. Of course, we thought him charming, especially when he propounded sundry games, among them the composition of impromptu verses on some given theme. My verses, unfortunately for my humility, were voted the best. I took to writing ballads, and there is no saying how far the poetic frenzy might have carried me had I not perused soon after The Lay of the Last Minstrel,—the finest poem, I think, Scott ever wrote. At that time, too, were just appearing Byron's best works : first, Childe Harold, then the Giaour, and the Corsair. I was fascinated by their fiery power, and thoroughly convinced that my vocation was not that of a poet.

Other works, of a very different character, fell into my hands about this time. Sir Charles Grandison, despite its stately formality, did me good. I think its tone of old-fashioned, homely chivalry has a healthy influence on young people. Paradise Lost had great attractions, but tended much to confuse my Biblical lore. As has doubtless happened to others, it was not till many years afterwards that I learned to distinguish between Milton's apocryphal story and the orthodox Bible narrative. The Pilgrim's Progress, too, which I read over and over again, further entangled my theolog-

ical ideas.   Christian's journey and adventures won my
belief as fully as those of the Israelites, led by Moses
toward the promised land.

These were works which the children of a former
century had read and pondered.   But my boyhood was
at a period when a branch of literature, till then underrated, and indeed little worth, suddenly assumed new
character and proportions.   One by one, the marvellous productions of the prince of novelists startled and
charmed the British public.   Guy Mannering, The
Antiquary, Rob Roy, Ivanhoe, and all the rest,—what
sunny memories, what hours of rapt enjoyment, do the
very titles still call up !

But events were approaching that were to leave a
deeper impress on my character than books, whether
of fancy or of graver tone.   I was a strong, hearty boy,
fond of all rough sports, a very fair rider, following the
fox-hounds on a clever dun pony in a manner that
called forth commendation from my companions.   The
young country gentry of that day, in the heart of
Scotland were a good-natured, rollicking set, given to
violation of the Third Commandment and quite willing
to risk their necks any day at a five-bar gate.

One instance of profanity, I remember, greatly scan-
dalized me, brought up as I had been to venerate ministers of the Gospel.   I was sitting on my impatient pony,
one gray morning, next to a jolly, well-mounted curate
who had just joined the hunt.   The hounds had been
turned into a dense copse, and we were in momentary
expectation of the signal announcing that Reynard had
got away before the dogs, when a horseman, riding up,
told us that " the stupid animal had suffered himself to be
killed only a few yards from where he was unearthed."

"D—n the creature!" broke forth my clerical neighbor; "God d—n such a fox!" Adding, perhaps in
reply to my look of astonishment, "And that's a
good deal for a clergyman to say."

After a time we came upon another, more satisfactory
specimen of the vulpine race, who got a fair start before
the hounds, and we followed him under full cry. Over
a field or two, where the fences were low, I kept up with
a young officer mounted on a beautiful hunter, nearly
thorough-bred. Finally, there presented itself before us
an enclosure of a formidable character, flanked by a
double ditch; between the two ditches a mound, on
which was a light fence with stakes and rail,—the whole
upwards of five feet high, and the stretch, from outside
to outside of the ditches, a good fourteen or fifteen feet.
They say that a thoroughly trained Irish hunter will
light, like a cat, sideways on the summit of such a
mound, and then, with a second bound, clear the farther
ditch. But I never witnessed such an exploit, and our
horses were incapable of performing it. I pulled up, of
course; but my military companion, after a good look
at what awaited him, patted his horse on the neck with
the words, "O, Jamie, lad, we're going to get a deevil
of a tumble," and put him unhesitatingly at the leap.
The spirited animal cleared it handsomely with his fore-
feet; but one hind foot caught in the top rail, and horse
and man rolled into the farther ditch. I held my breath,
fearing that the rider was killed; but he was up again in
a few seconds smirched, indeed, from head to foot with
the contents of the mud-puddle, but evidently unhurt;
for he sprang as lightly into the saddle as if nothing had
happened, and was off at a gallop before I recovered
from my surprise.

I rode ignominiously round by a farm-gate and was completely thrown out, while the young dare-devil came in triumphantly, first at the death.

But for me all such sports were soon to end. When about twelve years old I had the measles ; and, though I recovered easily, I had afterwards, from undue exposure I believe, a terrible relapse, resulting in high and unmanageable fever and some sort of inflammation of the chest. They gave me foxglove and other powerful medicines, and applied, on breast and stomach, a large Spanish-fly blister, which was kept open for a week. Every day during that week, as I was afterwards told, my death was expected; during a month I continued in great danger, and for six months more I was confined to the house.

By this illness my nervous system was completely unstrung; indeed, prostrated to such degree that the slightest noise, even an abrupt word or the unexpected opening of a door, caused me to start with terror. Some one had to remain constantly in the room ; for I could not endure to be left alone, even for a moment. So abnormal was the condition of my nerves of touch, that the sheets of my bed seemed to me thicker than sail-cloth, and the blankets like inch boards. Then, too, I had a constantly repeated sensation of sinking down, down, as to the centre of the earth ; and the slightest unforeseen incident, pleasant or unpleasant, moved me to tears. I remember that the doctor ordered my head to be shaved, and that a wig was bought for me ; but the sight of it and the idea of the head-shaving threw me into such a paroxysm of grief, that it was abandoned and the matter compounded by having my hair cut short.

These symptoms subsided very gradually, lingering after the first half-year had passed and I had been at last permitted once more to mount Donald—that was my pony's name—and enjoy a short ride daily. A full year elapsed before I was able to part with any intimate friend, even for a few days, with equanimity, or to read aloud any touching episode in history,—the death of Queen Mary of Scotland, for example.

My father and mother were very considerate, never adverting to this nervous weakness. I was terribly ashamed of it, but it was no more under my control than were the beats of my pulse. I did not regain reasonable command of my sensations till college-life, with regular gymnastic training, brought hardening influence. Then I gradually got rid of all mere physical nervous debility, so that throughout life my equanimity has not been easily disturbed by sudden danger, nor unduly excited by partisan abuse ; and even to this day I can carry a full cup or strike a billiard-ball as steadily as I could fifty years ago. The mental effects, however, of that sickness, carrying me to the verge of death, have never been wholly removed. Since then my emotions seem to lie nearer the surface than formerly ; to be more readily called forth by pity, by admiration, by love. I have continued to be more quickly excited by wrong to indignation, and more easily moved to tears; but though my emotional nature was thus intensified by the ordeal through which it passed, the change did not involve any tendency to nervous anxiety or to undue thought for the morrow,—still less to any dark forebodings as to the future. So little have I been prone to expect that things would turn out ill, that I have to set a constant watch on a disposition to careless incaution

Many of our friends said, and I think my parents believed, that my chance of attaining manhood was doubtful. But let those who find themselves, in youth, as
nigh unto death and as wearied waiters for convales-
cence as I, take heart. From that time to the present
I have not had what might be called a serious illness;
and, at this day, I am free from the infirmities—even
from the usual ailments—of age.

Before I finally recovered, however, I was overtaken
by a serious affection of the eyes, the balls becoming
blood-shot and the lids inflamed. The usual prescrip-
tions by an oculist proving ineffectual, my mother,
somewhat alarmed, decided to try the effect of sea-
bathing, renting two rooms for my brother William and
myself, in Portobello, the watering-place of Edinburgh,
where our windows looked out on the beautiful Frith of
Forth. There we were put in charge of a kind,
motherly old lady, with whom instructions were left
that, so we kept within reasonable bounds, we might
order what we pleased for dinner.

The first day, after mature deliberation, we concluded
that there was nothing, in the way of delicacies, superior
to mashed potatoes browned before the fire, and apple-
pie ; so we decided on that bill of fare. The second day,
failing to hit upon anything else as good, and seeing no
reason why we should have anything short of the best, we
renewed the order ; and so on for several days in succession, much to the amazement of our good hostess. It
was not until the sixth day, I think, that it occurred to
us that the *toujours perdrix* plan did not work quite sat-
isfactorily, and that we should like pie and potatoes
better if we tried something else for a few days.

Three or four months of relaxation, most agreeably

spent, sufficed to effect a radical cure ; and here, again, it may comfort others similarly afflicted to learn that my eyes have never troubled me since ; and that—though now on what is called the wrong side of seventy, but what I think ought to be called the *right* side, as being nearer home—my sight, at a distance, is nearly as good as it ever was, and spectacles are less necessary than they were twenty years ago ; for I can read fair-sized type by daylight without them.

When I returned to Braxfield, my father, rightly judging that further suspension of regular study and change of scene were needed to confirm my health, took me with him, in the summer of 1815, on a journey throughout England and Scotland, which he made for the purpose of collecting evidence touching the condition of children employed in the cotton, woollen, linen, and silk factories of the kingdom.

At a meeting which he had previously held at the Tontine, Glasgow, he had introduced two resolutions recommending petitions to Parliament,—one for the remission of the duty on imported cotton ; the other for the protection of factory children from labor beyond their strength. The first passed unanimously ; the second was lost by an overwhelming majority. Thereupon my father determined to agitate the matter himself.

As a preliminary measure we visited all the chief factories in Great Britain. The facts we collected seemed to me terrible almost beyond belief. Not in exceptional cases, but as a general rule, we found children *of ten years old worked regularly fourteen hours a day*, with but half an hour's interval for the mid-day meal, which was eaten in the factory. In the fine-yarn cotton mills (producing from a hundred and twenty to three hundred hanks to the pound), they were subjected to this labor in a temperature usually exceeding seventy-five degrees; and in all the cotton factories they breathed an atmosphere more or less injurious to the lungs, because of the dust and minute cotton fibres that pervaded it.

In some cases we found that greed of gain had impelled the mill-owners to still greater extremes of inhumanity, utterly disgraceful, indeed, to a civilized nation. Their mills were run fifteen and, in exceptional cases, *sixteen* hours a day with a single set of hands; and they did not scruple to employ children of both sexes from the age of eight. We actually found a considerable number under that age.

It need not be said that such a system could not be maintained without corporal punishment. Most of the overseers openly carried stout leather thongs, and we frequently saw even the youngest children severely beaten.

We sought out the surgeons who were in the habit of attending these children, noting their names and the facts to which they testified. Their stories haunted my dreams. In some large factories, from one-fourth to one-fifth of the children were either cripples or otherwise deformed, or permanently injured by excessive toil, sometimes by brutal abuse. The younger children seldom held out more than three or four years without severe illness, often ending in death.

When we expressed surprise that parents should voluntarily condemn their sons and daughters to slavery so intolerable, the explanation seemed to be that many of the fathers were out of work themselves, and so were, in a measure, driven to the sacrifice for lack of bread; while others, imbruted by intemperance, saw with indifference an abuse of the infant faculties compared to which the infanticide of China may almost be termed humane.

In London my father laid before several members of Parliament the mass of evidence he had collected, and a bill which he had prepared forbidding the employment in factories of child-workers under twelve years of age, and fixing the hours they might be employed at ten a day. Finally, he obtained from the elder Sir Robert Peel (father of the well-known Prime Minister, and then between sixty and seventy years old), a promise to introduce this humane measure into the House of Commons. Sir Robert, then one of the richest cotton-spinners in the kingdom, and a member of twenty-five years' standing, possessed considerable influence. Had he exerted it heartily, I think (and my father thought) that the measure might have been carried the first session. But, in several interviews with him to which I accompanied my father, even my inexperience detected a slackness of purpose and an indisposition to offend his fellow-manufacturers, who were almost all violently opposed to the measure. I think it probable that his hesitation was mainly due to a consciousness that it ill became him to denounce cruelties, in causing which he had himself had a prominent share. The bill dragged through the House for four sessions; and when passed at last, it was in a mutilated and comparatively valueless form.*

---

* Several of our manufacturing States have followed the English example, and have added a requirement that factory children shall attend a day-school during three months of each year. Massachusetts forbids the em-

Pending its discussion I frequently attended with my father the sessions of a committee of the House appointed to collect evidence and report on the condition of factory children. He was a chief witness, and one day had to stand (and did stand unmoved) a bitter cross-examination by Sir George Philips, a " cotton lord," as the millionnaires among mill-owners were then popularly called. This oppressor of childhood questioned my father as to his religious opinions, and other personal matters equally irrelevant, in a tone so insolent, that, to my utter shame, I could not repress my tears. They were arrested, however, when Lord Brougham (then plain Henry) called the offender to order, and after commenting, in terms that were caustic to my heart's content, on the impertinent character of Sir George's cross-examination, moved that it be expunged from the records of the committee,—a motion which was carried without a dissenting voice.

Throughout the four years during which this reformatory measure was in progress, my father (in truth the soul of the movement) was unremitting in his endeavors to bring the evidence he had obtained before the public. The periodical press aided him in this; and I remember that one touching story, in particular, had a wide circulation. It came out in evidence given

ployment of children under ten years, and limits the working time of children under fifteen to ten hours a day. Rhode Island forbids employment under twelve years, and limits the working time to eleven hours a day. Connecticut has stringent regulations in regard to school attendance, but does not specifically limit age nor hours of labor.

The English law, though passed at first in mutilated form, was at a later period and after a severe contest, amended and improved. It has doubtless saved hundreds of thousands of helpless little beings from slavish toil and premature death.

before the committee by an assistant overseer of the poor. He was called upon to relieve a father out of employment, and found his only child, a factory girl, quite ill; and he testifies further as follows : " Some time after, the father came to me with tears in his eyes. 'What's the matter, Thomas ?' I asked. He said, ' My little girl is gone ; she died in the night ; and what breaks my heart is this,—though she was not able to do her work, I had to let her go to the mill yesterday morning. She promised to pay a little boy a half-penny on Saturday, if he would help her so she could rest a little. I told her he should have a penny.' At night the child could not walk home, fell several times by the way, and had to be carried at last to her father's house by her companions. She never spoke intelligibly afterwards. She was ten years old."

Some poet of that day—true poets are the best friends of the Right—versified this incident :—

" THE FACTORY GIRL'S LAST DAY.

"'Twas on a winter morning,
    The weather wet and mild,
Two hours before the dawning
    The father roused his child :
Her daily morsel bringing,
    The darksome room he paced,
And cried: ' The bell is ringing ;
    My hapless darling, haste !'

" ' Dear father, I'm so weary !
    I scarce can reach the door ;
And long the way and dreary :
    O, carry me once more !'
Her wasted form seems nothing ;
    The load is on his heart :

He soothes the little sufferer,
    Till at the mill they part.

" The overlooker met her
    As to her frame she crept ;
And with his thong he beat her,
    And cursed her when she wept.
It seemed, as she grew weaker,
    The threads the oftener broke ;
The rapid wheels ran quicker,
    And heavier fell the stroke.

" She thought how her dead mother
    Blessed her with latest breath,
And of her little brother,
    Worked down, like her, to death:
Then told a tiny neighbor
    A half-penny she'd pay
To take her last hour's labor,
    While by her frame she lay.

" The sun had long descended
    Ere she sought that repose :
Her day began and ended
    As cruel tyrants chose.
Then home ! but oft she tarried ;
    She fell and rose no more ;
By pitying comrades carried,
    She reached her father's door.

" At night, with tortured feeling,
    He watched his sleepless child :
Though close beside her kneeling,
    She knew him not, nor smiled.
Again the factory's ringing
    Her last perceptions tried :
Up from her straw bed springing,
    ' It's time !' she shrieked, and died !

" That night a chariot passed her,
    While on the ground she lay :

> The daughters of her master
>   An evening visit pay.
> Their tender hearts were sighing.
>   As negroes' wrongs were told,
> While the white slave was dying
>   Who gained their father's gold."

While in London I became acquainted with another reformer, as zealous and persevering in his way as my father. It happened thus.

I had a standing invitation from William Allen—the same who refused me a second supply of roast-beef—to dine or sup with him any time I happened to be in the city. Entering Plough Court late one afternoon, I met him equipped for a journey, and he greeted me joyfully.

"Ah, Robert, thee comes just in time. Friend Thomas Clarkson will be here to take supper and spend the night. I am going into the country and cannot return till to-morrow. So thee must stay here to-night and take my place. Thee knows what a firm friend Thomas has been to the good cause."

I was overjoyed, and I told him so. Just before leaving Braxfield I had read "Clarkson's History of the Abolition of the Slave-trade," and had there inspected the famous print of the plan and sections of a slave-ship with its four hundred and fifty victims packed in like so many herrings,—a print which the anti-slavery committee had got up, I think in 1790. No pamphlet or book or speech was ever so eloquent as that mute appeal. I recollect laying down the print and pacing the floor with mingled feelings of horror and of burning indignation. From that day forth I had regarded Clarkson with a sentiment akin to hero worship.

But his genial manner soon put me at my ease. Alone

with him after tea, I plied him with eager questions. He must have been gratified by the enthusiasm shown by a youth not yet fifteen ; for we sat together from seven or eight until one or two in the morning ; and he gave me, in minute detail, many particulars of the great struggle which had terminated triumphantly eight years before. To me they were of absorbing interest, and I remember to this day much that he said.

Clarkson, then fifty-five years old, had written thirty years before (when senior bachelor in St. John's College, Cambridge), a successful essay on the question, " Is involuntary slavery justifiable ? " That essay determined the entire course of his life. He spent twenty years in gathering, arranging, and disseminating the sickening mass of facts that marked the character of the slave-trade.

He told me that, during the early portion of that period, there were many days during which he collected evidence so replete with horrors and atrocities that he returned home, in the evening, with a burning sensation in his head which rendered sleep impossible, until he had applied for hours bandages soaked in coldest water to forehead and temples, so as to allay the fever of the brain.

But what chiefly lives in my recollection is the graphic account he gave me of an interview which, after several years thus spent, he obtained, through the influence of Wilberforce, with William Pitt, then Prime Minister.

With the directness of a master-mind that great man plunged into the subject at once. " I know that you have bestowed much study on this matter, Mr. Clarkson," he said ; "but I want details. Can you give them ? "

"Yes, if you will allow your secretary to bring in some books which I left in the antechamber."

Four or five ponderous folios, labelled respectively Day Book, Journal, and Ledger were produced. Pitt mentioned the name of some well-known slaver (the ship Brooks, I think it was), and asked, "Do you know anything about her?"

"Yes; do you wish to see an account of her last voyage?"

Pitt assenting, Clarkson, after referring to the index of one of his journals labelled "Slave Voyages," handed the volume, open at the narrative demanded, to the minister, who read it with the closest attention; then asked, "Do you know the names of the officers and sailors who were shipped for this voyage?"

"Here they are,"—opening one of the ledgers at a page headed, "The Ship Brooks."

"Ah! did you take the testimony of any of these sailors?"

"I did, of this one,"—pointing to his name; "and here it is,"—opening the ledger at another page, headed with the man's name.

Pitt read his testimony from the first word to the last. "Any other?" he then asked.

Clarkson gave him three or four more to read, which he perused with the same care, then added, "The surgeon; did you examine him?"

"Here is his testimony."

The minister ran it over, taking notes as he did so. "An important witness that, Mr. Clarkson. Can you tell where he is to be found?"

"Just at present he is at sea; but the Brooks will be

in during the summer, and then his address will be—"
giving it.

" Can the sailor witnesses be procured if they are
wanted ? "

" Next summer they can easily be found." And
Clarkson, having copied from a ledger the names of the
boarding-houses in Liverpool which each respectively
frequented when on shore, handed them to the minister.

" Any more vessels ? " asked Mr. Pitt.

" Twenty or thirty more, if you have time to examine
the testimony regarding them."

" I shall *make* time. It is a very important inquiry."

This rapid cross-examination, Clarkson told me, lasted
three or four hours, during which, he said, Mr. Pitt
must have looked over attentively not less than a hundred
pages of manuscript. To every question put, Clarkson
had a satisfactory answer ready. When the slave-
voyages had occurred years before, and some of the
sailors could not be produced, it was stated what had
become of them, whether by death, discharge, or deser-
tion. Pains had even been taken, in every case, to record the former abode or service of each, together with
the time of his entry, copied from the books of the
vessel.

The effect produced on the Prime Minister, during
this memorable interview, exceeded, Clarkson said, his
most sanguine anticipations.

When Pitt had glanced over the last page submitted
to him, he closed the book and said : " That will do. I
doubted whether the slave-trade was the iniquitous
traffic which many good men have represented it to be.
You have removed these doubts, Mr. Clarkson ; and I
thank you for the wonderful pains you have taken and

the facts you have brought before me. You may depend
upon whatever I can do, upon all the personal influence
I can exert, to further your wishes. I may not be able,"
—he hesitated a moment,—" there are circumstances
that are likely to prevent this being made a Cabinet
question. But nothing shall prevent me from expressing, so far as I can benefit the cause by doing so, my
individual opinion on this subject. Come to me whenever you have anything important to communicate,
without ceremony or previous appointment. I shall give
instructions that, unless I am very specially engaged,
you be admitted at once. Any papers you want I will
order. Perhaps I may communicate with some of our
Continental neighbors on the subject. Can I do anything more for you?"

Clarkson begged to be allowed to lay before him some
African productions; and they were brought from the
next room. They included native manufactures of
cotton, leather, gold, and iron. Pitt examined them
with interest, and spoke with emotion.

"I fear that we have underrated these people, Mr.
Clarkson. We owe them a debt for the miseries we
have aided to bring upon them. It would be worthy
of England to bestir herself for the civilization of
Africa."

Then, after sitting silent for some time—much moved,
Clarkson thought—he dismissed him with a few brief
words of kindness and encouragement.

Doubts have been cast on Pitt's sincerity in this matter. I know that Lord Brougham was incredulous as to
his earnest desire for abolition. But Clarkson told me
that he regarded him as a firm friend of the African to
the last. The above interview took place in 1788; and

before the close of that year Pitt caused to be made to the French government a communication in which he urged a union of the two countries to abolish the slave-trade.   But the answer from France was unfavorable ; and as the correspondence was not made public at the time, few persons knew that it had taken place.   Pitt kept his word, also, to Mr.   Clarkson—giving him access at all times, and furnishing him with many important documents which could only be had by a government order.

" He was true to the cause," Clarkson said to me, " from the early years of our great struggle till his death in 1806.   He did not live to see the Abolition Bill passed ; yet had it not been for his assistance at critical moments, we might not have succeeded in passing it even to this day.   Fox, when that bill was on its passage, did him full justice on that score."

The circumstances alluded to by Pitt as likely to cramp his action were, Clarkson informed me, the course taken by three of the most influential members of this Cabinet—Lord Chancellor Thurlow, Lord Liverpool, and Mr. Dundas—who remained persistent in resisting abolition.

As late as 1799, during a debate in the Lords on a bill to terminate the trade, Thurlow declared that slavery was sanctioned by Scripture, adding, " The bill is altogether miserable and contemptible." *   With such comrades and with his powers taxed to the uttermost in that terrible struggle with Napoleon during which England herself was threatened with invasion, it is little wonder

* Lives of the Lord Chancellors, by Lord Campbell.   London, 1868. Vol. VII., p. 233.

that Pitt scrupled to adopt an extreme policy which might have broken up the Cabinet.

Perhaps that evening with Clarkson was the most important I ever passed. Its lesson, never forgotten, influenced my action during a long public life. I bore in mind that declamation, eloquence even, avails little in a practical way, without a basis of fact carefully prepared and consolidated; for what amount of empty brilliancy would have converted Pitt? I never brought forward a measure of any importance, either in the Indiana Legislature or in Congress, without first seeking out and systematizing, not only the facts which I proposed to use in opening debate, but all others which, in the course of the discussion, my opponents were likely to employ. It is chiefly, I think, to this habit that I owe what success I may have had as a member of deliberative bodies. As an author, also, my rule has been the same. I owe a great debt to Thomas Clarkson.

On my return, soon afterwards, to Braxfield, my time, aside from private lessons in the languages, was chiefly spent in our day and evening schools, where I gave occasional lectures to the older classes. Nor was the instruction afforded to these factory children restricted to the school-house. I remember taking several classes of the more advanced scholars to see a large collection of wild animals in a menagerie which was exhibited, for a few days, in the old town of Lanark. This incident is stamped on my recollection the more because of what might easily have proved a fatal accident which occurred on that occasion. Among the beasts were two lions, a male and a female, and a lion's cub a few months old. This cub, which was already heavier and stronger

than the largest Newfoundland dog, was in a separate
cage ; and one of the keepers, entering with a whip,
ordered it about like a dog, and chastised it when it
disobeyed.   The children, of course, were delighted,
and crowded close up, " to see the fun." But their
cheer was soon changed.   A blow struck by the keeper
caused the young brute to back against the front bars
of his cage.   These, being insecurely fastened, gave
way, and the whelp was precipitated into the midst of
the children.   At first he seemed almost as much
frightened as they ; but recovering himself, he turned
and sprang upon a little girl ten years old, named Mary
Morrison, his teeth just grazing the back of her head.
Meanwhile, however, the " lion-tamer," as he was called
in the bills, sprang from the cage after the fugitive and
struck him sharply with his whip, causing him to relinquish his hold of the terrified girl ; while another secured
the animal by throwing a noose over his neck.   Luckily
they were both brave and powerful men ; and they
picked up the creature, threw him back into his cage,
and secured the bars, without further accident.

My father sought to make education as practical as
possible.   The girls were taught sewing and knitting,
and both sexes, in the upper classes, besides geography
and natural history, had simple lessons in drawing.   Yet
it was not the graver studies that chiefly interested and
pleased our numerous visitors : the dancing and music
lessons formed the chief attraction.   The juvenile per-
formers were dressed alike, all in tartan, the boys
wearing the Highland kilt and hose.   Carefully instructed in the dances then in vogue, as a lesson, not as
a performance, they went through their reels and quad-
rilles with an ease and grace that would not have shamed

a fashionable ball-room, coupled with a simplicity and unconsciousness natural to children when they are not spoiled, but which in higher circles is often sadly lacking.

The class or vocal music numbered, at one time, a hundred and fifty, and under a well-qualified teacher they made wonderful progress. I selected, and had printed for them, on a succession of pasteboard sheets, a collection of simple airs, chiefly national Scottish melodies, which they rendered with a homely pathos scarcely attainable, perhaps, except by those who are "to the manner born."

Another feature in our schools which proved very popular with visitors was the military training of the older children. Drilled by a superannuated soldier whom my father had hired for the purpose, and preceded by a boy-band of a drum or two and four or five fifes, they made a very creditable appearance.

All this, unprecedented then in any spinning village, or indeed in any free public school throughout the kingdom, gradually drew crowds of travellers as witnesses. I have seen as many as seventy persons in the building at one time. The number of names recorded in our Visitor's Book, from the year 1815 to 1825, the year in which my father bought the village and lands of New Harmony and sold out of the New Lanark concern, was nearly twenty thousand.

There came, not only nobility and gentry from every part of Great Britain, but also many foreigners of rank from the Continent. Among these last the most notable was a nobleman who, nine years afterwards, became the most powerful emperor in the world.

It was in 1816 that Nicolas, Grand Duke of Russia,

then on a tour through Great Britain, visited Glasgow. There he received and accepted an invitation from my father; and he and the officers of his suite, to the number of eight or ten, spent two days with us at Braxfield. He was then twenty years old; fully six feet high; and, in face and figure, I thought him the handsomest man I had ever seen. His manner, in those days, was simple and courteous; and the dignity which marked it at times had not yet degenerated, as it is said afterwards to have done, into haughtiness.

My French tutor, in anticipation of this visit, had been drilling me in matters of etiquette. "Your Imperial Highness," he bade me bear in mind, was the only proper mode of address. I must be sure not to say *you*, and the "Imperial" was imperative—*de rigueur*, as he phrased it, not to be replaced by *milord* or any other common title. He would have me try it, in conversation with himself; but it did not come "trippingly on the tongue," as Hamlet required, and Monsieur Levasseur prophesied a failure.

My father, I could see, waited his guest's arrival with a little touch of nervousness. Somewhat inconsiderately, I think, he had instructed the village band to meet the Duke's carriage and escort it the last mile or two. I judged from some remarks made by a member of his suite, and not intended for my ears, that the delay and the indifferent music annoyed the Duke; but he was too well-bred to show it, causing fifty dollars to be handed to the band-leader.

The Duke's physician, a Scotchman named Sir Alexander Creighton, interpreted between his royal patient and my father, who spoke English only. A great relief it was to me, who had feared to be called upon in a similar capacity. And, as a listener, I was soon set at ease on another point. I observed that the officers of the Duke's suite, in addressing their master, ignored the " Imperial ; " said *you*, as to other people, and used no title except Monseigneur. Greatly relieved in mind, I concluded that Monsieur Levasseur was not *au fait* in regard to court etiquette ; and when the Duke addressed me in French, I replied without embarrassment.

I think, however, that I must have shared my father's feeling as to the importance of this visit ; for I can still recall some of the exact words of a conversation which I had with the Duke during a walk from Braxfield to the Mills. Among other questions touching our business, he asked me what was our daily produce. It so happened that some weeks before I had calculated that we spun, on the average, three hundred and sixty thousand miles of thread per week. So I was able to reply that we manufactured daily " autant de fil de coton qu'il faut pour entourer deux fois et demi le monde."

In my turn, I asked him if he had ever been in England before ; to which he answered, " Je la visite pour la première et pour la dernière fois,"—a mistake of his, however ; for twenty-eight years afterwards he crossed to London on a visit to Queen Victoria.

He next inquired if I would like to know by what name he was known in his own country ; and, on my assenting, said he was there called *Nicolas, Veliki Kneis Rouski*—wrongly spelt, probably, and perhaps bad Russian ; but he repeated it several times, laughing at my pronunciation, till I got it by heart ; and thus it comes to me now.

The Duke seemed to take a special fancy to a younger brother of mine, named David Dale, after his grandfather, and then nine or ten years old. He was a re-markable-looking boy, with handsome features, light-yellow curling hair, and dark eyes, eyebrows, and eye-lashes. The Duke had him on his knee, playing with him, during a considerable portion of the evening; and the child, flattered by such notice, took so cordially to our visitor that it appeared to win his heart. At all events, next day he caused it to be intimated to my father that, if he would give up the boy, he (Nicolas) would charge himself with his future. Whether my mother objected, or whether my father himself thought a court life an undesirable career, I know not; but the offer was gratefully declined.

If my impressions, such as they were at fifteen, are trustworthy, there was nothing, at that early age, in the future Emperor to indicate the arbitrary and cruel spirit which, in later years, marked his subjugation of Poland and his armed intervention against the Hungarian patriots; nothing in the appearance of the youth of twenty to prefigure the stern autocrat who was by and by to revive against his own subjects that capital pun-ishment which had been humanely abolished by the Empress Elizabeth. There have been many Hazaels who, while yet unhardened by the habit of irresponsible power, might exclaim, from the heart, " What! is thy servant a dog, that he should do this great thing?"

At all events, the young Duke's manner seemed to me unaffected, earnest, and cordial. He listened with marked attention for two hours or more to an exposition, by my father, of his peculiar views for the improvement of mankind, and showed a lively interest in all he saw, whether in school or factory, at New Lanark. Count Gurowski, who knew Russia well, and with whom Nicolas was no favorite, speaking of him as he was in youth, admits : " His primitive tendency was to be a reformer. . . . . He believed that his mission was to be the conductor of his people into light and civilization ; that he was to lay a corner-stone for their moral and social amelioration. This was more than a dream ; it was a reality of several years' duration." *

At the time of his visit to us, he was engaged to the Princess Charlotte, eldest daughter of the King of Prussia ; and he purchased at the company's store, and had sent to her, sundry specimens of goods manufactured from our yarns.

My father states in his Autobiography that his guest, alluding to Malthus's theory that Great Britain was over-peopled, expressed his willingness to receive and promote the advantageous settlement in Russia of as many British manufacturers and their operatives, including my father and the villagers of New Lanark, as might see fit to emigrate thither. But if I heard this at the time, I have since forgotten it. My father, successful and satisfied in his position, declined the offer.

Nicolas, as I remember, was frugal to abstemiousness in his mode of living, eating sparingly of the plainest food only, and scarcely touching wine. In some of his appointments he was homely—so it occurs to me now —to the point of affectation. He caused to be set up, in the handsome chamber which had been provided for him, a small iron camp-bed, with leathern mattress and

---

* Russia as It Is, pp. 51, 52. New York, 1854.

Gurowski also tells us that, in 1825, when the Czar's councillors urged him to restore capital punishment, bringing him a sentence of the criminal court condemning five conspirators to death, he refused, for three days, to give his signature in approval, and acquiesced, at last, with reluctance.

pillow stuffed with hay, and spread with the rudest covering.   An officer of his suite told us that such was his
constant habit.

One of his attendants slept on the floor across his
chamber-door, outside—a measure of precautionary
suspicion, probably of Oriental origin, and adopted, I
believe, by all Russian princes of the blood.

A trifling incident connected with the Duke's visit
to us occurs to me now, as characteristic of a weakness
into which my good father, prosperous and generous,
was occasionally betrayed.   The crest of our family,
two eagles' heads, had been, as is customary, engraved
on our service of plate.   At supper, one of the Duke's
suite, handing a silver fork to him, called his attention
to the engraving as being almost an exact copy of the
double-eagle, part of the blazon of the Russian coat-of-
arms.   Some jest as to right of property having passed,
in connection with the matter, and attracted my father's
attention, it suggested a gift to his guest.   Accordingly,
next morning he had a silver dessert-set packed up, and
handed, just as the party were starting off, to one of the
attendants, together with a letter begging the Duke's
acceptance of it as a memento of his visit to New
Lanark.

My mother, good, sensible matron, took exception to
any such proceeding.   In the case of a friend to whom
we owed kindness or gratitude, or to any one who would
value the offering for the donor's sake, she would not
have grudged her nice forks and spoons ; but to the
possessor of thousands, a two days' acquaintance who
was not likely to bestow a second thought on the
things !—in all which I cordially agreed with her, especially when I found William Sheddon, our butler,

lamenting over his empty cases, the glittering contents of which had often excited my childish admiration. But I think the worthy man was somewhat comforted when he estimated his lion's share of a ten-pound note which the Duke's purser had put into his hands for distribution among the servants.

My recollections of William Sheddon extend over more than twenty years. Careful, punctiliously respectful, order-loving even to fanaticism, a piece of animated clock-work in all his daily duties, how well I recollect the staid face, with a nervous twitching of the chin when at all excited! The best men have their failings, and I think Sheddon, after he had decanted, with infinite care, the old port and pale sherry, was wont to taste them, to assure himself that they had not lost their flavor. But, to atone, I have seen him spend full ten minutes over the dinner-table, after it had been all set, to give it a finishing touch; adjusting each cover, and every knife, fork, glass, and salt-cellar so scrupulously to its allotted spot, that a mathematician, with his compasses, might have found it difficult to detect an error of a quarter of an inch in their respective distances each from the other.

Peace to his shade! I wonder how many of his life-long peculiarities he carried with him to the next world.

But all these familiar scenes were soon to become, for me, things of the past. I was about to quit our quiet home, and to find, in a distant country, a new and more stirring life.

PAPER V.

EMANUEL VON FELLENBERG AND HIS SELF-GOVERN-ING COLLEGE.

GROWING up and educated, to the age of sixteen, in the country, and in the quiet and genial atmosphere of a domestic circle, I was isolated from a thousand temptations that are wont to assail boys in schools and cities. It was a civilizing circumstance, too, that our family consisted chiefly of cultivated women.

But the situation had its serious drawbacks also. It lacked bracing, case-hardening influences. While it nourished self-esteem, it failed to give self-assertion. I was in danger of reaching manhood devoid of that sterling quality, specially prized in England,—*pluck;* and this the rather because of the excessive sensibility which that grave fit of sickness had left behind. I was then little fitted to hold my place in the world as it is.

What effect a sudden transition to the buffetings of some such public school as Eton or Harrow, with its fag-tyranny and its *hazing*, and its squabbles settled by the fist, might have had I cannot tell. At all events, I think it fortunate that I was spared the trial; and for this I am chiefly indebted to an excellent man, Charles Pictet (de Richemont) of Geneva.

An enlightened agriculturist and firm friend of education; an intimate associate of Cuvier, La Place, and other distinguished scientists; one of the editors of the

Bibliothèque Britannique ; a diplomatist, too, trusted by his countrymen,—Pictet had been sent by the Swiss Republic as Envoy Extraordinary to the Congress of Vienna in 1814, and to that of Paris in 1815. In 1817 he visited New Lanark ; and he and my father contracted a warm and lasting friendship. They agreed to travel together to London, Paris, and Geneva ; and afterwards to visit in Switzerland a certain institution, the most re-markable of its kind then in the world, of which Pictet had been the historian* from the inception of the enter-prise in the first years of the present cent ury It em-braced the various establishments of M. de Fellenberg on his estate of Hofwyl, two leagues from Berne, con-sisting of a primary school, a college, an industrial school, and workshops for improved agricultural instruments.

That journey had an important influence on all my after life ; for my father was so much pleased with all he saw that, on his return, he engaged a private tutor to teach my brother William and myself German, and sent us to Hofwyl in the autumn of next year, my

* Chiefly in the pages of the *Bibliothèque Britannique,* or as it was after-wards called, the *Bibliothèque Universelle.* His first letter on the subject is dated December 20, 1807. In 1808 the French ambassador to Switzer-land had a public correspondence with Pictet on the subject. Count de Capo d'Istria, who was the Russian Envoy to the Congresses of Vienna and Paris, made to the Emperor Alexander, in 1814, an extended report on Hofwyl which, being widely circulated in book form, brought M. de Fel-lenberg's ideas into notice all over Europe. There were also published, about the same time, a Report made to the Swiss government by a special commission appointed to that effect ; another by M. Hoffman, special en-voy of the Princess of Swartzenberg Rudolstadt ; observations thereon by M. Thaer, Councillor of State of the King of Prussia ; a report by M. Schefold, Commissioner of the King of Würtemberg ; and various others. Sundry articles by Fellenberg himself, in German, were translated into French by Pictet, and attracted much attention.

brother being upwards of fifteen, and I upwards of sixteen years old.

We entered the college, then having rather more than
a hundred students, natives of every part of Europe, and
from fifteen to twenty-three years of age. But, as it
was early in August and during vacation that we reached
the place, we found only three or four of its inmates
there.

We were placed in charge of one of these, a Prussian
two or three years older than I, named Carl Bressler.
I shall never forget the considerate forbearance with
which this good young fellow treated two raw Scotch
lads, childish for their age, and the pains he took to
correct in us any habits that might have exposed us to
ridicule.   One example comes to me.

Walking with him some miles into the country, a large
and fierce dog from a neighboring farmhouse suddenly
rushed open-mouthed at us.   William and I shrank
back, and might have run away.   But Bressler, stopping
us with a word, struck the animal so sharply with a
stout cane that he fled, yelling.   Then he turned to us.

" Look here," said he, "this will never do. Remember! If you ever show the white feather, you're
done for with us.   I give you fair warning."

All we could plead was that we had no canes.

" Yes, that was my fault. You shall have a good
Ziegenhainer apiece, just as soon as we get back.   But,
anyhow, you ought to have stood your ground, and
kicked the brute, if you could not do better."

I thanked him, adding, " You'll see that this is the
last time anybody will have to find fault on that score."
(And I kept my word.)

" All right !"   Then, after looking me fixedly in the

eye: "I think you'll do. I'm glad I had a chance to warn you before the other fellows came. Raw young ones always need drilling."

Before the remaining six weeks of vacation had expired and the college began to fill again, we had already, in a measure, settled down into the ways of the place, and understood pretty much all that was said to us, a few slang phrases excepted.* Then began for me a marvellous life.

Marvellous, because the world and its institutions are *as* they are ; because of the much that we might be, compared to the little that we are. But, in those days, it did not strike me that there was anything marvellous about it. Just from the shelter of a refined and peaceful home, with the sunny hopes and high ideal and scanty experience of youth, I accepted, as but natural and in the due course of things, much that comes before me now, by the light of a life's teachings and by comparison with the realities of after years, more like a dream of fancy, seen under the glamour of optimism, than anything sober, actual, really to be met with in this prosaic world. I say this heedfully, after making what I deem full allowance for the roseate hue that is wont to linger over one's early recollections.

I was speedily inducted into some of the wonders, social and political, of the little republic of which I had become a member.

We of the United States assert that, in our country, the rights of the person are more liberally acknowledged and more strictly assured than in any other great nation.

* One especially puzzled me. It was some time before I discovered that " Es ist mir Wurst " had no reference whatever to German sausage, but meant, "What do I care ? "

We have beautiful theories of government. We boast of our universal suffrage. We live under a Constitution framed by wise ancestors. We are governed by laws enacted by the consent of the governed.

Yet if a governmental system is to be prized either according to the spirit in which it is administered, or by the practical results obtained through its agency, the democratic *Verein* (Union) of Hofwyl was, in a very small way, more of a success than the American Union with its forty millions.

I found the students living under a *Verfassung* (constitution) which had been drafted by a select committee of their number, five or six years before, adopted by an almost unanimous vote of the whole body, and approved by Mr. Fellenberg's signature. This constitution and the by-laws supplemental to it (drawn up by the same committee) were subject to amendment, Fellenberg retaining a veto ; but during the three years I remained at college, scarcely any amendments were made.

This embraced the entire police of the institution. Neither the founder and president nor the faculty issued any rules or regulations. Our professors had no authority whatever except within their class-rooms. Our laws, whether defining official duties, or relating to household affairs, hours of retiring, and the like, or for the maintenance of morality, good order, cleanliness, and health, were stringent, but they were all strictly self-imposed. A breach of the laws was an offence against the Verein ; and as to all such we ourselves had sole jurisdiction. I cannot doubt that Fellenberg kept unobtrusive watch over our doings ; but while I remained at Hofwyl he never openly interfered with our legislation or our domestic proceedings, by veto or otherwise.

And while punishment by the college authorities held no place, as restraining motive, among us, neither was any outside stimulus of reward, or even of class rank, admitted. Emulation was limited among us to that which naturally arises among young men prosecuting the same studies. It was never artificially excited. There were no prizes or college honors, no "double-firsts" to be won; there was no acknowledged position, marked by numbers, giving precedence and conferring name and fame; there was not even the excitement of public examinations; we had no Commencement exercises that might have assembled the magnates of Switzerland to criticise or to applaud.

A dangerous experiment it would usually be pronounced; the more dangerous because of the heterogeneous materials that had come together at Hofwyl from half the nations of the world,—Swiss, Germans, Russians, Prussians, French, Dutch, Italians, Greeks, English, and I know not of what other nationalities,—some having been nursed and petted in luxury, others sent thither, probably, because their parents could not manage them at home. The difficulties were the greater on account of the comparatively late age at which students were received, many of them just from schools where teachers were considered natural enemies, where severity was the rule, and artificial reward the trusted stimulant to exertion. Yet I am witness to the fact that this hazarded experiment was an eminent success. It was a triumph in self-government. The nobler elements of our nature had been appealed to, and the response was prompt and ardent.

I think I may say that I had been nurtured at home in an atmosphere of purity and rectitude, no ignoble

motive, as of fear or jealous rivalry, called into play;
no bribe offered for behaving well ; self-respect encouraged by absence of all mean suspicion.   Once, when
my father had occasion to leave me in London for a few
weeks, William Allen had warned me : " Thee will be
exposed to great temptation here, and I am afraid for
thee.   Our nature is desperately wicked.   Thee must
resist the Devil ; for he is ever tempting youth to its
ruin."   But all my father had said, in taking leave of
me, was, " You've been well trained, Robert ; you
know what is right, and I'm sure I can trust you till I
return."   Well do I remember, still, the glow of indignation with which I listened to the one speech, and the
blush of glad pride called forth by the other !

But there was no jar to my sensitive nature, even
from the first, at Hofwyl.   I was trusted there as I had
been trusted at Braxfield.   Of course I had hardships.
I was jostled and bandied about and shaken into place,
roughly enough sometimes.   But there was no bitterness or ill-will mixed in : that hard novitiate was wholesome, not degrading, and after some months it gradually ceased.   There were no coarse incentives, no
mean submissions, no selfish jealousies.   There was
pride, but it grew chiefly out of a sense that we were
equal members of an independent, self-governing community, calling no man master or lord : Fellenberg, our
president, preferred to be called, and was usually called,
Pflegevater (foster-father).   We were proud that our republic had no laws but those we ourselves had made.
It had its Council of Legislation, its court of judges, its
civil and military officers, and its public treasury.   It
had its annual elections, by ballot, at which each student
had a vote ; its privileges and honors equally accessible

to all ; its labors and duties shared by all. In its Council of Legislation laws were repealed or changed ; yet our system was stable, few and not radical changes being proposed. And never, I think, were laws framed or modified with a more single eye to the public good, or more strictly obeyed by those who framed them.

Nor was this an unwilling obedience ; nothing resembling that eye-service, which springs from fear or force. It was given ungrudgingly, cheerfully, honestly. It became a point of honor to conform in spirit as in letter to laws that were our own.

I do not recollect, and perhaps never knew, whether the idea of this self-regulating society originated with Fellenberg or with some of the older students. The memory of several of its founders was as gratefully cherished by us as, in the American Union, is the fame of the Revolutionary fathers. But whether the first conception was theirs or Fellenberg's, the system thence resulting was the chief lever that raised the moral character of our college to the height at which I found it. It gave birth to public spirit and to social and civic virtues. It nurtured a conscious independence that submitted with alacrity to what it knew to be the will of the whole, and felt itself bound to submit to nothing else. It created, in an aristocratic class, young Republicans, and awakened in them that zeal for the public good which we seek too often in vain in older but not wiser communities.

Our system of rule had another wholesome ingredient. The annual election to the offices of the Verein acted indirectly as a powerful stimulus to industry and good conduct. The graduated scale of public judgment might be read as on a moral thermometer, when the result of these elections was declared. That result informed us who had risen and who had fallen in the estimate of his fellows ; for it was felt that public opinion among us, enlightened and incorrupt, operated with strict justice. In that youthful commonwealth, to deserve well of the republic was to win its confidence and obtain testimonial of its approbation. I was not able to detect one sinister motive swaying the votes given,—neither favoritism, nor envy, nor any selfish inducement. There was nothing even that could be called canvassing for candidates. There was quiet, dispassionate discussion of relative merits ; but the one question which the elector asked himself or his neighbor was, " Who can best fill such or such an office ? " And the answer to that question furnished the motive for decision. I cannot call to mind a single instance, during the years I spent at Hofwyl, in which even a suspicion of partisan cabal or other factious proceeding attached to an election among us. It can scarcely be said that there were aspirants for office. Preferment was, indeed, highly valued, as a token of public confidence ; but it was not solicited, directly or indirectly : it was accepted rather as imposing duty than conferring privilege. The Lacedæmonian who, when he lost his election as one of the three hundred, went away rejoicing that there were found in Sparta three hundred better men than he, is lauded as a model of ideal virtue. Yet such virtue was matter of common occurrence and little remark at Hofwyl. There were not only one or two, but many among us, who would have sincerely rejoiced to find others, more capable than themselves, preferred to office in their stead.

All this sounds, I dare say, strangely Utopian and extravagant. As I write, it seems to myself so widely at variance with a thirty years' experience of public life, that I should scruple, at this distance of time, to record it, if I had not, forty years ago, carefully noted down my recollections while they were still fresh and trustworthy. It avails nothing to me that such things cannot be, for at Hofwyl *they were*. I describe a state of society which I saw, and part of which I was.

As partial explanation it should be stated that no patronage or salary was attached to office among us.

To our public treasury (*Armenkasse*, we called it) each contributed according to means or inclination, and the proceeds were expended exclusively for the relief of the poor. We had an overseer of the poor, he being the chairman of a committee whose duty it was to visit the indigent peasantry in the neighborhood, ascertain their wants and their character, and afford them relief, especially in winter. This relief was occasionally given in the form of money, more frequently of food, clothing, or furniture. In other cases, we lent them goats, selected when in milk, from a flock which we kept for that purpose. Our fund was ample, and, I think, judiciously dispensed.

The article in our Verfassung relative to moral government provided for the division of the students into six circles (*Kreise*); and for the government of these each circle elected a councillor (*Kreisrath*). These were held to be our most important officers, their jurisdiction extending to the social life and moral deportment of each member of the Kreis. This, one might imagine, would degenerate into an inquisitorial or intermeddling surveillance, but in practice it never did. Each Kreis was a band of friends, and its chief was the friend most valued and loved among them. It had its weekly meetings ; and, during fine summer weather, these were usually held in a grove (*das Wäldchen*) near by.   In all my experience I remember no pleasanter gatherings than these.   During the last year of my college life, I was my- self a Kreisrath ; and I carried home no memorial more valued than a brief letter of farewell, expressing affection and gratitude, signed by all the members of my Kreis.

These presiding officers of circles constituted a sort of grand jury, holding occasional meetings, and having the right of presentment, when any offence had come to their knowledge.

Our judiciary consisted of a bench of three judges, whose sessions were held in the principal college-hall with due formality, two sentinels, with drawn swords, guarding the doors.   Its decisions were final.   The punishments within its power to inflict were a vote of censure, fines, which went to the Armenkasse, depriva- tion of the right of suffrage, declaration of ineligibility to office, and degradation from office.   This last punish- ment was not inflicted while I remained in the college. Trials were rare, and I do not remember one, except for some venial offence.   The offender usually pleaded his own cause ; but he had the right to procure a friend to act as his advocate.   The first public speech I ever made was in German, in defence of a fellow-student.

The dread of public censure, thus declared by sen- tence after formal trial, was keenly felt, as may be judged from the following example :—

Two German princes, sons of a wealthy nobleman, the Prince of Thurn and Taxis, having been furnished by their father with a larger allowance of pocket-money than they could legitimately spend at Hofwyl, fell upon a somewhat irregular mode of using part of it.   Now and then they would get up of nights, after all their comrades had gone to bed, and proceed to the neighboring village of Buchsee, there to spend an hour or two in a tavern, smoking, and drinking lager-beer.

Now, we had no strict college bounds and no prohibition against entering a tavern, though we knew that M. de Fellenberg objected to our contracting the habit of visiting such places. Our practice on Sundays may illustrate this. That day was strictly kept and devoted to religious exercises, until mid-day, when we dined. After dinner it was given up to recreation ; and our favorite recreation was, to form into parties of two or three, and sally forth, stout stick in hand, on excursions of many miles into the beautiful, richly cultivated country that surrounded us, often ascending some eminence which commanded a view of the magnificent Bernese Alps, their summits covered with eternal snow. It sometimes happened that, on such excursions, we were overtaken by a storm ; or perhaps, having wandered farther than we intended, we were tired and hungry. In either case we did not scruple to enter some country tavern and procure refreshments there. But whenever we did so, it was a custom—not a prescribed law, but a custom sanctioned by college tradition—to visit, on our return, the professor who overlooked the domestic department of our institution,—a short, stout, middle-aged man, the picture of good-nature, but not deficient in energy when occasion demanded,—it was our uniform custom to call upon this gentleman, Herr Lippe, and inform him that we *had* visited such or such a tavern, and the occasion of our doing so. A benignant smile, and his usual "It is very well, my sons," closed such interviews.

But the use of tobacco—strange, in a German college !
—was forbidden by our rules ; so also was a departure,
after the usual hour of rest, from the college buildings,
except for good reason shown.   Thus Max and Fritz
Taxis (so the youths were called) had become offenders
amenable to justice.

The irregularity of which they had been guilty—the
only one of the kind which I recollect—became known
accidentally to one of the students.   There existed
among us not even the name of informer ; but it was
considered a duty to give notice to the proper authorities of any breach of law.   Accordingly the fact was
communicated by the student to his Kreisrath, who,
thereupon, called his colleagues in office together.
Having satisfied themselves as to the facts, they presented Max and Fritz for breach of law.   The brothers
were then officially notified that, on the second day
thereafter, their case would be brought up before the
Tribunal of Justice, and they would be heard in defence.

Max, the elder, held some minor office ; and the sentence would probably have been a vote of censure, or a
fine for both, and a dismissal from office in his (Max's)
case.   But it would seem that this was more than they
could make up their minds to bear.   Accordingly, the
night before trial, they decamped secretly, hired a *post-
kalesche* at Buchsee, and, being well provided with
money, returned to their parents.

We afterwards ascertained that our president did not
send after them, in pursuit or otherwise, not even writing
to their parents, but quietly suffering the fugitives to tell
their own story in their own way.

The result was that, in a few weeks, the father came,
bringing with him the runaways, and asking, as a favor,

that M. de Fellenberg would once more take them on probation, which he very willingly did. They were received
by us with kindness, and no allusion was ever made to
the cause of their absence. They remained several
years, quiet and law-abiding members of our Verein, but
neither attained to any office of trust again.

I think this habit of our founder—to let things have
their course, whenever interference could be dispensed
with—had much to do with the success of his college experiment.

Emanuel von Fellenberg was one of the men of mark
who arose during those exciting times when liberty,
cheated in France, triumphed in America. He came of
a patrician family of Berne, his father having been a
member of the Swiss government and a friend of the
celebrated Pestalozzi,—a friendship afterwards shared
by the son. His mother was granddaughter of the stout
Admiral Van Tromp,—the Nelson of Holland,—who
was victor in more than thirty naval engagements, and
who died in that fatal battle which lost forever to his
country the supremacy of the seas. Frau von Fellenberg seems to have inherited her grandfather's spirit and
courage ; and to this noble woman her son owed ideas of
freedom and philanthropy beyond the age in which he
lived, and foreign to the aristocratic class to which he
belonged. " My son," she used to say, " the great
have plenty of friends : do thou be the friend of the
poor." *

Educated at Colmar and Tübingen, the years succeeding his college life were spent in travels which

* *Biographie Universelle*, Article *Fellenberg*. At one time Fellenberg
planned emigration, with several friends, to the United States, but gave up
the idea when offered important public service in his own country.

brought him, at the age of twenty-three, and just after the death of Robespierre, to Paris, where he had opportunity to study men in the subsiding tumult of a terrible revolution.

The result—partly determined, no doubt, by recollection of the atrocities committed during the Reign of Terror, then fresh in all men's minds—was to make the young Fellenberg a Republican, but not a leveller. Appointed to an important military command, he quelled an insurrection of the peasantry in the Oberland; but, true to his mother's injunction, he granted these people terms so liberal that his government refused to ratify them. Thereupon he threw up his commission, and served, for a time, on the Board of Education in Berne.

The one great idea of his life appears to have been, not (as Madame Roland and the Girondists thought possible) to fuse, in the crucible of equality, what are called the upper and the lower classes, but to seize the extremes of society, and carefully to educate them both : the one to be intelligent, cultivated workers; the other to be wise and considerate legislators, enlightened and philanthropic leaders of civilization. I believe he imagined that there would be rich and poor to the end of the world ; and he restricted his endeavors to making the rich friends of the poor, and the poor worthy of such friendship. To carry out this last he considered agriculture, when intelligently followed as a calling, to be an essential aid.

On his estate of Hofwyl, purchased in 1809, he commenced first a workshop for improved farm implements; ten years later an industrial school, called the Vehrli School, from the excellent young man who conducted it. It had thirty scholars in 1815, and forty or fifty when I first saw it. The children, from seven to fourteen years old, and chiefly destitute orphans or sons of indigent peasants, were employed in farm work eight or nine hours a day, and had two hours' instruction in summer and four hours in winter. This school became self-supporting after a few years. Besides the ordinary branches, the children were taught drawing, geometry, natural history, and music. We did not see much of the *Vehrli-Knaben* (Vehrli boys), as we called them; but there was the kindest feeling between our college and their school; and I never saw a happier-looking set of children than they. I think M. de Fellenberg considered this industrial experiment of more importance, as a reformatory agency, than our college.

There was, in addition, supplementary to the college, at Diemerswyl, a few miles from Hofwyl, a primary school, for boys up to the age of thirteen or fourteen; but there was little intercourse between us and them.

The habits and tone of all these establishments seemed to have been colored by their founder's democratic leanings. The Vehrli boys, though always respectful, had a look of bright, spirited independence about them. Among us students, in spite of what might have been disturbing causes, the strictest equality prevailed.

Though our habits were simple, the college was an expensive one, our annual bills, everything included, running up to some fifteen hundred dollars each; and thus those only, with few exceptions, could obtain admission whose parents had ample means; the exceptions being the sons of a few of Fellenberg's Swiss friends, in moderate circumstances, whom, when they showed great promise, he admitted with little or no charge. We had among us many of the nobility of the Continent—dukes, princes, some of them related to crowned heads, and minor nobles by the dozen; yet between them and others, including the recipients of Fellenberg's bounty, there was nothing, in word or bearing, to mark difference of rank.

No one was ever addressed by his title; and to the tuft-hunters of English universities it will appear scarcely credible that I lived several weeks among my college-mates before I accidentally learned who were the princes and other nobles, and who the objects of Fellenberg's charity; my informant being my friend Bressler.

"Carl," said I one day, "what's become of all the nobility you used to have here?   I heard, before I came, that there was quite a number."

"Why," said he, smiling, "they're all here still."

"Indeed!   Which are they?"

"See if you can't guess."

I named several who had appeared to me to have the greatest consideration among the other students.

"Out!" said he, laughing; "these are all sons of merchants and commoners.   Try your hand again."

I did so, with no better success.   Then he named, to my surprise, several young men who had seemed to me to command little influence or respect; among them, two sons of the Duke of Hilburghausen, the two princes of Thurn and Taxis, and three or four Russian princes; at which last item a good-natured young fellow named Stösser, a room-mate of ours, looked up from his desk and laughed, but said nothing.   "Then," added Bressler, "there's Alexander; he's another prince, nephew of the King of Würtemberg." I had especially observed that this young man was coldly treated—indeed, avoided rather than sought—by his companions.

A few days later I obtained two additional items. Bressler had said nothing to me of himself as having a title, nor did I suppose he had any ; but I happened to see, on his desk, a letter addressed, " A Monsieur le Comte Charles de Bressler." *Stösser* I found to be a nickname (literally *Jolter*, from a sort of pounding gait he had) ; and the youth who bore it turned out to be a Russian prince, grandson of a celebrated general, Catherine's Suwarow. Bressler had told me that there *were* two young Suwarows, but left me to find out that our room-mate was one of them. He (Stösser) had charge of our flock of goats, above referred to ; and he took to the office very kindly.

And, as of rank, so of religion ; neither introduced among us any disturbing element. We had Protestants, Catholics, members of the Greek Church, and members of no church at all ; but I recollect not a single word, nor other evidence of feeling, indicating any shade of coldness or aversion, which had rise in theological differences. It might have puzzled me, after a three years' residence, to call to mind whether those with whom I was intimate as with my own brother were Protestants, or Catholics, or neither : and long ere this I have quite forgotten. We never debated controversial points of belief. M. de Fellenberg read to us occasional lectures on religion ; but they were liberal in tone, and practical, not doctrinal ; embracing those essentials which belong to all Christian sects, and thus suiting Protestants and Catholics alike. The Catholics, it is true, had, from time to time, a priest who came, in a quiet way, to confess them, and, no doubt, to urge strict observance of the weekly fast ; yet we of the Protestant persuasion used, I believe, to eat as much fish and as many frogs on Fridays as they.

So, also, as to the various nationalities that made up our corps of students ; it caused no dispute, it gave rise to no unkindness.   Duels, common in most of the German universities, were an unheard-of absurdity ; quarrels ending in blows were scarcely known among us. I recall but two, both of which were quickly arrested by the bystanders, who felt their college dishonored by such an exhibition.   One of these was commenced by a youth fresh from an English school.   The other occurred one evening, in a private room, between a fiery Prussian count and a sturdy Swiss.   When the dispute grew warm, we pounced upon the combatants, carried them off, each to his own room, on our shoulders, and there, with a hearty laugh at their folly, set them down to cool.   It was so good-humoredly done, that they could not help joining in the merriment.

1 have heard much of the manliness supposed to grow out of the English habit of settling school-quarrels by boxing.   But I do not think it would have been a safe experiment for one of these pugilistic young gentlemen to insult a Hofwyl student, even though the manhood of this latter had never been tested by pounding another's face with his fist.   His anger, when roused, is most to be dreaded who so bears himself as to give no one just cause of offence.

But though little prone to quarrel, our indignation, on occasion, could be readily roused.   Witness this example.

It happened that three officers of distinction from the Court of Würtemberg, coming one day to visit M. de Fellenberg, desired to see their sovereign's nephew, the same Prince Alexander of whom I have already spoken as no favorite among us. The interview took place in front of Fellenberg's *Schloss*, where four or five students, of whom I was one, then happened to be, not more than eight or ten steps distant. The officers, as they approached the prince, uncovered, and stood, their plumed caps in their hands, while conversing with him. The young man, whose silly airs had chiefly caused his unpopularity among us, did not remove the little student-cap he wore, nor say a word to his visitors about resuming their hats.

This was more than I could stand, and I knew that my companions felt as I did. "Alexander," said I, loud enough to be heard by all concerned, "take off your cap!"

But the cap did not stir. We took a step or two nearer, and another of our party said, "Alexander, if you don't take that cap off yourself, I'll come and take it off for you."

This time the admonition took effect. The cap was slowly removed, and we remained to make sure that it was not resumed until the officers, bowing low, took their leave,—carrying, I dare say, to their royal master no favorable report of the courtly manners of Hofwyl.

Such an institution naturally awoke the jealousy of European legitimacy; and it was probably with feelings more of sorrow than surprise that Fellenberg, about the year 1820, received official notice that no Austrian subject would thereafter be allowed to enter the college, and an order that those then studying there should in-

stantly return home.   No greater compliment could
have been paid to Fellenberg and our college than this
tyrannical edict of the Austrian Emperor,—the same
Francis who did not blush to declare that he desired to
have loyal subjects, not learned men, in his dominions.
" Je ne veux pas des savans dans mes Etats : je veux des
bons sujets," were his words.

I don't think, however, that any of us gave promise
of becoming very learned men.   I am not sure whether
classical proficiency did not suffer, in a measure, from
the lack of artificial stimulus.   I am not sure whether
some sluggards did not, because of this, lag behind.
Yet the general advancement in learning was satisfactory ;
and the student, when he entered the world, bore with
him a habit of study needing no excitants, and which
insured the continuance of education beyond his college
years.

Our course of instruction included the study of the
Greek, Latin, French, and German languages, the last
of which was the language of the college ; history, natural philosophy, chemistry, mechanics ; mathematics, a
thorough course, embracing the highest branches ;
drawing, in the senior class, from busts and models ;
music, vocal and instrumental ; and finally gymnastics,
riding, and fencing.   There was a riding-school with a
considerable stable of horses attached ; and the higher
classes were in the habit of riding out once a week with
M. de Fellenberg, many of whose practical life-lessons,
given as I rode by his side during these pleasant excursions, I well remember yet ; for example, a recommen-
dation to use superlatives sparingly, in speech and writing, reserving them for occasions where they were
needed and in place.

The number of professors was large compared to that of the taught, being from twenty-five to thirty ; and the classes were small, containing from ten to fifteen. Twice or thrice only, during the term of my residence, one of the students, on account of repeated inattention during a recitation, was requested by the professor to leave the room. But this was quite an event to be talked of for a week. No expulsion occurred while I was there. I do not myself remember to have received, either from M. de Fellenberg or from any of the faculty, a single harsh word during the happy years I spent at Hofwyl.

Latin and Greek, though thoroughly taught, did not engross as much attention as in most colleges. Not more time was given to each than to ancient and modern history, and less than to mathematics. This last, a special object of study, was taught by extempore lectures, of which we took notes in short-hand ; and in after years, when details and demonstrations had faded from memory, I have never found difficulty in working these out afresh, without aid from books.

I look back on one incident connected with our mathematical studies—always my favorite pursuit—with a pleasant impression. My chief college friend was Hippolyte de Saussure, grandson of the eminent Swiss naturalist of that name, who the first, with a single exception, reached the summit of Mont Blanc. The subject of our lecture was some puzzling problem in differential calculus ; and De Saussure propounded to the professor a knotty difficulty in connection with it. The reply was unsatisfactory. My friend still pressed his point, and the professor rejoined, learnedly and ingeniously, but without meeting the case ; whereupon the other silently assented, as if satisfied.

" You were *not* satisfied with that explanation," said I to De Saussure, as we walked to our rooms.

" Of course not," was his reply ; " but would you have had me, before the class, shame the good man who takes so much pains with us and is usually so clear-headed ? We must work it out ourselves to-night."

This trifle gives a glimpse of the relation between professor and student at Hofwyl. There was no antagonism between them. The former was regarded, not as a pedagogue from whom to stand aloof, but as an elder friend with whom it was a privilege to converse familiarly out of college hours. And the professors frequently joined in our sports. Nor did I observe that this at all diminished the respect we entertained for them.

Our recreations consisted of public games, athletic exercises, gymnastics, and—what was prized above all— an annual excursion on foot, lasting about six weeks.

A favorite amusement in the way of athletic exercise was throwing the lance (*Lanzenwerfen*). The weapons used were stout ashen spears, six or seven feet long, heavily pointed with iron; the target a squared log of hard wood, firmly set in the ground, about six feet high, —the upper portion, or head, which it was the chief object to hit, a separate block, attached to the trunk by stout hinges. A dozen or more engaged in it at a time, divided into two sides ; and the points gained by each stroke were reckoned according to power and accuracy. We attained great skill in this exercise.

We had a fencing-master, and took lessons twice a week in the use of the rapier, skill in the management of which was then considered, throughout Continental Europe, indispensable in the education of a gentleman.

There are many swordsmen in the upper classes who need not have feared any ordinary antagonist. I was exceedingly fond of this exercise ; and I suppose our teacher may have thought me his best pupil, for he said to me one day, " Herr Owen, I expect a friend of mine, who is professor of fencing in Zurich, to visit me in a few days. He will expect, of course, to try his hand with some of the class, and I've chosen you to represent us. If you don't hit him first, I'll never forgive you."

" I think that's hard measure," I replied ; " he has made fencing the business of his life, and I haven't taken lessons three years yet."

" I don't care. I know his strength. I'd be ashamed not to turn out a pupil who could beat him."

I told him I would do my best. He let me into his visitor's play, as he called it, warning me of the feints likely to be employed against me. Yet I think it was by good fortune rather than skill that I made the first hit. Our professor assumed to take it as a matter of accident, yet I could see that he was triumphant.

Much has been said for and against gymnastic exercises. We spent an hour a day, just before dinner, in the gymnasium. And this experience causes me to regard these exercises, judiciously conducted, as essential to a complete system of education. They induce a vigor, an address, a hardihood, a presence of mind in danger, difficult of attainment without them. While they fortify the general health, they strengthen the nerves ; and their mental and moral influence is great. I know that, in my case, they tended to equalize the spirits, to invigorate the intellect, and to calm the temper. I left Hofwyl, not only perfectly well, but athletic.

Our annual excursions, undertaken, in the autumn of that bright and beautiful climate, by those students who, like myself, were too far from home to return thither during the holidays, were looked forward to, weeks beforehand, with brilliant anticipations of pleasure ; which, strange to say, were realized. Our favorite professor, Herr Lippe, accompanied us ; our number being commonly from thirty to thirty-five.

It was usually about the first of August that, clad in the plain student-uniform of the college, knapsack on shoulder, and long, iron-shod mountain-staff (*alpenstock*) in hand, we sallied forth, an exultant party, on " the journey," as we called it. Before our departure Herr Lippe, at a public meeting, had chalked out for us the intended route ; and when we found, as on two occasions we did, that it was to extend beyond the valleys and mountain passes of Switzerland to the lakes of Northern Italy, our enthusiasm burst forth in a tumult of applause.

Our day's journey, usually eighteen or twenty miles, sometimes extended to twenty-five or more. We breakfasted early, walked till mid-day ; then sought some shady nook where we could enjoy a lunch of bread and wine, with grapes or goat's-milk cheese, when such luxuries could be had. Then we despatched in advance some of our swiftest pedestrians, as commissariat of the party, to order supper preparatory to our arrival. How joyfully we sat down to that evening meal ! How we talked over the events of the day, the magnificent scenes we had witnessed, the little adventures we had met ! The small country taverns seldom furnished more than six or eight beds ; so that three-fourths of our number usually slept in some barn, well supplied with hay or straw. How soundly we slept, and how merry the awaking !

There were among us, as among German students there always are, good musicians, well trained to sing their stirring national airs, together with gems from the best operas or the like,—duets, trios, quartets. After our frugal noonday meal, or, perhaps, when we had surmounted some mountain-pass, and came suddenly, as we reached the verge of the descent, upon a splendid expanse of valley or champaign, stretching out far beneath us, it was our habit to call a halt for music. The fresh grass, dotted with Alpine roses, furnished seats ; our vocalists drew from their knapsacks the slender *cahier* containing melodies arranged, in parts, for the occasion ; and we had, under charming circumstances, an impromptu concert. I have heard much better music since, but never any that I enjoyed more.

On one of these expeditions we passed, by Napoleon's wonderful road, the Simplon, into one of the most beautiful regions of Piedmont. How amazing the change ! How lovely that first night at Baveno ! The sweet Southern air ; the moonlight on the placid lake, on the softly-rounded, olive-clad hills, on the trellised vines, so picturesque compared to the formal vineyards of France, in such contrast to the scenes we had left behind,—to the giant mountain-peaks of granite, snow-covered, piercing the clouds : to the vast glacier, bristling with ice-blocks, sliding down, an encroacher on the valley's verdure,—all in such marvellous contrast to that region of rock and ice and mountain torrent and rugged path and grand, rude majesty of aspect,—it seemed like passing, in a single day, into another and a gentler world.

The morning after our arrival we crossed to the Isola Bella, once a barren island of slate rock, then a gorgeous garden, teeming with the vegetation of the tropics. We explored its vast palace, lingered in its orange groves, where I exchanged the few words of Italian of which I was master with a fair and courteous Signora who crossed our path. In returning from this abode of luxurious and elegant leisure, we touched at the little Isola dei Pescatori, a desolate island dotted with rude hovels, occupied only by poor fishermen and their families, who won, from the waters of the lake, a precarious and scanty subsistence. They seemed far more destitute and careworn than the Swiss peasant on his mountains. Perhaps the contrast, daily before their eyes, between their own cabins perched on the bare, hot rock, and the stately grandeur of that fairy palace, rising from the cool and fragrant groves that sheltered its base and swept down even to the water's edge, may have had something to do with the hard, hopeless air that darkened these weather-beaten features.

Then we made other charming excursions on the lakes,—Maggiore, Lugano, Como,—rowed by young girls with pensive, oval faces, who sang barcaroles as they rowed. I don't know which we enjoyed most,— the sight of these comely damsels, in their picturesque costume, or the rest to our blistered feet. Those blisters *were* a drawback; but what episode in human life has none? We might have had rest on the road by hiring mules for a day; but none of us had been willing to venture on that. What college lad was ever willing to incur, in the eyes of his mates, the charge of effeminacy? So we had drawn worsted threads through the blisters and walked on, the thoughts of the Italian paradise before us, and the boating on its sunny lakes, shedding hope and comfort over craggy path and rugged pilgrimage.

One of our excursions on Lago Maggiore brought us to the town of Arona, on an eminence near which stands the gigantic bronze statue of that cardinal and saint, Carlo Borromeo, illustrious for more than piety,—of all his compeers, perhaps, the most worthy ; for he not only devoted much of his life to reform the morals of the clergy and to found institutions for the relief of the poor, but also, when the plague raged at Milan nearly three hundred years ago, gave unremitting personal attendance on the sick at risk of his life, and spent his entire estate in ministering to their wants. We ascended this memento of a good man, first by a ladder, then by clambering up within one of the folds of the saint's short mantle; sat down inside the head, and looked out through the eyebrows on the lake, under whose waters lies buried the wide-brimmed shovel-hat which once covered the shaven crown, but was swept off by a storm-wind one winter night.*

Throughout the term of these charming excursions the strictest order was observed. And herein was evinced the power of that honorable party spirit which imposed on every one of us a certain charge as to the good conduct of the whole—making each, as it were, alive to the faults and responsible for the shortcomings of our little

* His death seems to have affected men as did that of Abraham Lincoln. Here is the record : "It was such a lament as had been given to no prince or hero within the memory of man. At the first alarm that their bishop was dying, a cry went up in the streets which reached to every house and convent and chamber. Some ran to the churches to pray. Some waited at the gate of the palace for instant tidings. All Italy was mourner for this good man."—*Amer. Cyclo.*, Art. *Borromeo.*

community.   Rude noise, unseemly confusion, the least
approach to dissipation at a tavern, or any other violation of propriety on the road, would have been considered an insult to the college.   And thus it happened
that we established, throughout Switzerland, a character for decorum such as no other institution ever obtained.

Nor did influences thus salutary cease with the term
of our college life.   So far as I know anything of the
after-fortunes of my college-mates, they did honor to
their *alma mater*—if older and more learned foundations
will not grudge ours that name.   As a body, they were
distinguished for probity and excellent conduct, some
attaining eminence.   Even that Alexander of Würtemberg whom we so lightly esteemed seemed to have
profited by the Hofwyl discipline; for I heard him
spoken of, at a later period, as one of the most estimable young princes of the court he graced.   Fifteen years
ago I met at Naples (the first time since I left Hofwyl)
our quondam master of the goats, now an officer of the
Emperor of Russia's household, and governor of one of
the Germano-Russian provinces.   We embraced after
the hearty German fashion—a kiss on either cheek—
still addressed each other, as of old, with the familiar *du*
and *dich;* sat down, forgetting the present, and were
soon deep in college reminiscences, none the less interesting that they were more than thirty years old.

So also of the Vehrli institution.   It assumed a normal character, sending forth teachers of industrial
schools, who were in great request and highly esteemed
all over Europe.   I found one of them, when, more than
forty years since, I visited Holland, intrusted by the
Dutch government with the care of a public school of

industry; and his employers spoke in the strongest terms of his character and abilities.

It does not enter into my present purpose to consider whether, in the hundred universities that are springing up throughout our country, from the Atlantic to the Pacific, it is practicable to reproduce, under a system of self-government, the noble spirit that animated the Hofwyl College. But one conviction it may not be out of place here to record. I regard such reform as this to be impracticable, unless, in the persons of those who preside over these learned foundations, we can unite, with the highest cultivation, literary and social, not only eminent administrative talent, but, above all, a devotion such as marked the Alsatian Pastor Oberlin, Thomas Arnold of Rugby, or our own Horace Mann. The soul of Hofwyl was its great president and founder; its palmy days ceased with Fellenberg's life. Under the inefficient management of his son and the son's successors, it gradually dwindled into an ordinary seminary, with little to distinguish it from many other reputable boarding-schools to be found throughout Switzerland.

But, while I live, the golden memories of our college, as it once was, can never fade. With me they have left a blessing—a belief which existing abuses cannot shake nor worldly scepticism destroy, an abiding faith in human virtue and in social progress.

PAPER VI.

I LEFT Hofwyl sadly, as if departing from a life-home; a fair Latin scholar, an indifferent Hellenist, thoroughly grounded in mathematics, with a minutely detailed knowledge of German history, that has served me but little since; in the other college branches pretty well up; in one only, according to the judgment of our teachers, had I outstripped my fellows, namely, in literary composition.

In connection with this last item, there lingers, in vivid colors still, a trifling reminiscence from my college life; one that would not be worth recording except that it may serve to indicate what it was that replaced, at Hofwyl, the honors and distinctions which await favored students in other institutions of learning. It would probably have faded long since from memory but' for the love of approbation which Dr. Spurzheim set down (as my readers will see hereafter), among the prominent organs in my brain.

Our professor of German literature, a warm-hearted, genial man whom we all liked, gave monthly to the senior class a subject for a thesis. It was his custom, in returning our papers, to read each to the class, pointing out errors or shortcomings, and usually appending a written word of approval or censure, nothing more. A month or two before I left, the theme propounded had been *Hope ;* and when the professor reached my essay, he said : " I read this to the class, not to point out errors, though it has a few, but to set before you an example which you would all do well to emulate. No effort of equal merit has come into my hands during all the years that I have been professor among you."

I listened, bewildered by surprise and pleasure ; and when, on receiving my manuscript, I glanced at its close, my eyes were moist, and I could not utter a syllable ; for there were a few cordial, loving words, in literal translation these : "Strive ever onward thus, thou dear Robert; and the fair *Hope* which all thy teachers have of thee will one day be brightly fulfilled."

No college honors could have moved me as did these simple words. They caused throbbings of joy such as I had never felt before.

The congratulations I received, when this was bruited about, were honest and unstinted : and when I finally took leave of my college mates, so cordial were their well-wishes that I felt a doubt whether I should ever spend such happy years again.

M. de Fellenberg bought, for my brother and my-self, a stout, light, open calèche ; we took post-horses, and, passing by way of Zurich and Basel, and travelling by easy stages, we descended the Rhine. What an era in one's life is that !

I shall not describe our journey. Half a century ago, when it was made, its details might have interested the American public. Now, the Rhine is almost as well known to us as our own Hudson. To me, in those days,.that magnificent valley was hallowed ground. I had imbibed, during three years of German thought and German study at Hofwyl, a portion of that love, tinged with veneration, which the entire German family entertain for their Great River. Every town, almost every castle, along its banks had, for me, historical associations; and the verses we used to sing in its praise were familiar as household words. * Thus I seemed to be journeying through a fairy-land of legend and of song.

A few incidents, that especially stamped themselves on my memory, may be worth recalling.

We visited at Stuttgart the studio of the German sculptor Dannecker, pupil of Canova, and at that time second only to him, and perhaps to Thorwaldsen, among the sculptors of Europe. He was then upwards of sixty years old, with that sort of native dignity which belongs to genius; yet I chiefly remember the simplicity and benevolence which marked his appearance and bearing. He seemed as much pleased with our enthusiasm, and took as much good-natured pains to show us over his studio, as if we had been connoisseurs. And it was a studio well worth seeing. There were many admirable busts of distinguished persons, of which the one that dwells most in my memory was that of Schiller, then my favorite above Goethe. This, from the manner in which the artist spoke of it, must have been a labor of love; for in early life they had been comrades, and it would seem sworn friends, in the School of Design at Ludwigsburg,—a friendship which lasted until the day when all Germany mourned her gifted poet. It was an inspired face, and Dannecker had caught and embodied in marble the very soul of its

---

* " Am Rhein, am Rhein, da wachsen unsere Reben;
Gesegnet sei der Rhein!" etc.

inspiration. He afterwards made a copy of this noble bust for the king of Bavaria.

There also was the original cast of Ariadne mounted on the panther, the best known perhaps of this artist's works : we saw it soon after, in marble, in the garden of the banker Bethman, in Frankfort ; where, as it had been purchased but a few years before, it drew together admiring crowds.

But it scarcely attracted my notice compared with the great work, the masterpiece of all that ever came from Dannecker's chisel, the colossal statue of Christ, on which he was then engaged, and had been for five years. It was an order from the Dowager Empress of Russia, and was afterwards presented by her to her son Alexander I. ; but it was not completed and sent to St. Petersburgh until three years after I saw it. The head, throat, and shoulders, however, were finished ; at least, I thought them so : and never have I seen, in sculpture or in painting, such an expression of mingled grandeur and sweetness, filling my conception of the Great Teacher, as on that wonderful countenance. It was something to remain stamped on the memory for a lifetime. A more princely gift was never, I think, presented by mother to son.

At Mannheim we hired a boat of size sufficient to float us with our carriage down past Mayence and "Bingen on the Rhine," to Coblentz, through that world-renowned valley, narrow, hedged closely in by mountain ranges. Is its scenery, with all the romantic accessories, equalled, within the same number of miles, on any other river-course in the world ?

I know not. But when I recall my emotions during that dreamlike and luxurious trip, drifting down silently and without perceptible motion past towering walls of cliff, abrupt as the sides of a Yosemite cañon, and scarce leaving, sometimes, between their base and the river-bank, apparent space for a bridle-path ; past time-worn fortresses perched on what seemed inaccessible rock-pinnacles, where clouds might settle ; then gliding by many gentler banks that slope far back and are clothed, to their top, with terraced vineyards; then coming, here and there, on some quaint old remnant of a walled and moated town, cramped, struggling for room be-tween mountain and river, but adorned with gray cathe-dral, rising from narrow and crooked streets that were darkened by the projection of massive gable fronts ; then occasionally spying, far up on the heights, a soli-tary peasant hut, or perhaps the slate roof and pointed spire of some lone cloister, aspiring toward heaven,— when I recall what I felt while there swept before me, lighted by bright autumnal skies, that magical panorama of beauty and romance,—I am tempted to join that most eloquent and artistic of all eccentrics,—adorer of Turner and detester of steamer and rail-car,—John Ruskin, in his notable crusade against all desecrating innovations in travel, and all modern scientific encroach-ments on time-honored modes of locomotion. Lazily floating on at the rate of five miles an hour, we certainly revelled in enjoyments which elude the time-pressed traveller of our day, busy and swift as bee on the wing, thinking no " shining hour " improved in which five times five miles are not left, forever, behind him.

Such a traveller would not have tarried, as we did, at Worms, attracted by the recollection that several of the scenes of the *Nibelungen Lied*—the Iliad of Germany, and a favorite text-book at Hofwyl—were laid at that town and in the surrounding country, called by the

Minnesänger *Wonnegau* (Land of Joy). Yet how themes of interest change with age ! To-day I barely remember the names of Brunhild and Siegfried ; and if I were now to stop at Worms, the first spot I should visit would be the site of that *Bischofshof* where Luther confronted Charles V. and his magnates ; and, when called upon to recant, replied in the memorable words : " It is neither safe nor advisable to do anything against conscience. Here I stand; I cannot otherwise ; God help me ! Amen ! "

Our trip was made at an interesting period. Napoleon's meteor career had ended at Waterloo six years before ; and, as the result of his fall, the valley of the Lower Rhine (from Carlsruhe down) had been freed from what Germans called French desecration. They might well exult ! The French rule on the Rhine, whenever their armies reached that river, had commonly been a rule of iron. We witnessed some of the desolation it had left behind. We found the luckless town of Speyer (Spires) still half in ruins, just beginning, under Bavarian rule, to recover from the atrocities which it suffered at the hands of France under her " Grand Monarch " and later,—atrocities with the details of which our professor of history, narrating to our class with flashing eyes that terrible episode which the Germans still call the *Mordbrenner Krieg* (the Murder and Burning War), had made us familiar. We thought of the miserable inhabitants driven forth by beat of drum ; of the seven-and-forty streets of the town ablaze for three days and nights ; and of the miners afterwards employed to blow up walls, fountains, convents, the cathedral, even the tombs of the Emperors ; till what had been Speyer was but a desolate heap of rubbish.

Mannheim fared little better.   After the French general had announced to the townspeople that his master (Louis *the Great!*) had resolved to raze their city to the ground, he told them that, as a special favor, they would be allowed twenty days in which to complete the work of destruction themselves.   When they refused to execute this atrocious order, they too were driven forth like cattle, and the soldiers did the work of destruction ; leaving fourteen houses only standing.   We found this town fully rebuilt, but in rectangular monotony.

I remember that at Coblentz we visited a trifling but characteristic memento of the recent decadence of the Empire.   In the square fronting the Church of St. Castor we found a pretty fountain, erected in 1812, during a season of elation, by the French.   It was intended as a monument of triumphs still to be achieved ; bearing an inscription to commemorate the passage through the city of the French Emperor on his way to Russia.   Little more than a year later, the Russians passing through the city in pursuit of the miserable remnant of one of the greatest armies of the world, their commander Priest left this monument, with its pompous boast, intact ; but we found, below the French inscription, the formal and quiet, but bitterly significant words : " *Vu et approuvé par nous, Commandant Russe de la Ville de Coblentz, Janvier 1ᵉʳ, 1814.*" *

On the opposite bank we inspected another remembrancer of then recent political revolutions ; finding the celebrated Ehrenbreitstein, as Byron had done a few years before, still

" Black with the miner's blast upon her height."

* The form used in viséing passports was adopted : " Seen and approved by us, Russian Commandant of the City of Coblentz, January 1, 1814."

The Prussians had made good use of the six years since which this fortress had passed, in ruins, into their hands. We saw hundreds of workmen busy in restoring its walls and removing the traces of French devastation. It is now, I believe, after a cost of five millions, one of the strongest fortified posts in the world; five thousand men sufficing to defend it, and its magazines capable of containing wherewithal to victual that number throughout a siege of fifteen years.

Cologne—encompassed by its seven miles of castellated walls with their eighty-three picturesque flanking towers and their twenty-four redoubt-defended gates, and exhibiting perhaps the most perfect remaining example of the great fortified cities of the Middle Ages— seemed to have escaped the invader's destroying hand, but not her own folly. From her high estate—her period of prosperity and splendor, five centuries ago, when she could send thirty thousand men into the field —she had fallen, not by the ravages of war, but by the madness of intolerance. They showed us the Hebrew quarter of the city where, in 1349, the principal Jews who occupied it, to escape intolerable persecutions, shut themselves up with their wives and children, set fire to their houses and perished in the flames. In 1425 every Jew, and in 1618 every Protestant, had been ignominiously exiled. The absolute rule of bigoted ecclesiastics worked desolation as real as that by fire and sword; and the deserted city had little left in the way of consolation save the reflection that there rose from her religious buildings as many spires as there are days in the year.

Her cathedral, too, remained to her; an unfinished dream, indeed, but when to artistic dreamer ever came such a magnificent conception of beauty embodied in stone ?—its towers to reach nearer to heaven than Egypt's pyramids ; its choir, from floor to ceiling, full a hundred and sixty feet. We ascended one of the unfinished towers on which, they told us, one layer of stone had lain undisturbed for three centuries before the next layer was superimposed. After six centuries we found the estimated cost of its completion still put at five millions of dollars.

From Düsseldorf, where modern art had not then established a school of painting, we crossed, chiefly, by level, sandy roads, through Hanover to Hamburg. One of our Hofwyl college-mates, Adolph von Münch- hausen, had given us a letter of introduction to his father, an old baron living a few miles from Hanover, and had exacted a promise that the letter should be de- livered in person.

It was a charming visit, and we, fresh from legends of which the story of Götz von Berlichingen is the type, were at an age thoroughly to enjoy it. The Baron's château, a few centuries old, was moated and turreted, though no portcullis rose to admit us. Without, de- spite the clustering ivy, it had a touch of stately gloom about it ; but within, from the first moment, we found bright cheerfulness and a cordial welcome. A few min- utes after we had sent up our letter of introduction, there rushed rather than swept into the room the eldest daughter of the house, who, when I advanced to meet her, gave me both hands, led me to the sofa, and seating herself beside me, exclaimed : " And so you have seen my dear, dear Adolph ; and you've lived three years with him ! I'm so glad he gave you that letter to us. You must tell me all about him—everything."

The deep blue eyes that met mine were moist with emotion; and their owner, a blonde of some twenty summers, without being regularly beautiful, had a face singularly expressive and attractive. Abashed, at first, by such unwonted cordiality, I found myself, after half an hour, conversing with her as frankly as if she had been my sister, instead of Adolph's. Then came in the father and mother; and it has never been my good fortune since to see a finer or more favorable specimen of the old *noblesse*, in its paternal type. Dignity was allied in their kindly features to a simple and benevolent grace. The white hair dropped to the Baron's shoulder, and the gray curls stole from under the bright old lady's cap; and Nature had set her grand seal of goodness on these genial faces, an earnest that was fulfilled, if four or five days' visit enabled me to judge, in that worthy couple's daily demeanor.

At a mid-day dinner we were introduced to a feudal dining-hall, its lofty walls half covered with old family portraits; and we had an opportunity of realizing what used to be meant by the expression, " below the salt." The Baron and Baroness sat at the head of the long table, opposite each other; next to them my brother and myself; then the young ladies, for there was a second daughter, prettier, but less interesting, I thought, than the first; then some relatives of the family; and below them the house steward, the factor who managed the estate, a gamekeeper, and two or three other dependants. It had a patriarchal look; and it was pleasant to hear the kindly tone in which the Baron occasionally addressed some remark or behest to those sitting at the lower end of the board.

During the afternoon, which was bright and warm,

we strayed, under guidance of the young ladies, through the large, old-fashioned garden, and over the stately park. When, on our return, we found the table already laid for supper, the elder exclaimed to her mother, "Liebe Frau Mutter, it's a shame to stay in the house losing a glorious sunset. Can't we have the evening meal (*Abendessen*) out on the lawn, in the shade?"

"Certainly, if you'll take the trouble, my children," said the old lady.

"It will be fun." Then to us: "You'll help us?"

But there seemed little need. In a twinkling, covers and dishes were removed to the sideboard, and the two girls were about to carry off the table, when William and I interposed. The table laid (under one of several magnificent limes just in front of the house), my brother and I returned for the chairs; but we were not suffered to take peaceable possession. The damsel who had first welcomed me, bounding lightly over a low ottoman while I was walking quietly round it, pounced upon the chair I had my eye on, and laughingly carried off the prize before I had recovered from my astonishment.

That little improvised banquet, literally "unter den Linden," has never faded from my memory. It was a jovial merry-making. Parents and children kept up the light shuttlecock of jest; and so catching was the genial laughter of that charming old couple, so winning the frank and graceful familiarity of the girls, that, ere the meal was over, two bashful college lads began to feel as if they were at home for the holidays with some fairy godfather and godmother, and two newly found sisters, "wonder-beautiful" as the Germans phrase it, to match. We asserted brotherly authority over chairs and tables, restricting women's rights to the transport of plates and dishes, until all was in due order again.

Next day Baron von Münchhausen conducted us over his farms, which seemed to be admirably managed. As we neared a pretty cottage, a young peasant girl of fourteen or fifteen, with comely features imbrowned by exposure, approached us, but stopped at some distance, shy and embarrassed, curtseying.

" Come hither, my daughter," said our host, in his cheery tones ; and the girl, encouraged, came up to us. " Ah, it is thou, Lisbethchen ? How thou'rt grown ! we shall have a woman of thee, one of these days ; and then a wedding, no doubt. I see thou hast a story to tell ; what is it ? "

The girl made some humble demand on behalf of her parents, which the Baron granted on the spot ; dismissing her with a kiss on the forehead, while she reddened with pride and pleasure.

We had a cordial invitation, earnestly pressed by parents and daughters, to remain with them for a month, and the promise of a ball which was to come off the following week. I was sorely tempted to stay ; but anxiety to reach home, and a promise to my mother not to delay on the journey, hurried us off. If fate *had* detained us there a month or two, I am not sure but that my father might have had a chance of welcoming a German daughter-in-law ; at all events I dreamed several times of the deep blue laughing eyes, before we reached Hamburg ; and I have preserved to this day, warm in my memory, a tender recollection of that fine old château, with its large-hearted, bright-spirited inmates.

At Hamburg we came upon traces, recent then, of

French inhumanity during the empire. In 1810 the city had been conquered, its Constitution abolished, and the city declared a French town. In 1813 the inhabitants, who hated their conquerors, welcomed the Russians, who restored the old Constitution ; but toward the close of that year, the French, under Marshal Davoust, retook the place, and were afterwards besieged by the allies. During that siege Davoust robbed the bank of Hamburg of three millions and a half of dollars ; and drove out, in the very depth of winter, forty thousand of the inhabitants. Of that number eleven hundred and thirty-eight perished miserably, from famine and exposure. We visited the monument that had been erected to their memory at Altona, which is close to the city.

Throughout this journey we were not once taken for foreigners, but by every one supposed to be German students. Indeed, by this time we thought in German, dreamed in German, spoke in English with a slight German accent ; and my brother and I, for a year after our return, conversed in German only, when alone. At Hamburg we chanced to make acquaintance with a young Swiss, and sauntered with him, one day, into a shop where pipes were sold. While he was bargaining for a Meerschaumer, I had a chat with the shopkeeper ; and when the bargain was made he said to my Swiss friend,

" Are you a Russian ? "

" No."

" Then you are Swiss."

To this the other assented, asking, " How could you possibly know that ? "

" Ah, I never mistake nationalities. I can tell, by

the accent, even from what part of Germany any one comes."

"Then perhaps you know where I am from?" I said.

"Yes, from Hanover." I told him he was mistaken. He made several other guesses, coming back, however, to his original opinion: "I know you must be from Hanover."

I told him I was a Scotchman; but had to confess that two thirds of the professors at Hofwyl were Hanoverians. I have never lost facility either in reading or in speaking German; and this has been of great advantage to me throughout life.

Wind-bound for three weeks, we sailed, at last, in a British vessel, to meet with heavy gales and foul weather. Thrice we were compelled to put back to Cuxhaven, the last time under circumstances of great danger. We had been three days beating about some seventy or eighty miles on our way, dead-lights up all the time, and without a glimpse of the sun at noonday, whence to determine our exact position; off a sand-bar coast too, and a lee-shore. The captain's state-room was next to ours; and the third evening we overheard this:—

Mate. The dead-reckoning brings us awfully near them cursed sand-bars.

Captain. We carried on too long. She's a jewel, close-hauled, and I hated to put back the third time; but it won't do: three hours more of this, and the masts would have to go to lighten her. We must lay her for Heligoland. We ought to see the light by eight bells, or soon after.

Mate. And if we miss it?

Captain. God help us! But the wind's in our favor;

and we must trust to luck to make it.   Go up and put her about at once.

Pretty serious! we thought it was.   On cross-questioning the captain, he admitted that the coast to leeward of us and toward which, beating up under a heavy norwester, we had all day been drifting, was a very dangerous one, often strewed with wrecks.   He said, however, that he thought we had a fair chance to make the lighthouse on Heligoland between twelve and one that night.   If we did, it would give us our precise position, and the chief danger would be over.

" But if we did not? " I asked, as the mate had done.

The captain saw, I think, that I took it quietly; for after a pause he said, " I'll tell you the truth.   We *may* be out of our reckoning, having only the log to trust to ; and we might run on some sand-bar, inside the island, and have to take to the boats.   But say nothing to the rest about it."

I asked him if we might lie down ; and he said yes, in our clothes ; and that he would wake us in time, if there was any danger.

In the cabin we found that the bad news had already spread.   Some were bitterly bemoaning their hard fate ; others sat, their heads buried in their hands, sobbing or rocking themselves to and fro : a small minority remaining self-possessed.   My brother and I turned in, tired and sleepy, having been all day on deck, and never opened our eyes till seven o'clock next morning.   Then we sprang up eager for the news.

" What ! " said one of the passengers—for they were all still assembled in the cabin, where they had passed a sleepless night—" don't you know that we made the

lighthouse at one o'clock ? Didn't you hear the rejoicing ? Where have you been, in God's name ? "

" Asleep," we told him ; " the captain had promised
to wake us up in good time."

They all stared ; and I believe that our avowal caused
us to be credited rather with callous apathy than with
fortitude. I think youth and sound health and nerves
braced by hardy exercise had more to do with it than
either.

We made a fourth start, deserted, however, by some
of the passengers ; and a short run to London, under
favorable winds, repaid us who still held to the vessel for
past mishaps.

At home we found our father doing well in business ;
but, as a radical reformer, having lost much ground in
public estimation.

He had been misled by prosperity, by benevolent
enthusiasm ; and there had been lacking, as steadying
influence, thorough culture in youth. He had risen, with
rare rapidity and by unaided exertion, to a giddy
height. At ten years of age, he had entered London
with ten dollars in pocket ; at forty-five, he was worth
quarter of a million. Then his Essays on the Formation of Character, backed by his success, pecuniary and
social, at New Lanark, had won him golden opinions.
He had been received, respectfully and sometimes with
distinction, by those highest in position ; by Lords Liverpool, Sidmouth, Castlereagh, and by Mr. Canning ;
by the Royal Dukes York, Cumberland, Sussex, Cambridge, and especially by the Duke of Kent ; by the
Archbishop of Canterbury (Sutton) and the Bishops
of London, St. David's, Durham, Peterborough, and
Norwich. Besides Bentham, his partner, he was more

or less intimate with Godwin, Ricardo, Malthus, Bow-
ring, Francis Place, Joseph Hume, James Mill, O'Con-
nell, Roscoe, Clarkson, Cobbett, Vansittart, Sir Francis
Burdett, the Edgeworths, the statistician Colquhoun,
Wilberforce, Coke of Norfolk, Macaulay (father of the
historian), and Nathan Rothschild, the founder of his
house. He had received as guests at Braxfield, among
a multitude of others, Princes John and Maximilian of
Russia, the Duke of Holstein Oldenburg, Baron Gold-
smid, Baron Just, Saxon Ambassador, Cuvier, Henry
Brougham, Sir James Mackintosh, and Lord Stowell,
father-in-law of Lord Sidmouth. When he visited Paris,
he took letters from the Duke of Kent to the Duke of
Orleans (Louis Philippe), and from the French Ambassador to the French Prime Minister ; and he was invited
to a visitor's chair by the French Academy. In Europe
he made the acquaintance of La Place, Humboldt, La
Rochefoucauld, Boissy d'Anglas, Camille Jourdain,
Pestalozzi, Madame de Staël, Pastor Oberlin, and many
other celebrities. Then, too, his popularity among the
masses quite equalled the favor with which men of rank
and talent received him.

Is it matter of marvel that a self-made and self-taught
man, thus suddenly and singularly favored by fortune,
should have miscalculated the immediate value of his social methods, and overestimated the influence of the
position he had gained ?

He worked, at that time, to disadvantage in another
respect. He saw the errors of orthodox theology, and
keenly felt their mischievous influence ; but he did not
clearly perceive the religious needs of the world.

He was a Deist. He stated his belief in an " eternal
uncaused Existence, omnipresent and possessing attri-

butes whereby the world is governed ; " and that " man, the chief of terrestrial existences, has been formed by a Power, in our language called God, that eternally acts throughout the universe, but which no man has yet been able to comprehend." *

As to religion he said, " I am compelled to believe that all the religions of the world are so many geographical insanities." Nor did he except Christianity, for he added : "I should therefore as soon attempt to contend against the Christian religion in a Christian country as to contest any question with the inmates of a lunatic asylum." †

His strong, original mind, lacking the habit of critical study, tempted him to discard in gross, without examining in detail ; and to overlook a fact of infinite importance in morals and legislation, to wit, that reverence, acting on man's spiritual part, is a legitimate and cogent motive that has influenced human actions in all ages of the world.

He was one of those who, like many of the ablest scientists in all countries, need experimental proof to convince him that, when the body is discarded at death, the man himself does not die, but passes on to another and higher phase of being ; and till he was nearly eighty years old he never obtained such proof.

Through all the active portion of his life he was a Secularist ; not denying a world to come, but believing that man had no proof of it, could have no knowledge of it, and ought not to trouble himself about it. Therefore he omitted from his system, as a motive to hu-

---

* Debate between Robert Owen and the Rev. J. H. Roebuck, London and Manchester, 1837, pp. 7 and 25.

† Debate quoted, p. 106.

man conduct, all reference to another life; believing
that men can be made to see so clearly how much it.is
for their interest to be temperate and industrious, just
and kind, that, in virtue of such insight and without
other prompting, they will act uprightly through life.
He trusted to man's desire for happiness, aside from religion, to reform the world.

It may be set down, also, as partly due to his lack of
critical scholarship, that he failed correctly to estimate
Christianity ; freely admitting, indeed, the truth and
beauty of its precepts of peace and charity and loving-
kindness, yet rating it no higher than Socrates's philosophy or the religion of Confucius.   When he spoke of
Christianity he meant, not the teachings of Christ himself,
as an exact and patient student may fairly construe them
from the narrative as it comes down to us through the
synoptical gospels, but that orthodox theology, loaded
down by extrinsic dogmas, which, ᴕspecially in its Calvinistic phase, may properly be termed an Augustinian
commentary on certain scholasticisms of St. Paul.

Some of the very truths he perceived tended further
to discredit the Christian record in his eyes.   He rejected, as an enlightened portion of mankind are learning to reject, the miraculous and the infallible ; and he
supposed, because King James's translators told him
so,* that Christ claimed for himself miraculous powers.
It did not suggest itself to him that the gifts or powers
exercised by Jesus, though spiritual, might be natural,

---

* Every tyro in Greek knows that *dunamis* (which, in accordance with
King James's instruction to his translators that "the old ecclesiastical
words should be kept," is rendered, in our authorized version, *miracle*)
means simply "power, faculty, efficacy : " the word "dynamics" (certainly
not a miraculous science) being derived from the same root.

as occurring strictly under law.   He did not believe that they occurred at all.   He thought, as Rénan does, that Christ, governed by expediency, lent himself to imposture ;   and this, in his eyes, tended to disparage the person of Jesus, and to cast suspicion on the narrative of his life.

So, also, as to inspiration.   Unable to accept it, in its orthodox sense, as a special and miraculous gift direct from God, it did not occur to him that it might be an element of culture, traceable throughout the history of all ages and nations ; a class of influences, ultramundane but not miraculous, coming to us, in virtue of intermundane laws, from a higher phase of being ; and that, in this broad sense, inspiration more or less pure might be, as Bishop Butler suggests,* the original of all the religions of the world.

But for these errors and oversights, I think a spirit like my father's—benevolent, merciful, forgiving—would have felt that there *are* no such lessons taught by ancient philosophy, Oriental or European, as are embodied in parables like that of the Pharisee and Publican at prayer, and of the Prodigal Son ; or in the record of that memorable scene in the Temple when the woman, who was a sinner, was brought up for judgment before Christ.

Robert Owen's mistakes, then, as a practical reformer, were, in my judgment, twofold.

First. He regarded self-love, or man's longing for happiness, rationally educated, as the most trustworthy foundation of morals.   I think that the hunger and thirst after the Right,† which is induced by culture of the con-

---

* Analogy of Religion, Part II., Chap. II., pp. 195, 196, of London ed. of 1809.

† Matthew v. 6.

science, is a higher motive, and, because higher, a motive better fitted to elevate our race, than selfishness, however enlightened.   Honesty *is* the best policy; truth *is* the safest course.   But he who is honest and true for the sake of the Right is more worthy, alike of trust and of love, than he who is honest and true for the sake of profit to himself.

Secondly.   He limited his view of man to the first threescore and ten years of his life, ignoring the illimitable future beyond.   But the Secular school can never prevail against the Spiritual.   It has nothing to offer but this world, and that is insufficient for man.

Acting upon his ardent convictions, and subordinating to these all considerations of money or fame, my father, in the autumn of the year 1817, after elaborate preparation, held three public meetings in the great hall of the City of London Tavern.   In the two first he set forth his views on education and on the social arrangement of society ; and these seem to have been favorably received, eliciting commendatory notices from the Times and other leading journals.   Thereupon several sectarian papers called upon him to declare his views on religion, which, till then, he had withheld.   And this appears to have produced a sudden resolution which he disclosed to no one, wishing to take the sole responsibility; namely, at the third meeting (as he himself expresses it), to " denounce and reject all the religions of the world."

The day before this meeting (August 20) he had an interview, by appointment, with Lord Liverpool, who received him graciously ; and when my father asked permission to place his name and the names of other members of the Cabinet on the committee of investigation, the appointment of which he proposed to move at the meeting next day, the Minister replied, " You may make any use of our names you please, short of impli- cating the government."

The meeting was crowded by thousands, and thou- sands more went away unable to find even standing room. My father began by putting the question, " What has hitherto retarded the advancement of our race to a high state of virtue and happiness ? " The words of his reply clearly indicate the enthusiastic ex- citement under which his mind was laboring : " Who can answer that question ? who dares answer it but with his life in his hand ?—a ready and willing victim to truth, and to the emancipation of the world from its long bondage of error, crime, and misery. Behold that victim ! On this day ! in this hour ! even now ! shall those bonds be burst asunder, nevermore to reunite while the world lasts ! "

Then he proceeded to declare that the arrest of hu- man progress toward a rational state was due to the " gross errors underlying every religion that has hitherto been taught to man." *

These sweeping and extravagant sentiments were doubtless uttered with the same sincerity, and in some- what the same state of feeling, that prompted the monk Telemachus to confront in the arena of the Coliseum the anger of Roman Emperor and populace, in an effort to put an end to the barbarity of gladiator shows. My father spared no cost in publishing what he had said ; purchasing of the London newspapers which appeared on the day succeeding each of his three lectures respectively

* Autobiography, p. 161.

thirty thousand copies. These papers, then heavily stamped, sold at fifteen cents apiece. In addition to this he printed forty thousand copies of each in pamphlet form, at a cost of more than six thousand dollars. In two months he had expended, for paper, printing, and postage, twenty thousand dollars.* The London mails, on the three days succeeding his lectures, were delayed, by the unexampled increase of mail-matter, twenty minutes beyond their set time.

My father, with fervid and exaggerated ideas of his mission, was evidently prepared for violence, even for outrage ; † and he had enough of the martyr in him to face it : yet he need not have feared. The ages have long gone by when a self-sacrificing reformer imperils life, or loses it as the noble Roman monk did at the hands of the very sufferers for whose liberties and lives he was pleading, ‡ by an honest endeavor to benefit his race. The day is past, even, when, in a free-minded country like England, one incurs personal risk by expressing, however boldly, if only honestly and decorously and without exciting to revolutionary violence, any opinions, no matter how extreme or unpopular.

What he did incur was a certain measure of ostracism. The Times led on, wheeling into line against him, and other periodicals followed its lead. He lost caste in the eyes of the pious, the conservative, and, in a general way, of the influential classes ; though some of these last, including the Duke of Kent and Lord Brougham, stood by him to the end. A few of his personal friends

---

* Autobiography, p. 156.   † Ibid., p. 161.

‡ Telemachus was slain by the gladiators themselves, incensed at his interference, about A.D. 400, under the Emperor Honorius.—Milman's *History of Christianity*, Vol. III., Book IV., Chap. II.

avoided his society, and many more were alarmed and dispirited.

He retained his hold, however, upon the working-classes ; and in the sequel he extended and fortified an influence over them which is sensibly felt, alike in its truths and its errors, to this day. An official Report on Religious Worship, made in connection with the British census of 1851, to the Registrar-General, speaks of the prevalence of secularism among the laboring classes ; its principal tenet, the reporter says, being that, as another world is matter of uncertainty, it is wise not to waste our energies on so remote a contingency, but to restrict our thoughts and exertions to the present life, adding : " This is the creed which probably with most exactness indicates the faith which, virtually though not profess-edly, is entertained by the masses of our working popu-lation." * Thirty years ago the Westminster Review had said : " The principles of Robert Owen are, in one form or another, the actual creed at the present time of a great portion of the working-classes." †

The reviewer speaks here, of course, of my father's ideas on co-operative industry as well as on religion. I learned recently from an English gentleman who has taken the lead in forming co-operative unions, that the amount of capital now invested in co-operative stores, manufactories, and the like throughout Great Britain, reaches some twenty millions of dollars ; that, with scarcely an exception, these have been a financial suc-cess ; and that they are rapidly on the increase.

While all earnest believers in a better world than this

---

* Report on Religious Worship made by Horace Mann, barrister of Lincoln's Inn, to the Registrar-General, under date December 8, 1853.
† Westminster Review for April, 1839.

must regret the prevalence of materialistic opinions among England's laborers, it is an open question whether the fallow ground of secularism be not better fitted to receive the good seed of vital religion than the dogmatic field of theology, often choked with a thousand noxious weeds.

There are various niches to be filled by those who would render service to their fellows; and the ultra-reformer's is one of these. It needs a violent wrench to unsettle the deep-seated errors of centuries, before quiet truths and well-considered opinions—the sober second-thought which succeeds agitation—can take their places.

The pioneer, meanwhile, suffers for his rashness. Yet on my return to Braxfield, I found my father as sanguine as ever, busy in perfecting his educational reforms, and apparently thinking little, and caring less, about the loss of his popularity. I myself was much occupied, for several years, in the personal supervision of the village schools, both day and evening. Several incidents that influenced, more or less, my after-life grew out of this occupation,

In the summer of 1824, when I was twenty-two years old, the first book I ever wrote, a small octavo volume of a hundred pages, was published in London and Glasgow: its title, An Outline of the System of Education at New Lanark. It was favorably received by the public; and in glancing over its pages, now after an interval of half a century, I do not find much to retract. Left free by my father to say just what I pleased, I did not follow his religious lead. In our schools he had not only scrupulously excluded all opinions, such as he himself held, against the religions of the day, but he allowed brief portions of the Scriptures to be statedly read by the children, because their parents wished it. Their time, however, was mainly occupied, aside from lessons in reading, writing, and arithmetic, in mastering the more important facts taught by natural science, geography, and history.

The ground I assumed was this : " A knowledge of these facts is a necessary preliminary to the study of the science of religion ; and a child, at an early age, should become acquainted with them, instead of being instructed in abstruse doctrinal points. . . . . An acquaintance with the works of the Deity, such as these children acquire, must lay the basis of true religion ; because true religion must be in unison with all facts." *

In those days Jeremy Bentham was my favorite author, and I was deeply read in his Principles of Morals and Legislation. From him and from my father I accepted the theory that utility is the test and measure of virtue ; and this caused me to fall in with what I now regard as one of Robert Owen's mistakes ; to wit, the assuming enlightened selfishness as the most trustworthy basis of elevated morality. In the introduction to the account of our school system I find myself saying : " A clear knowledge and distinct conviction of the necessary consequences of any particular line of conduct is all that is necessary to direct the child in the way he should go ; provided common justice be done to him in regard to the other circumstances which surround him in infancy and childhood." †

* New Lanark Schools, pp. 52, 53, 56, 57.
† Work cited, pp. 12, 13, 16. I admitted elsewhere, however, that convictions as to our true interests might be counteracted by the influence of evil associates ; confessing that "man is gregarious ; and he might

The publication of these and similar opinions pro· cured for me, some time afterwards, an interesting introduction. Having accompanied my father on one of his visits to London, I told him that I much wished to make Jeremy Bentham's acquaintance. He replied that Bentham's aversion to new faces was such that his most intimate friends could not take the liberty even to propose an introduction, unless he had himself expressed a desire on the subject. But a week or two later he informed me that he had visited Bentham, who said to him, in his abrupt way: " Owen, I like that son of yours. I've been reading his book. Send him to see me, will you ? No, I'll write him myself."

Ten days later, I had an invitation to his *symposium*, as he sometimes called his seven o'clock evening meal ; at which, however, there was abundance to eat as well as to drink : the profane vulgar would have called it a late dinner—and a very good one.

I preserve a most agreeable recollection of that grand old face, beaming with benignity and intelligence, and occasionally with a touch of humor, which I did not expect. The portrait of him which is prefixed to the later English editions of his Morals and Legislation is very like him, as I saw him then, at the age of seventy-eight, six years before his death.

I do not remember to have met any one of his age who seemed to have more complete possession of his faculties, bodily and mental ; and this surprised me the more because I knew that, in his childhood, he had been a feeble-limbed, frail boy, precocious, indeed,—

choose to traverse a desert in the company of others, though it led to danger and death, in preference to a solitary journey, though it conducted through gardens to a paradise."—p. 21.

taking his degree of A. M. at eighteen,—but with little
of that health of body which is sometimes spoken of as
indispensable to health of mind. I knew, also, that, in
his early years, in that gloomy "Lincoln's Inn garret"
(as he himself called it), and before he had made the
acquaintance of the cheerful and talented circle at Lord
Shelburne's, he had been sad and desponding, dispirited
by the world's lack of appreciation of youthful efforts,
which to-day are admitted to have given evidence of
marvellous acuteness and promise. Add to this that his
later attempts to have his principles of jurisprudence
adopted, at first by his own government, afterwards
by the United States, and, not long before I saw
him, by Spain, had all been unsuccessful; and yet there
I found him, having over-passed by nearly a decade
the allotted threescore years and ten, with step as active
and eye as bright and conversation as vivacious as one
expects in a hale man of fifty.

Our dinner party consisted of John Neal of Maine,
the author of Logan and other novels, and then, I think,
an inmate of Bentham's house; and three or four others
whose names I can no longer recall. I shall never forget my surprise when we were ushered by the venerable
philosopher into his dining-room. An apartment of
good size, it was occupied by a platform about two feet
high, and which filled the whole room, except a passage-
way, some three or four feet wide, which had been left
so that one could pass all around it. Upon this platform stood the dinner-table and chairs, with room
enough for the servants to wait upon us. Around the
head of the table was a huge screen, to protect the old
man, I suppose, against the draught from the doors.

The dinner passed cheerfully, amid the lively, and to

me most interesting, conversation of our host ; but I observed that he did not touch upon any of the topics of the day, nor allude to recent events, political or social ; while his recollections of the past were vivid and ready. His talk ran chiefly on those principles of morals and jurisprudence which have made his name famous.

When the cloth was drawn and we had sat for some time over our " wine and walnuts," Bentham pulled a bell-rope that hung on his right. " John, my marmalade !" he called out to the servant who entered ; then, to us : " That Scotch marmalade is an excellent digester. I always take a litle after dinner."

When another half hour had passed, he touched the bell again. This time his order to the servant startled me : " John, my nightcap !"

I rose to go and one or two others did the same ; Neal sat still. " Ah !" said Bentham, as he drew a black silk nightcap over his spare gray hair, " you think that's a hint to go. Not a bit of it. Sit down ! I'll tell you when I am tired. I'm going to *vibrate* a little ; that assists digestion, too."

And with that he descended into the trench-like passage, of which I have spoken, and commenced walking briskly back and forth, his head nearly on a level with ours, as we sat. Of course we all turned toward him. For full half an hour, as he walked, did he continue to pour forth such a witty and eloquent invective against kings, priests, and their retainers, as I have seldom listened to. Then he returned to the head of the table and kept up the conversation, without flagging, till midnight ere he dismissed us.

His parting words to me were characteristic : " God

bless you,—if there be such a being; and at all events, my young friend, take care of yourself."

Bentham's standing as a reformer of jurisprudence was not, at that time, what it afterwards grew to be, especially in England: thanks to the translations and able editing of his works by Dumont, he was more highly appreciated in France. Yet his posthumous fame was greater than his reputation while living. I heard him often spoken of as an ultra radical by those who thought that one of the gravest terms of reproach. It is true that after I saw him, but while he yet lived, Mackintosh admitted that "Bentham had done more than any other man to rouse the spirit of judicial reformation." But it was years after his death that Macaulay paid him this higher tribute: "Posterity will pronounce its calm and impartial decision; and that decision will, we firmly believe, place in the same rank with Galileo and with Locke the man who found jurisprudence a gibberish and left it a science. In some of the highest departments in which the human intellect can exert itself, he has not left his equal nor his second behind him."

With John Neal I kept up the acquaintance thus begun. My father, ardent in his love of civil and religious liberty, had brought me up to think highly of America and Americans; and the young man's enthusiastic admiration of Bentham fell in well with my own. He was then engaged in writing, for Blackwood, sketches of the literary and political celebrities of the United States, which I read eagerly; and the stories he told of his native country had for me all the charm of romance.

One day, when I was walking with him in Hyde Park, we met Henry Brougham, who accosted me, Neal saun-

tering on. I had spent several days of the previous
week near Birmingham, with the Hills; Rowland, afterwards Sir Rowland, author of the penny-postage system,
and for many years at the head of the British post-
office; together with two other brothers, Frederick and
Matthew; the former noted in later years for his work
on Crime and its Causes; the latter, for his exertions in
procuring law reform. They were then conducting a
large boarding-school or private college for boys, justly
celebrated in its day; and, as Brougham knew of my
visit, he had stopped me to learn what I thought of that
institution. I spoke of it, as I felt, in terms of the
warmest approval. I remember that one trifling peculiarity which I related to him took his fancy, as it had
taken mine; we were roused in the morning, not by the
harsh clang of a bell, but by the soft tones of a cornet,
gradually swelling until the musician concluded that
they were loud enough to awaken the sleeping population of the house,—a most pleasant and harmonious
ushering in of a new day, it had seemed to me.

Our conversation ended, I rejoined Neal. "Some
schoolmaster, was it not?" he asked in an indifferent
tone.

"No, indeed," said I; "that was Henry Brougham.
I should have introduced you, if you hadn't walked
off."

Neal stopped dead short, and stared at me. "Henry
Brougham!" he cried out at last. "The man of all
others I wanted to see and know! What an ass I was!
not to see, in his face, the power and talent he has,—to
mistake him for some old pedagogue."

Henry Brougham, though then without title, had
been, for years, a distinguished member of Parliament,

eminent for his passionate eloquence and vehement invective ; famous, too, as the legal defender of Queen
Caroline. He had also been chosen a year or two before, though Walter Scott was his competitor, Lord
Rector of the University of Glasgow, and his recent
work on the Education of the People was attracting universal attention. No wonder, then, that my friend
Neal, sanguine, impressible, and a worshipper of genius,
was provoked with himself for having missed an introduction.

I may state here that there was, between Brougham
and my father, so great a personal resemblance, alike in
face and person, that the one was frequently mistaken
for the other. A year or two after Brougham obtained
his title, my father, passing through Macclesfield in the
mail-coach, was accosted, while it stopped there, by a
gentleman who said he was glad to see his Lordship
again so soon, My father, guessing the mistake, pro-
tested that he was not Lord Brougham ; but the other
rejoined, " You wish to travel incognito ; but you forget that I had the honor of dining with your Lordship
three weeks ago." This was noised about ; a crowd
collected ; and when the coach started again, they gave
three hearty cheers for Lord Brougham, the people's
friend.

My father, while I was with him in London, introduced me to a noted author, already known to me
through two of his works,—Political Justice and Caleb
Williams,—and as the husband, thirty years before
that time however, of the celebrated Mary Wollstonecraft. William Godwin was then seventy years old ;
but he seemed to me older than Bentham. Feeble and
bent, he had neither the bright eye nor the elastic step

of the utilitarian philosopher. In person he was small and insignificant. His capacious forehead, seeming to weigh down the aged head, alone remained to indicate the talent which even his opponents confessed that he had shown, alike in his novels and in his graver works. His conversation gave me the impression of intellect without warmth of heart; it touched on great principles, but was measured and unimpulsive; as great a contrast to Bentham's as could well be imagined.

His face, however, twenty years before, if one might judge by what seemed a capital oil-painting that hung over the mantel-piece, must have had a noble expression. A head of Mary Wollstonecraft, in another part of the room, was inferior as a picture. But the face, less masculine than I had figured it to myself, was very beautiful; a peculiar soft and loving expression about the eyes mingling with a look of great intelligence. Godwin assured me that it was an excellent likeness. I gazed at it, calling to mind some of the sad passages of her life as recorded by her husband, and wondering whether her brief union with him had made up for previous sufferings.

My visits to London were occasional, only when my father needed an amanuensis. After writing many hours for him, I used, by way of exercise, to take riding lessons at Astley's amphitheatre, and there learned some of the simpler feats of horsemanship which, in the evening performances, I had admired.

At New Lanark I spent part of my time, during two or three years, in my father's counting-house, greatly to my after-advantage. I mastered, also, every operation by which cotton yarn is produced, so that I was able to give practical directions to the work-people in each branch if they were doing bad work ; for my father left me manager in his absence, intending that I should by and by take his place. This was not to be.

Meanwhile there occurred what forms one of the most romantic episodes of my life ; of which I give the details in the next paper.

PAPER VII.

EDUCATING A WIFE.

WE had much gay society at Braxfield ; and among
the visitors who almost daily thronged our table were
many young ladies, very eligible matches, and some
almost as charming as that dear Fräulein Münchhausen.

Two of them, I remember, came from Dublin with
their father, who was physician to the Lord Lieutenant
of Ireland, and had apartments at the castle. They
were splendid specimens of the old Milesian race : fair
girls, with finely formed, well-developed figures, strong
and stately, and just evading the exuberance of *embon-
point ;* with brilliant complexions, the rich red in their
cheeks such as only the "weeping skies" of the Green
Island call out ; with magnificent auburn hair, and large
blue eyes that looked filled to the brim with merry
thoughts. They were highly accomplished, too; dressed
with simple elegance, and were modish and well-bred,
as far as that irrepressible spirit of fun and frolic which
seems inborn in spirited Irish girls would let them.

The first evening, after the elder of these dashing
Milesians had given us, with stirring effect, " The Harp
that once through Tara's Halls," while she accompanied
herself admirably on the harp, gracefully displaying
arms of marvellous whiteness that a sculptor might have
yearned to copy, it chanced that their father and mine
became deeply engaged in a grave conversation touch-

ing the formation of human character. Meanwhile, on a sofa at some distance, I had commenced a low conversation on some light topic with the fair songstress, who seemed indifferent to metaphysics; when the younger sister, touching me so as to call attention to her movements, stole slyly up behind her father, and, cautiously raising her hands to his head, twitched off his wig while he was in the very midst of some learned reply, and made off with it to our end of the room. I shall never forget my father's look of amazement. From his guest I expected an outburst of anger, but he only said, " Come back this minute, you monkey ! Do you think I can talk philosophy without a wig ? "

They stayed with us several days ; and I was quite dazzled and somewhat overwhelmed by their beauty and spirit.

A complete contrast in character to these stylish perpetrators of fun, less bewildering but far more interesting, were two young ladies whose acquaintance I had previously made. They also were from Ireland, indeed from one of its noted families ; daughters of a nobleman whose name is still cherished by the Irish people as one of the most daring and disinterested defenders of their political franchises.

Lord Edward Fitzgerald, younger son of James, first Duke of Leinster, seems, despite his rank, to have been born a democrat. A mere stripling in our Revolutionary days, and barely of age when France quailed under her " Reign of Terror," he warmly sympathized, during both revolutions, with the oppressed millions struggling for freedom. As a member of the Irish Parliament toward the close of the last century, he took a stand for the independence of his country (then in imminent danger of subversion) as daring as that of Patrick Henry for ours. Brooding over her oppression, impatient under her sufferings, and finding words unavailing to effect redress, Lord Edward appears to have felt that the time for action had come. He joined the secret society of " United Irishmen," and was enthusiastically elected its president. That society virtually adopted as its motto the same which had been the watchword of our own Revolution, " Peaceably if we can, forcibly if we must ; " and ere long it counted its members by hundreds of thousands, scattered over every parish in the island ; many of them devoted men, nerved to a stern purpose by sacred incentives, national and spiritual. At that time the Irish Parliament enjoyed absolute independence of all power but the Crown. Grattan, in 1780, had procured the passage of a resolution, " that the king's Most Excellent Majesty and the Lords and Commons of Ireland are the only powers competent to make laws to bind Ireland." The British Government, acquiescing at the time, sought now to abolish this only competent power ; replacing a national and independent legislature by the admission into the British Parliament of a few Irish members, none of whom, however, it was lawful to choose from among professors of the Catholic faith. Then the " United Irishmen " plotted treason. The plot was prematurely revealed, and their leader betrayed, for money—by an informer. Lord Edward, after killing with a dagger one of his assailants, and severely wounding another, would doubtless have been tried for treason and sentenced to the gallows, but that he died in a Newgate prison-cell two weeks after his capture, of wounds envenomed by disappointed hopes. With a refinement of cruelty for which government policy, except it be such as is utterly disgraceful in a civilized nation, furnishes not a shadow of excuse, his wife had not been permitted to see him ; and permission was given to his brother and sister only when it was certain he must die, and then but for a few minutes, just three hours before his death. This was in 1798 ; and two years afterwards, despite the noble stand taken by a talented band of patriots, the outrage was consummated, and the Irish Parliament was merged in that of Great Britain.

Some years before his death, Fitzgerald had won and married the beautiful Pamela, daughter, by more than adoption, it seems,* of the celebrated Madame de Genlis. By her he had two daughters, Pamela and Lucy. These young ladies were connections of a kindly neighbor of ours, Lady Mary Ross, who lived two miles off at Bonnington, a romantic country-seat near the Falls of the Clyde ; Lady Ross's son, Sir Charles, having married their father's sister, Lady Mary Fitzgerald. During a visit of some months at Bonnington they were frequent visitors, and always welcome ones, to Braxfield.

We found them charming girls ; charming and estimable ; but one would never have imagined them sisters. The elder, Pamela, inheritor of her mother's personal gifts, but without the gayety of her mother's country, was a handsome brunette, small of stature and beautifully formed, with large, dark pensive eyes that seemed still to mourn her father's untimely fate ; the

---

* Pamela, the adopted, or (as may now be said without scruple) the actual daughter of Madame de Genlis by the Duke of Orleans (Egalité), etc.''—Memoirs of Lord Edward Fitzgerald, by Thomas Moore. London, 1831, Vol. i. p. 178.

younger, Lucy, a delicate blonde, tall and graceful, sprightly and sympathetic ; Irish evidently, not French, of origin ; her enthusiastic father's true child. Both had the charm of perfect manners, noble, simple, and kindly, rather than demonstrative.

One of them became a connection of ours. It chanced that Sir Guy Campbell, my mother's first cousin, a dashing young officer, came to us on a visit for a few days ; and that my father invited Lady Ross and the two Miss Fitzgeralds to dinner to meet him. That evening decided his fate. The dark eyes, with their depths of wistful expression, made an immediate conquest of the lively and brilliant youth. Next day he rode over to Bonnington, and the next, and the next. His visit to us was finally prolonged into a three-weeks' stay, and every forenoon, during that time, Sir Guy's charger was brought regularly to the door, not to return with his master, after the first week, till late at night. At the end of the three weeks, the rider's furlough drawing to a close, there was a wedding at Bonnington, and my father (who had been appointed Pamela's co-trustee with the Duke of Leinster, her uncle) gave away the bride.

I, in the officer's place, should have preferred Lucy. As it was, she being five or six years older than myself, I did not presume to think of her, except as a boy thinks of a beautiful woman, with reverential admiration and, as Tennyson has phrased it, with " tender dread." She was to me a sort of ideal being, removed beyond the actual and the familiar. Perhaps this was in part due to the fact that my affections had already begun to attach themselves elsewhere.

I have stated that, as a boy, I had read a work of

Thomas Day's; the same of which Leigh Hunt says, "the pool of mercenary and time-serving ethics was first blown over by the fresh country breeze of Sandford and Merton." But I do not think that, up to the time of which I am writing, I had read the author's life; or found out that he had selected, from a foundling hospital, two young girls of twelve, intending to educate them on Rousseau's system, and to make one of them, by and by, his wife; and that this strange contrivance did not succeed.

An experiment which, at the age of twenty-one, I commenced, was, I think, better deserving of success than Thomas Day's; inasmuch as it was not founded on the cold-blooded calculation of educating first and taking the chance of falling in love afterwards; also, because, instead of wandering off to French philosophy, I trusted to the domestic influences of Braxfield House.

Among the young girls in our village school was one, ten years old, and whom, as she may be still alive, I shall call Jessie. Her father was foreman of a room in one of our mills, an ordinary character; her mother (often familiarly going among her neighbors, according to the custom of the country, by her maiden name, Peggy Gardiner) seemed, by beauty and demeanor, and to judge by the exquisite cleanliness, order, and good taste that marked her humble apartments, quite above her station. From her, no doubt, had come to Jessie the nameless grace, the native refinement that distinguished the child, not in my eyes alone, from all her schoolmates.

I should not trust myself to describe this young girl, as I first remember her, did I not call to mind what my mother, six or seven years later, confessed to me, on her return from a visit to Glasgow, on which Jessie had accompanied her. " I could not walk the streets with her," she said, " without serious annoyance. Almost every gentleman we met turned round to look at her, and several contrived to pass and repass us several times, evidently smitten by her beauty. In the shops it was little better; business seemed half suspended, customers and shopmen alike pausing to admire."

" You don't think it was Jessie's fault, mother ? " I asked.

" No ; I think the poor girl's modest and quiet bearing only attracted people the more ; but it was very unpleasant."

This was when she was fifteen or sixteen ; as a child of ten she was scarcely less noticed by the fashionable visitors who thronged our school. Not in music and dancing alone did she excel all her fellows. I gave occasional lessons in geography and history to the elder girls' class to which she belonged; and while I found her first in almost every branch, she seemed quite unconscious of her superiority.

Her complexion was fair and of unrivalled purity, her face a perfect Grecian oval ; the eyes deep blue, and filled with a dancing· light when she smiled ; the chestnut hair long and silky. Every feature was cut with singular delicacy ; the only deviations from strict regularity being that the mouth was, in proportion, a trifle larger than that of the Venus of Milo, but then the teeth, dazzlingly white and perfect, atoned ; and that the nose was just a little bit what the French call *retroussé ;*—though one need not now have recourse to French ; Tennyson has coined just the word. To Jessie, as to Lynette, the lines apply,—

" And lightly was her slender nose
   Tip-tilted like the petal of a flower."

Only that, in Jessie's case, the divergence from the
classic line was so slight that the simile of the flower-
petal does not quite suit the occasion.

Though she afterwards grew to medium height only,
she was, in those days, rather tall for her age. Her
person was perfect in its form and proportions ; and this
has always had a singular charm for me.   Spurzheim
set down *form* large, and *color* small, in my phrenological chart, telling me I should make a good sculptor or
architect ; and, in effect, I have always found more
pleasure in going over a collection of the best-statuary
than in viewing the finest gallery of paintings.   I recollect reading casually, in some newspaper, the lines,

   " She had a form—but I might talk till night,
      Young as the sun is now upon our watch,
      Ere I had told its beauties.   It was slight,
      Even as yon willow, and, like its soft stem,
      Fell into thousand motions and all lovely,"

and thinking that they must have been written expressly
to describe Jessie.   Yet I believe it was not so much
her beauty, alike of form and feature, that first awoke
in me a sentiment seldom felt, I think, by an adult, for
a child so young, as another peculiarity.   She was a
creature of quick sensibilities, which she had not learned
to conceal.   Her countenance, always an interesting
one, was, if love be dangerous, a somewhat dangerous
one to watch.   She had a habit—painful, I knew she
herself often found it—of blushing at the touch of any
emotion, whether of joy or sorrow ; at trifles even, as
at the unexpected sight of some girl-friend ; and when

deeply and suddenly moved, the flush would overspread face and neck. This happened, on one occasion, when I had taken her by surprise in addressing to her a few words of commendation ; the tell-tale blush which my praise called up first awoke in myself the consciousness how dear she was to me.

I was very much ashamed when I became aware of this ; knowing that if it were observed it would expose me to ridicule ; not so much on account of the girl's social position,—I did not care for that, it being already an article in my social creed that Love, like God, is no respecter of persons,—but a mere child ! not half my own age, and I but just out of my minority : that *was* ridiculous ! I could not even call to mind that any hero of a novel had ever indulged in so absurd a fancy.

The parents of Jessie belonged to the sect over which my grandfather had presided,—the Independents ; and my mother attended service twice every Sunday in a small chapel or hall which my father had set apart for these worshippers. When I returned from college, my mother, feeling that her authority in such matters had ceased, merely asked me if I chose to go with her. She was greatly delighted when she found me a willing attendant both· at morning and evening service ; and I am glad the dear, good lady never guessed what the attraction was, never knew how often I might have played truant if Peggy Gardiner, a regular church-goer, had not brought her little daughter with her, looking as fresh and lovely as a spring flower ; dressed simply but with scrupulous neatness, and recalling to me what Christ said of the lilies of the field,—that even Solomon, in all his glory, was not arrayed like one of these.

Luckily our pew was square and spacious, and I al-

most always contrived so to select my place (facing the
congregation) that I could see that charming young face.
My sisters, and even William, would now and then drop
to sleep when the sermon overran an hour and a half;
but I know that grave, serious audience must have been
greatly edified, and my mother quite comforted, by my
wakefulness, and by what must have seemed to them
my unwavering attention, during endless disquisitions
on free-will and election and predestination, on vicarious
atonement and original sin. The preachers were too
gloomily in earnest ever to select so cheerful a theme
as that embodied in my favorite text, " Love is the fulfilling of the law ; " and, fortunately for their good opinion of me, thoughts are not read in this world as no
doubt they will be in the next.

It has sometimes occurred to me, however, that this
sudden attachment of mine might have proved a passing fancy only, had not my eldest sister, Anne, very
innocently and unintentionally given it food and encouragement.

Anne was then a thoughtful girl of seventeen or
eighteen, shy, and a little awkward in manner, not
handsome nor even pretty, but thoroughly good and
practical ; domestic in her tastes, a skilful needle-woman
who had worked a wonderfully elaborate sampler, em-
broidered with crowns, royal, baronial, and I know not
how many others, and bearing, in various colored
worsteds, a stanza, selected, I think, by her mother as a
bit of quiet consolation for lack of beauty, and reading
thus : —

> " Can comeliness of form or shape or air
> With comeliness of words or deeds compare ?
> No ! those at first th' unwary heart may gain,
> But these—these only—can the heart retain."

Anne was very fond of children and a born teacher ; attending the village school almost daily, and often taking part in the instruction of the various classes.   In the spring or summer of 1822 she selected two of the best pupils (of whom Jessie was one and a certain Mary the other), who came to Braxfield after school-hours and had lessons from her in music, reading, and some-times in other branches.   After a time, Mary being re-quired at home for domestic duties, Jessie remained sole scholar.   Toward the close of the year, her mother be-gan to talk of sending her into the mills ; but pupil and teacher having by this time become strongly attached to each other, a respite of a few months was obtained, and her daily visits, which were uninterrupted even by the rigor of a severe winter, were continued into the next spring.

During all this time, however delighted I was with Anne's proceedings, I set special guard on my looks and actions.   Yet I was unable to refrain from frequent attendance at my sister's private lessons, especially in music.   In eight or ten months Jessie had made won-derful proficiency on the piano, and sang duets with my second sister, Jane, to the admiration of the household ; with all of whom, I may add, she had become a favor-ite.   As I look back on those days, this seems to me strange ; for marked favor to one of humble rank is wont, in a class-ridden country like England, to produce envy and ill-will.   It was Jessie's idiosyncrasy, I think, which averted such results.   She had that innate refine-ment which is sometimes held to belong only to " gen-tle blood ; "" coupled with a simple bearing, alike re-moved from servility and presumption, which seemed to accept a new position, gladly indeed, but quietly and as a matter of course. Less than a year's daily inter-course with a cultivated circle had so wrought on that delicate nature that, by personal carriage and good breeding, she seemed "to the manner born." The ser-vants instinctively treated her as one of our family; yet to her school companions she was still the same lively and cordial playmate as before. Need I add that the impression she had made on me deepened daily?

About the 1st of March, 1823, I had a conversation with Anne. , She began by saying Jessie's mother had been telling her that her husband thought it was time that their child should begin to defray her own support by tending a throstle-frame. I could not help redden-ing, almost as Jessie herself might have done.

" You don't like that ? " said Anne.

" Of course not. Do you ? "

" It would give me great pain. I love the dear child, and I should feel almost as if I were to lose a little sister. But, Robert, I think you would care more still."

" What makes you think that ? "

" Well, you have a tell-tale face ; but that's not all. I found out some time since. A man who has a secret to keep ought not, when he reads his favorite authors, to make marginal references."

" I can't imagine what you mean, my dear."

" You and I are pretty much in the habit of reading the same books, and in half a dozen places lately I've found passages marked that showed what you were thinking about; one of them in Thomson's Seasons, in that story about the 'lovely young Lavinia' who 'once had friends,' and married so nicely at last."

My consciousness must have betrayed me at this

point, for she added, " It's no use denying it, Robert. You wish some day to make Jessie your wife."

" You think me an idiot for falling in love with a mere child ? "

" No ; one may admire a rose-bud as well as the full-grown flower ; and such a sweet rose-bud, too !"

" But I'm more than twice her age."

" You won't be, by and by. When you're thirty, Jessie will be nineteen. That's not out of the way. You're willing to wait ? "

" Willing ? " I felt pretty much as a Peruvian wor-shipper might, if he had been asked whether he was willing to await the rising of the sun ; but I only said, " Will you help me, Anne ? "

Thereupon, after consulting together, we concocted a scheme. My father was then on a visit to Ireland, where he had been lecturing in furtherance of his plans of social reform ;* and my sister told me she intended, as soon as he returned, to ask his permission to adopt Jessie, charging herself with the child's education. When I heard this, I thought Providence must be help-ing me ; for that was just what I had been wishing for months to bring about, without daring to suggest it, and not knowing whether the girl's parents would con-sent. Anne thought they would ; for the mother had ex-pressed to her doubts whether her daughter, who, though healthy, was far from being robust, could endure without injury the confinement of the mills at so early an age.

---

* He was then and later popular in Ireland, even among the upper classes. On March 18, 1823, he held a meeting, very numerously attended, at the Rotunda, Dublin ; at which the Lord Mayor presided, and the Duke and Duchess of Leinster, the Earl of Meath, Lord Cloncurry, Lady Rossmore, and a long list of nobility and gentry, were present.

Thus reassured, I suggested that it might be weeks before my father returned, and that it would be best to send him a letter, carefully prepared, at once. A copy of this letter, covering sixteen pages of note-paper and dated March 3, 1823, lies before me. It was in my sister's handwriting and signed by her, though in truth a joint production. I had put my heart into it; and, for that matter, so had Anne, who made some excellent points. Here is one :—

" Do not imagine, my dear papa, that I intend to make a fine lady of this little girl ; nothing is further from my thoughts. I wish to render her independent, and able by and by to take care of herself. With such an education as I propose to give her, she will, when she grows up, be a valuable instructress of youth ; and how rarely do we meet with such a one ! It shall be my study to prevent her acquiring idle or expensive habits ; and to make my little charge much more diligent and orderly than you have ever seen *us*."

Then followed a diplomatic suggestion, intended, I am afraid, to put my father off the true scent. She told him :—

" In case I kept house for one of my brothers, she would, I am sure, prove a most agreeable companion for me ; and, by affording me a never-failing source of amusement and interest, might enliven many hours I should otherwise spend in solitude."

The sly gypsy knew well enough that her elder brother, at least, was not likely to set up bachelor's hall and there to need a sister to preside ; and that her pupil, instead of proving an amusement to her in the fraternal mansion, would probably there become a domestic blessing to somebody else. But of course it would never have done prematurely to suggest such a contingency as that.

Anne waited with an anxiety only less profound than my own for a reply. It was kind and favorable; and, my mother acquiescing, Jessie became a member of our family circle.

I was exultant; yet I put a still stricter guard than before on all I said and did when Jessie was present. It was a great exercise of self-control. No matter how numerous and brilliant the company in our drawing-room, I knew, by instinct, whether Jessie was there, and missed her at once if she withdrew. Young girls of my own age, beautiful, cultivated, and well-born,— and many such were, from time to time, inmates of Braxfield House,—all failed to awaken in me an emotion comparable to the feeling which the sight of that child, scarcely eleven years old when she came to us, uniformly called forth.

She seemed to win my parents' hearts, and they behaved admirably, making no distinction between her and their own children; and for this I was the more grateful, because it placed them, now and then, in an awkward position. They would have to listen, for example, while some casual visitor descanted in warm terms on the singular beauty of their youngest daughter; and I overheard one preposterous flatterer tell my father how much she was like him: about as like, I longed to tell him, as I to Hercules. My father took it very quietly, smiling, and saying only, "she is not mine,— an adopted child." But I think my mother didn't quite like it.

I came very near betraying myself one evening; but fortune stood my friend. We had a young folks' party, and a number of both sexes had gathered together. A proposal was made that we should " draw for sweethearts,"—for the evening, of course ; but some one added jestingly, " Perhaps for life,—who knows ? " So we wrote the name of each young lady (Jessie included) on a slip of paper, then folded these and shook them up in a hat which I handed round. It so happened that the number of young ladies exceeded by four or five that of the young gentlemen ; so that when all had drawn and my turn came last, there were still several slips remaining. I glanced at that which I drew and saw Jessie's name. In a moment, what Anne had said of my tell-tale face flashed across me ; I turned instantly to hide my confusion by depositing the hat ; and, as I did so, dropped into it the name that was hidden away in my heart, and stealthily abstracted another unperceived. This time it was the plainest girl in the room ; to whom, grateful for danger past, I cordially offered myself as partner.

But before the evening was over, I contrived to get possession of the slip with Jessie's name. This I secreted within the lining of a small bead purse which one of my sisters had worked for me. That purse and its enclosure exist still. I kept it hidden away in the secret drawer of a writing-desk.

Our experiment proceeded smoothly and successfully, for more than two years,—two of the brightest years of my life ; even though I had no means of judging whether Jessie's heart, in after years, would turn to me or not.

I have heard the question debated, which is the greater happiness,—to love or to be loved. Theoretically, on purely ethical principles, one is led to the conclusion that to love is the higher privilege ; and practically the experience of a lifetime confirms to me that view of the case. To love is the best. It wears better, it has a nobler influence on a cultivated heart, than the mere consciousness of being loved, however grateful that consciousness may be to self-love ; however, too, it may minister to vanity. The tendency of loving, if one loves truly, is to eliminate selfishness ; but it often fosters selfishness to be the object of love. It is better to love without requital, than to be loved unless one can render double in return. It is not of love received, but of love given, that Paul, faithfully translated, speaks, in memorable words : Love, greater than faith, greater than hope, suffereth long, envieth not, seeketh not her own, endureth all things, never faileth. But the recipient even of the purest love may be dead to long-suffering, may nourish envy, may cherish self-seeking, may lack patience under adversity, and may fail when the hour of trial comes. Not he on whom love is bestowed is the favored one, but he by whom love is conferred. It is more blessed to give than to receive.

I never swerved in my loyalty to Jessie ; yet, though I could not help being uniformly kind to her and watchful for her welfare, I tried hard never to give the child any reason to believe that I loved her otherwise than as I did my three sisters. They, on their part, treated her at all times with sisterly affection, as one of themselves ; and this was greatly to their credit ; for Jessie not only quite outshone them in beauty, but in musical talent, in grace in the ball-room and elsewhere, and ultimately in ease of manner. If, at the end of two years, a stranger had been asked to say which of the four girls had been raised from an humble home to her

present position, I think Jessie was the last he would
have been likely to select.

If I had remained at Braxfield, this novel experiment
of mine could have had, I incline to believe, but one
issue. It was otherwise ordered, however. In the
winter of 1824–5, my father purchased a village and a
large tract of land in Indiana, with what result I shall
state by and by; and in the autumn of 1825, when
Jessie was little more than thirteen years old, I emigrated to this country. I was sorely tempted, before I
left home, to tell the girl how much I loved her, and
that I hoped some day, if she should ever come to love
and accept me as a husband, to make her my wife.
But, while I was romantic enough in those days and
later, to do many foolish things, common-sense suggested that to a child such a declaration was ill-judged
and out of place. So I departed and made no sign.
With Anne, however, I conferred in secret; and she
promised me, if I could not return in three or four
years, to come to the United States herself, and bring
Jessie with her.

Though it is anticipating dates, I may as well here
state the ultimate issue of that episode in my life. Two
years later, namely, in the summer of 1827, longing to
see Jessie once more, I joined an English friend and re-
crossed the Atlantic. I found the young girl beautiful
and interesting even beyond my remembrance or expectation; and, what moved me still more, she received
me so cordially and with such evident emotion, that—
though I think I may say that I have never been guilty
of the presumption of imagining myself loved when I
was not—it *did* seem to me the chances were fair that,

if I remained some months and spoke out, she would
not say me nay.

But I determined first to make a confidant of my
mother, in whose good sense and deep affection for me
I placed implicit trust.

" My son," she said, " I saw, before you went to
America, that you loved this girl, and had already
thought of her as a wife. But there is much to be
taken into account in such a matter."

" You would prefer to have a daughter-in-law from
our own rank in life ? "

" If I could have chosen, yes ; but I do not think
that a sufficient objection. My own good father worked
his way up from a position as humble ; and Jessie's appearance and manners are as ladylike as if she had
been my own child."

" But you *have* objections, dear mother. Do not
withhold them from me, I entreat you."

" At least I should like to see what will be the result,
on her character, of the next three years. I know you,
Robert ; you have a very high ideal of what a wife
ought to be ; unreasonably high, I am afraid. You
think this girl perfect, but she is not. I should like to
be sure that she will grow up free from undue love of
admiration, and, what is more important, perfectly sincere."

" Not truthful, mother ? "

" I do not say that ; though, when she first came to
us, I sometimes thought it. She is very anxious to
please, and occasionally says things rather because she
thinks they will be agreeable than because they square
with her convictions. I should like a more earnest and
downright character in your wife."

"You wish me to give her up?"

"No; she has many excellent qualities; she has so affectionate a heart, and such winning ways, that there is not one of us who can help loving her. But I *have* something to ask of you, for your sake, dear Robert, not for mine. This girl is only fifteen, a child still; and you have to return with your father very soon to America. Do not commit yourself: you ought not to marry any one younger than eighteen or nineteen. Let three years pass. I'll take as much pains with Jessie, meanwhile, as if she were already my daughter; and I will report to you faithfully the result. Come back when the three years are passed; and, if I am then alive and you still wish to marry her, I will not say a word, except to wish you both all the happiness this world can afford." The tears rose to her eyes as she added, in a lower tone, "I only ask for delay; it may be the last request I shall ever make of you."

I have never made up my mind, since, whether I did right or wrong. But my mother was in very feeble health at the time, and I felt no assurance that I should ever see her again, as, indeed, I never did. If she had objected to Jessie because of her lowly birth, if she had spoken harshly of her, if she had told me she would never consent to receive her as a daughter-in-law, I should have sought to engage the girl, young as she was, then and there. But all she said was so reasonable, and the unfitness of marriage before three years so apparent, that I hesitated as she went on. Her tears, at the last, decided the matter. I gave her the promise she wished.

My word thus pledged, I felt that I must hasten my departure for London, whence we were to embark.

The day before I set out, I asked Jessie if she would not like to visit her parents in the village ; and when she assented, I proposed that we should take a circuitous route through the Braxfield woods, the last time, as it proved, that I ever saw them.

On no occasion of my life have I suffered from a struggle between duty and inclination as I did during that walk. As we passed, deep in the woods, a rural seat whence, through the foliage, glittered, in the autumn sun, the rippling waters of the Clyde, I proposed to Jessie that we should sit awhile, to rest and talk. What we said and how long we remained there I cannot tell. All I remember is, feeling at last that, if we sat there half an hour longer, I should break the solemn promise I had made to my mother. So we rose, went on, half in silence, to the village, where we separated,— and dream and temptation were over !

Ere the three years of probation had passed, Anne had died,* and Jessie had married a most amiable and estimable young man, in easy circumstances,— had married before I knew, even, that she had been sought in marriage. More than thirty years passed after that walk through the wooded braes of Braxfield before I saw Jessie again.

It was in Scotland we met, both married persons. I

---

* In a letter from my father to myself, written soon after Anne's death, he says of her : " I never knew a judgment more severely correct than her's, upon all subjects connected with the mind and disposition. Whatever was needed to assist her in the education of her pupils she studied with unabating interest ; and even you would be surprised to hear of the number of works which she read to store her mind with useful facts on all subjects for the benefit of those under her charge. She had patience, perseverance, and an accurate knowledge of human nature, and took an interest in the progress and happiness of her pupils, such as I have never seen excelled."

found her in her own handsome house, in a beautiful situation, surrounded by every comfort and some luxuries. So far as I could learn, she had so borne herself through life as to secure esteem and love from a cultivated circle of acquaintances.

Just at first I could scarcely recognize, in the comely matron, the Jessie of my youth, until she smiled. But we met twice or thrice, and talked over the olden time, very quietly at first. During my last visit I asked her if she had ever known that I loved her and that I had wished to make her my wife. She said it had several times occurred to her as possible, even before I left Braxfield, the first time, for America; that she felt sure of it during the woodland walk, and especially while we sat together in that secluded spot, with the birds only for witnesses; but when I had departed to another hemisphere with no promise of return, and without declaring myself, she had felt sure it was because of her humble parentage, and so had given up all idea that she could ever be my wife. Then, with a frankness which even as a child she had always shown toward me, she added that she never could tell when she first loved me; and that if, during that last walk, I had asked her to become my betrothed, she would have said yes with her whole heart and soul. The tears stood in her eyes as she made this avowal; and she followed it up by saying, " I wished to meet you once, and to tell you this. But I know you will feel it to be best that we should not see each other, nor write to each other, any more."

I told her she was wise and good, and that I would strictly conform to her wishes; thinking it best so, for both our sakes. So even an occasional exchange of letters which, throughout our thirty years' severance, had been kept up at long intervals, has ceased from that day. And now, when more than another decade has passed, I am uncertain whether Jessie is still in this land of the living, or has gone before to another, where many dear friends who have been life-long apart will find no cause for further separation.

Here let me confess that it needed, as prompting motive to overcome the natural reluctance one feels to confide to the public such details of inner life as one has seldom given even to intimate friends, a sense of the duty which an autobiographer owes to his readers. They are entitled, in the way of incident, to whatever of interest or value is strictly his own to relate ; the secrets of others, however, not being included in that category.

When my father returned from Ireland to find Jessie a member of his family, he related to us an anecdote which pleased me much, in the state of mind I then was, and which may be acceptable to others.

In the winter of 1818–19 a party of bright and lively young people had assembled, to spend the period of Christmas festivity at a spacious old country-seat not very far from Dublin. Several of them, ladies as well as gentlemen, had already acted creditably on the amateur stage·; so they fitted out a large hall as theatre, and got up several standard comedies in a manner that elicited hearty applause. Encouraged by this success, they thought they might manage one of Shakespeare's tragedies ; and their choice fell on Romeo and Juliet. They succeeded in casting all the characters except one, that of Juliet herself. It was offered to several young ladies in succession ; but they all persistently refused, fearing to attempt so arduous a part. In this dilemma some one suggested an expedient. Miss O'Neill, then in the zenith of her fame, was an actress of unblemished reputation, most ladylike demeanor, and eminent talent, whom I once saw as Juliet. She was then regarded, justly I imagine, as the most perfect interpreter of Shakespeare's embodiment of fervid passion and devotion in the daughter of Capulet that had ever appeared on the London boards ; her singular beauty admirably seconding her rare powers, and turning the heads of half the fashionable young men of the day. She was universally respected, was often admitted to the best society, and had several times assisted at private theatricals.

It so happened that she was then in Dublin, and, for the time, without an engagement. The proposal was, to write to her and ask her, on her own terms, to come to them and take the part of Juliet. This was eagerly acceded to, and a letter despatched accordingly.

The part of Romeo had been assigned to a gentleman of fortune and family, Mr. Becher of Ballygibbon, County Cork ; *jeune encore*, as the French say, for he was still on the right side of forty, and excelling all his companions in histrionic talent. To him, as soon as the invitation had been given, came one of his intimate friends. " Becher," said he, " take my advice before it is too late. Throw up the part of Romeo. I dare say some one else can be found to take it."

" Back out of the part ? And why, pray ? Do you think my acting is not worthy to support Miss O'Neill's ? "

" You act only too well, my good fellow, and identify yourself only too perfectly with the characters you undertake. I know Miss O'Neill well ; there can't be a

better girl, but she's dangerous.   She's perfectly be-
witching in her great *rôle*.   It is notorious that no man
ever played Romeo to her Juliet without falling in love
with her.   Now I'd be sorry to see you go to the stage
for a wife."

"Marry an actress! and at my age! Do you take
me for a fool?"

"Anything but that, Becher.   I *do* take you for a
whole-souled, splendid fellow, with a little touch of
romance about him, impressible by beauty, and still
more alive to grace and talent, and I really can't make
up my mind to address even that glorious creature as
Mrs. 'Becher.'"

"Do talk sense, Tom.   If I hadn't agreed to play
Romeo, I'd go and offer to take the part now, just to
convince you how ridiculous you are."

"Well, all I hope is that the enchantress will decline."

But she accepted.   Becher played Romeo, shared the
fate of his predecessors ; was engaged within the month,
and married a few weeks afterwards.

My father spent several days with them at their
country-seat.   He was charmed with Mrs. Becher, in
whom, he said, he could not detect the slightest trace of
the actress.   And the marriage, my father told us,
seemed to have been eminently fortunate, though up to
that time they had no children.

In the sequel they had several children.   Mr. Becher,
eight years later, was created a baronet, lived thirty years
with his wife, and was succeeded, in 1850, by their son,
Sir Henry Wrixon Becher, the present baronet.   Lady
Becher died only last winter, loved and mourned by

friends and dependants ; having survived her husband more than twenty years. *

With one other love-story, also brought by my father from Ireland, I shall conclude this chapter.

The names I have forgotten, but the circumstances happened in a country-house, the hereditary seat of an ancient and wealthy Irish family.

There, to its owner then only a few years married, was born a son and heir. There was, in his household at the time, a young woman of eighteen, fairly educated, but in humble circumstances, who had been retained as dependant rather than servant, filling the posts of nursery-governess and assistant housekeeper. Let us call her Miss Norah Fitzpatrick. She was faithful, industrious, and good-looking, but with no pretension to beauty.

The infant heir of some thirty or forty thousand a year, committed to her care and daily carried about in her arms, became much attached to his nurse. His affection seemed to increase with years ; and at the age of eight or ten, he used to call her his wife, and say he intended to marry her by and by. This, of course, was only laughed at, but when he repeated the same protestations four or five years later, it began to look a little serious, and he was sent to college. He returned from college some months before he was eighteen, and, true to his first

---

* In a London journal, of November, 1872, is the following paragraph :
" The remains of Lady Becher were interred, on November 1, in the family vault in Castlemartyr Churchyard, Ireland. The funeral cortège was more than a mile in length. The chief mourners were Sir Henry Wrixon Becher, Bart., Mr. John Wrixon Becher and Mr. William Wrixon Becher, the three sons of the deceased. The tenantry of Sir H. W. Becher, to the number of four hundred, walked four abreast. The windows of the Ballyhass National School, in which the deceased lady took a deep interest, were draped in black."

fancy, after a time he proposed to Miss Fitzpatrick, then just twice his age. She told him that both for his sake and hers, such a marriage was not to be thought of; the great disparity of age, she said, was alone reason suffi- cient; but, aside from that, the marriage with one so far beneath him in social position would go nigh to break his parents' hearts and would make himself unhappy; for which she could never forgive herself, and which would render her miserable even as his wife. And in this she persisted.

Thereupon the youth ceased to urge his suit; but after moping about for some weeks in a listless way, took to his bed with a low fever. When the family physician, an enlightened man, found the usual reme- dies unavailing and the mother in despair, he said to her, "Madam, it is my duty to tell you that your son's condition seems to me the result of deep-seated mental depression. Something preys on his mind; try to find out what it is; you may then be able to do more for him than all the medicine in the pharmaco- poeia."

The next day the mother did her best to call forth her son's confidence, but for a time in vain. All she could get from him, was, "It's no use, mother dear. It will only vex you."

But when she implored him, weeping, to tell her all, he said at last: "I have loved Norah all my life. I asked her, since I came home, to marry me; but she refused me, because she said it would make us all un- happy. And, say what I will, she sticks to it."

"My son, my son, how *could* you think of such a thing?"

"I told you it was no use, mother; I knew you

would take it just so; but I haven't spirit to live without her."

Then the father was consulted; he was furious; but the patient's fever increased from day to day, and the mother's heart began to relent. "If it should kill him!" she said to her husband; "you know how you felt when I refused you the first time."

That touched him, but he held out three days longer, the young man appearing to sink all the time. Then, one morning, he got up with a sudden resolution and sought his son's bedside. "Listen to me, dear boy," he said; "your happiness is my first object, but it is my duty to prevent you from doing anything rashly, which you may repent all your life afterwards. You are scarcely eighteen; that is too young to marry. I want you to make the tour of Europe before you settle down. I will find you an excellent tutor as companion. But I ask from you that you will not return to Ireland till you are twenty-one, nor correspond meanwhile with Miss Fitzpatrick. I must say she has acted very honorably; and if, when you return, you still remain of the same mind and she will accept you, your mother and I will not withhold our consent. But you must promise on your honor as a gentleman."

And so the bargain was struck, the parents doubtless believing that three years would cure a boyish fancy. Two weeks saw the son well again, and prepared for his journey. On the very day he was twenty-one, he returned to claim his parents' promise; overpersuaded Norah; and my father, invited to their country-seat ten years afterwards, found them, he told us, one of the happiest-looking couples he had ever seen. The lady *did* seem more like the young man's mother than his wife ; but a thousand nameless, unobtrusive attentions testified that a marriage which the world doubtless pronounced preposterous was a true conjugal union, after all.

This story of my father's, coupled with my own experience, caused me to conclude that, while Love is no respecter of persons, he is no respecter of ages either.

PAPER VIII.

THE SOCIAL EXPERIMENT AT NEW HARMONY.

IN the summer of 1824 there came to Braxfield a gentleman whose visit to us there determined, in great measure, the course of my future life.

Richard Flower, an experienced English agriculturist, possessed of considerable means, had emigrated, some years before, to the United States; and had settled at Albion, in the south-eastern part of Illinois, and about twenty-five miles distant from a German village founded by emigrants from the Kingdom of Würtemberg, schismatics of the Lutheran Church, led by their pastor, George Rapp. These people came to America in 1804, settling first on the waters of Conequenessing, Pennsylvania; afterwards, namely in 1813, on the Lower Wabash River and about fifteen miles from the town of Mount Vernon on the Ohio. There they purchased thirty thousand acres, chiefly government land, and erected a village containing about a hundred and sixty buildings, one half brick or frame, the other half of logs. They held it to be a religious duty to imitate the primitive Christians, "who had all things in common;"* to conform to St. Paul's opinion that celibacy is better than marriage;† and desiring also to be, like

---

* Acts iv. 32.   The land was entered in the name of the entire community; and was conveyed by Rapp, under a power of attorney from them, to my father.

† 1 Corinthians viii. 8.   They lived together as the Shakers do.

the early disciples, " of one heart and of one soul," * they called their little town *Harmonie.*

Their experiment was a marvellous success in a pecuniary point of view; for at the time of their immigration their property did not exceed twenty-five dollars a head, while in twenty-one years (to wit, in 1825) a fair estimate gave them *two thousand dollars* for each person,—man, woman, and child; probably *ten times* the average wealth throughout the United States; for at that time each person in Indiana averaged but a hundred and fifty dollars of property, and even in Massachusetts the average fell short of three hundred dollars for each adult and child. Intellectually and socially, however, it was doubtless a failure; as an ecclesiastical autocracy, especially when it contravenes an important law of nature, must eventually be. Rapp was absolute ruler, assuming to be such in virtue of a divine call; and it was said, probably with truth, that he desired to sell out at Harmonie because life there was getting to be easy and quiet, with leisure for thought; and because he found it difficult to keep his people in order, except during the bustle and hard work which attend a new settlement. At all events, he commissioned Mr. Flower to offer the entire Harmony property for sale.

The offer tempted my father. Here was a village ready built, a territory capable of supporting tens of thousands in a country where the expression of thought was free, and where the people were unsophisticated. I listened with delight to Mr. Flower's account of a frontier life; and when, one morning, my father asked me,

* Acts iv. 8.

"Well, Robert, what say you—New Lanark or Har-
mony?" I answered, without hesitation, "Harmony."
Aside from the romance and novelty, I think one
prompting motive was, that, if our family settled in
Western America, it would facilitate my marriage with
Jessie.

Mr. Flower could not conceal from us his amazement,
saying to me, I remember, "Does your father *really*
think of giving up a position like his, with every comfort and luxury, and taking his family to the wild life of
the far West?" He did not know that my father's one
ruling desire was for a vast theatre on which to try his
plans of social reform. Robert Owen thought he had
found one; crossed the Atlantic (taking my brother
William with him, and leaving me manager of the mills)
in the autumn of 1824; completed, in April, 1825, the
purchase, for a hundred and fifty thousand dollars, of
the Rapp village and twenty thousand acres of land;
and in the course of the summer some eight hundred
people had flocked in, in accordance with a public
invitation given by him to "the industrious and well
disposed" of all nations and creeds. Every dwelling-
house was filled.

This purchase, though not judicious merely as a pecuniary investment, seeing that the estate lay in an interior nook of country off any main line of travel, actual
or projected, and on a river navigable for steamers during a few months of the year only, was eligible enough
for my father's special purpose. The land around the
village, of which three thousand acres were under cultivation, was of the richest quality of alluvial soil,
level but above the highest water-mark, and in good
farming order. This valley-land was surrounded by a

semicircular range of undulating hills, rising sixty or
seventy feet above the plain below, and sweeping round
about half a mile from the village on its southern side.
On a portion of these hills where the descent was steep
were vineyards in full bearing, covering eighteen acres,
and partly terraced.   On the west, where this range of
hills increased in height, it terminated abruptly on a
cut-off of the Wabash River, which afforded water-
power used to drive a large flour-mill ; and near by, on
the precipitous hillside, was a quarry of freestone.
Across the cut-off was an island containing three thousand acres, affording excellent woods-pasture.

The village had been built on the bottom land,
quarter of a mile from the river.   Seen from the brow
of the hill-range as one approached it from Mount Vernon, it was picturesque enough ; literally embowered
in trees, rows of black locusts marking the street lines.
Several large buildings stood out above the foliage ; of
which a spacious cruciform brick hall, the transept a
hundred and thirty feet across, was the chief.   There
was also a church, a steam mill, a woollen factory, and
several large boarding-houses.   The private dwellings
were small, each in a separate garden-spot.   Adjoining
the village on the south were extensive apple and peach
orchards.

When my father first reached the place, he found
among the Germans—its sole inhabitants—indications
of plenty and material comfort, but with scarcely a touch
of fancy or ornament ; the only exceptions being a
few flowers in the gardens, and what was called " The
Labyrinth," a pleasure-ground laid out near the village
with some taste, and intended—so my father was told—
as an emblematic representation of the life these colo-

nists had chosen. It contained small groves and gardens, with numerous circuitous walks enclosed by high
beech hedges and bordered with flowering shrubbery, but
arranged with such intricacy, that, without some Dæda-
lus to furnish a clue, one might wander for hours and
fail to reach a building erected in the centre. This was
a temple of rude material, but covered with vines of the
grape and convolvulus, and its interior neatly fitted up
and prettily furnished. Thus George Rapp had sought to
shadow forth to his followers the difficulties of attaining
a state of peace and social harmony. The perplexing
approach, the rough exterior of the shrine, and the elegance displayed within were to serve as types of toil
and suffering, succeeded by happy repose.

The toil and suffering had left their mark, however,
on the grave, stolid, often sad, German faces. They
looked well fed, warmly clothed (my father told me),
and seemed free from anxiety. The animal had been
sufficiently cared for ; and that is a good deal in a world
where millions can hardly keep the wolf from the door,
drudge as they will, and where hundreds of millions,
manage as they may, live in daily uncertainty whether,
in the next week or month (chance of work or means of
living failing), absolute penury may not fall to their lot.
A shelter from life-wearing cares is something : but a
temple typifies higher things—more than what we shall
eat and what we shall drink, and wherewithal we shall
be clothed. Rapp's disciples had bought these too
dearly,—at expense of heart and soul. They purchased
them by unquestioning submission to an autocrat who
had been commissioned—perhaps as he really believed,
certainly as he alleged—by God himself. He bade them
do this and that, and they did it ; required them to say,

as the disciples in Jerusalem said, that none of the things they possessed were their own, and they said it; commanded them to forego wedded life and all its incidents, and to this also they assented.

Their experiment afforded conclusive proof that, if a community of persons are willing to pay so high a price for abundant food, clothing, shelter, and absolute freedom from pecuniary cares, they can readily obtain all this, working leisurely under a system of common labor, provided the dictator to whom they submit is a good business manager. The success of the Rappites, such as it was, wonderfully encouraged my father. He felt sure that he could be far more successful than they, without the aid either of bodily and mental despotism or of celibacy. Aside from rational education, which he deemed indispensable, he trusted implicitly, as cure for all social and industrial ills, to the principle of co-operation.

There was much in the economical condition of England to lead a mind like my father's, accustomed to generalizations and imbued with sanguine confidence in whatever he desired, to such a conclusion ; and, unless I here devote a page or two to a succinct statement —in mere outline it must be—of the main statistical facts which go to make up that strange, unprecedented condition, I shall leave my readers without a clue to the motives which caused a successful business man like my father to relinquish wealth, domestic ease, affluent comforts, and an influential position, and to adventure, with a faith which admitted not even the possibility of failure, an untried experiment in an unknown field, then little better than a wilderness.

As a large manufacturer, much cogent evidence bearing on that condition had been brought home to him.

Ten years before, Colquhoun had published his work on the Resources of the British Empire, and that had supplied important additional data.

My father felt that there was then—as there is now—one of the great problems of the age still to be solved. I can here but briefly state, not seek to solve it. It connects itself with the unexampled increase of productive power, which human beings in civilized life have acquired in little more than a single century, and with the momentous question whether this vast gift of labor-saving inventions is to result in mitigation of the toil and melioration of the condition of the millions who have acquired it. Few persons realize the extent of this modern agency, the changed state of things it has brought about, or the effect of its introduction, so far, upon the masses, especially in European countries.

From certain Parliamentary reports made in 1816, in connection with Sir Robert Peel's Factory Bill (already alluded to), my father derived data in proof that the machinery employed in Great Britain in cotton-spinning alone—in *one* branch, therefore, of *one* manufacture—superseded at that time the labor of eighty million adults ; and he succeeded in proving, to the satisfaction of England's ablest statistician,* that if all the branches of the cotton, woollen, flax, and silk manufactures were included, the machine-saved labor in producing English textile fabrics exceeded, in those days, the work which two hundred millions of operatives could have turned out previous to the year 1760.†

* Colquhoun, whose celebrated work on a cognate subject is above referred to. See, for Robert Owen's conversation with Colquhoun on this subject, his (Owen's) Autobiography, p. 127.

† A few trustworthy figures may give confidence in this calculation. McCulloch (**Dict**ionary of Commerce, published 1832, Art. *Cotton*) sets

This statement of my father's attracted the attention of the British political economists of that day, was virtually adopted by them soon after,* and became, as these vast inanimate powers increased, the foundation of successive calculations touching their aggregate amount in all branches of industry carried on in Great Britain and Ireland. In 1835 my father put down that aggregate as equal to the labor of four hundred million adults ; and estimates by recent English statisticians, brought up to the present time, vary from five hundred to seven hundred millions. We may safely assume the mean of these estimates—*six hundred millions*—as closely approximating the truth to-day.

But the population of the world is, in round numbers, twelve hundred millions ; and the usual estimate of the

down " 800,000 as the total number of persons directly employed in the various branches of the cotton manufacture." Of these nearly two-thirds (42 out of each 67, by actual returns, " Report of Factory Commissioners," in 1833, pp. 123, 124, 136) were employed in cotton *spinning :* say 500,000. That was in 1832 ; in 1816 the number did not probably exceed 400,000. But McCulloch, on the authority of Kennedy (" Rise and Progress of the Cotton Trade "), states that, as early as 1815, one person, aided by machinery, could produce as much cotton yarn as 200 could have produced in 1760: this agrees with my own calculation made at New Lanark in 1817.—See preceding page 33.

Then, if we multiply 400,000 by 200, we have *eighty millions* as the number of adults who, half a century before, would have been needed to produce the quantity of cotton yarn which 400,000 men, women and children, in 1816, actually did turn out.

The aggregate number of operatives in other English textile manufactories was, in 1832, nearly as great as the number in cotton mills: namely, woollen, 350,000 ; silk, over 200,000 ; linen, nearly 200,000 ; together, 750,000.

* John Quincy Adams accepted it in his Report from the Committee of Manufactures, made to Congress in 1832. He there estimates that, at the conclusion of the war in 1815, the mechanical inventions of Great Britain were equivalent to the labor of two hundred millions of persons.

productive manual labor of a country is, that it does not exceed that of a number of adult workmen equal to one-fourth of its population. Thus, the daily labor of three hundred million adults represents the productive *manual* power of the world.

It follows that Great Britain and Ireland's labor-saving machinery *equals*, in productive action, *the manual labor-power of two worlds as populous as this.*

It follows, further, inasmuch as the present population of the British Isles is less than thirty millions, that seven millions and a half of adults represent the number of living operatives who control and manipulate that prodigious amount of inanimate force.

Thus, in aid of the manual labor of seven and a half millions of human workmen, Great Britain may be said to have imported, from the vast regions of invention, six hundred millions of powerful and passive slaves ; slaves that consume neither food nor clothing ; slaves that sleep not, weary not, sicken not ; gigantic slaves that drain subterranean lakes in their master's service, or set in motion, at a touch from his hand, machinery under which the huge and solid buildings that contain it groan and shake ; ingenious slaves that outrival, in the delicacy of their operations, the touch of man, and put to shame the best exertions of his steadiness and accuracy ; yet slaves patient, submissive, obedient, from whom no rebellion need be feared, who cannot suffer cruelty nor experience pain.

These unwearying and inanimate slaves outnumber the human laborers who direct their operations as *eighty to one.** What is the result of this importation ?

* It may be truly objected that, in one vast department of industry—the agricultural—labor-saving machines, though of late introduced to a cer-

If we shut our closet doors and refuse to take the answer from the state of things as it actually exists, we shall probably say that inestimable aid, thus sent down from Heaven as it were, to stand by and assist man in his severest toils, *must* have rendered him easy in his circumstances, rich in all the necessaries and comforts of life, a master instead of a slave, a being with leisure for enjoyment and improvement, a freeman delivered from the original curse which declared that in the sweat of his brow should man eat bread all the days of his life.   But if, rejecting mere inference, we step out among the realities around us, with eyes open and sympathies awake, we shall see, throughout the Old World, the new servants competing with those they might be made to serve.   We shall see a contest going on in the market of labor, between wood and iron on the one hand, and human thews and sinews on the other; a dreadful contest, at which humanity shudders, and reason turns, astonished, away.   We shall see masters engaging, as the cheapest, most docile, and least troublesome help,* the machine instead of the man.   And we shall see the man, thus denied even the privilege to toil, shrink home, with sickening heart, to the cellar where his wife and children herd, and sink down on its damp floor to ask of his despair where these things shall end,—whether the soulless slaves, bred year by year

tain extent, furnish but insignificant aid compared to that which they render in manufactures : much farm labor being still but unaided manual labor.   Then let us suppose our estimate reduced to one-half, and say that, practically regarded, each British workman, on the average, has but *forty* inorganic slaves to help him.   The argument remains equally good.

* " The self-acting *mule* has the important advantage of rendering the mill-owners independent of the combinations and strikes of the working-spinners."—Baines's Cotton Manufacture, p. 207.

from the teeming womb of science, shall gradually thrust aside, into idleness and starvation, their human competitors, until the laborer, like other extinct races of animals, shall perish from the earth.

I have made a special study of the statistical facts which go to justify more than all I here assert. But the limits of this narrative allow me to give only a condensed abstract of the results.

For two centuries after the Conquest, feudal oppressions and intestine wars grievously oppressed British labor. At any moment the serf might be taken from the plough to arm in his liege lord's quarrel; and if, spite of all such interruptions, the seed was sown and the harvest ripened, the chance remained that it might be cut down by the sword of the forager or trampled under the hoof of the war-horse. Nothing is more characteristic than the Borderer's account of an ancient raid, in Scott's Lay :—

> " They crossed the Liddell at curfew hour,
>   And burnt my little lonely tower.
>   The fiend receive their souls therefor :
>   It hadn't been burnt this year or more ! "

The peasantry, or rather *villeinry*, of those days,— many of them thralls—had the scantiest wages, often mere food and clothing, living miserably.* But during Edward the Third's wars with France, he was compelled to manumit many bondsmen, in order to recruit his armies ; and the forced services of villeinage were gradually exchanged for free labor, often fixed by statute.

* " Their habitations were without chimneys, and their principal furniture consisted of a brass pot valued at from one to three shillings, and a bed valued at from three to six shillings."—Wade's History of the Working Classes, pp. 11, 12.

In the middle of the fourteenth century, common labor on a farm was set at *three pence halfpenny a day ;* in harvest, four pence. But at that time wheat did not exceed *six pence* a bushel, and other staple articles of food were in proportion. So in the fifteenth century, harvest wages were *five pence,* and wheat was *seven pence halfpenny* a bushel. With all this accords what Sir John Cullum, the English antiquarian (quoted as reliable authority by Hallam), tells us, namely, that in the fourteenth century a week's wages in harvest enabled the laborer to buy four bushels of wheat. The weekly wages of *common* farm labor, however, throughout the year, were the equivalent of *three bushels of wheat* only. This last may be safely assumed as the purchasing power of ordinary farm labor in England four hundred and five hundred years ago.*

* Those interested in such researches, may verify the above, by consulting the Act of 23d of Edward III. (that is, in 1350) commonly called "The Statute of Laborers," which fixed rates of wages as follows : for common labor on a farm, three pence halfpenny per day ; a reaper, per day, four pence ; mowing an acre of grass, six pence, etc. The act of 23d of Henry VI. (in 1444), fixes the reaper's wages at five pence, and others in proportion.

As to the price of wheat, in Bishop Fleetwood's "Chronicon Preciosum," a work of reputation, we find many accounts of bursars of convents, in which wheat is usually set down in the fourteenth century, at three shillings and four pence a quarter, or five pence a bushel : but Fleta, who wrote about 1335, and gives four shillings a quarter, or six pence a bushel, as the average price in his day, is probably nearer the true retail price to the general public. In the fifteenth century, Sir Frederick Eden, after examining various account-books kept in convents from 1415 to 1425, gives us five shillings as the price of a quarter of wheat, at that time (seven pence halfpenny a bushel). Hallam's general estimates agree with the above ; and he calculates butchers' meat, in the fifteenth century, at a farthing and a half a pound. In the sixteenth century, the price of beef or pork was limited by statute (24th of Henry VIII.) to a halfpenny per pound.

After many fluctuations, weekly wages of ordinary
labor settled down, in the middle of the eighteenth century, to about a bushel and a half of wheat.* By the
middle of the present century a common farm laborer
could purchase, with his eight shillings for a week's
work, but ONE BUSHEL of wheat. Since then wages
have slowly risen ; and to-day a farm laborer, with nine
and sixpence to ten shillings a week, can earn a bushel
and a quarter of wheat.†

Though, for brevity's sake, I have here confined the
comparison to staple bread-stuff alone, I have verified
the fact that it applies equally to other articles of common use or necessity. In the fifteenth century a week's
labor bought *sixty-four* pounds of butchers' meat ; now
it will hardly purchase *nineteen.* So, instead of *ten*
geese, *three* would now absorb a week's labor ; instead
of *a sheep a week*, a laborer must toil *four weeks for a
single sheep.* Again, a day's wages will now buy, not
eight dozen of eggs as then it did, but *three* dozen ; not
eight pounds of cheese, but *three;* not *five* pounds of
butter, but *two.*—Even in some staple articles of clothing, the balance is against the peasant of to-day. Three
days' labor will now hardly procure him the stout pair

* See table of wages and prices from 1813, back to 1495, by Barton, in
his Enquiry into the Depreciation of Labor.

† About the year 1844, the exertions of that excellent Association, the
Anti-Corn-Law League, supplied, as the Westminster Review expressed it,
"an accumulation of facts so incontrovertible, that no person who has any
reputation for accuracy or intelligence will risk it on the denial of the terrible
truth." They inform us that the average wages of farm laborers, at that
time, *was rather under than over eight shillings a week :* just the average
retail price in that country, for years past, of a bushel of wheat.

At this time, wages in husbandry are from nine shillings and six pence, to
ten shillings ; the price of wheat remaining the same.

of shoes which a single day formerly paid for; and nine days' labor, instead of six, are needed to obtain the material for a winter coat; that is, if a farm laborer should be extravagant enough to buy coarse broadcloth for such a purpose.

Labor in factories is somewhat better paid than farm labor; adult operatives receiving 'from nine to eleven shillings a week when fully employed. But there are thousands, weavers and others, in every manufacturing district, who have only occasional work at home, and live in squalid wretchedness,—wretchedness that has often but five cents a day to keep each human body and soul together,* —wretchedness that terribly shortens life. †

---

* In Minutes of Evidence before a Select Committee of the House of Commons, 1833, Mr. William Stocks, secretary of a committee of factory owners, deposed to certain facts obtained and verified by that committee during visits to the cottages of laborers in and around Huddersfield, thus summing up the results: " We found 13,226 individuals that averaged two pence halfpenny (five cents) per day to live on. That sum included all parish relief; and it was not wholly applicable to meat and drink, for they had rent and everything to pay out of it, including wear and tear of looms."—Minutes of Evidence, July 28 and August 3, 1833.

The Report of the Liverpool Branch of the Anti-Corn-Law League for 1833 shows a similar state of wholesale misery. It states that "in Vauxhall Ward, Liverpool, containing, in all, 6,000 families or 24,000 souls, the number of 3,462 families had but two pence halfpenny (five cents) per individual to live on."

† In Chadwick's well-known "Report of the Sanitary Condition of the Laboring Population of Great Britain," are tables, based on official statistics, showing the average duration of life, of different classes in manufacturing districts. In Manchester and Liverpool, where the proportion does not vary materially from that in other manufacturing cities, the average of life is found to be:

IN LIVERPOOL, 1840.

Among gentry, professional persons, etc., . .	35 years.
Among laborers, mechanics, etc., ...	15 years.

Another most significant fact is, that whereas, three hundred years ago, the poor-law system of England scarcely existed,* my father found one in ten of all the inhabitants of Great Britain a pauper, receiving parish relief.† Without the English poor-laws, there would long since have been wholesale starvation among those willing and able to work, and, probably, a rebellion instigated by despair.

With all the foregoing data tallies an estimate made by Hallam, in his History of the Middle Ages, of the relative value of money ; which is, that any given sum in the fourteenth century must be multiplied by twenty, and in the fifteenth century by sixteen, to bring it to the standard of our day. If so, then a common laborer's wages in the fourteenth and fifteenth centuries were equivalent to five shillings of the modern English currency per day, or to thirty shillings per week ; at least *three times as much* as such a laborer receives at present.

IN MANCHESTER (same date).

Among gentry, professional persons, etc.,	38 years.
Among laborers, mechanics, etc.,	17 years.

Thus, in these cities, persons in easy circumstances live, on the average, *more than twice as long* as the laborer does.

* The poor-law system of England was first rendered secure and permanent, by the famous statute of 43d Elizabeth, ch. 2 : (that is, in 1601.)

† "In our manufacturing districts every *eleventh* inhabitant, and in our agricultural counties every *eighth* inhabitant, receives parish relief. But this by no means represents the whole mass of suffering. The horror of being branded as a pauper is so prevalent among the industrial population, that *thousands prefer death by gradual starvation, to placing themselves on the parish funds.*"—Report of Liverpool Branch of the Anti-Corn-Law League, 1833.

These calculations are, however, for the middle of the present century. Wages having since risen twenty or twenty-five per cent., the proportion of paupers is very considerably less to-day.

But to guard against possible exaggeration, let us deduct one third from this result; and the startling fact still forces itself on our attention, that the working-classes employed in tilling the garden soil of Great Britain, or in tending her magnificent machinery, *receive now*, as the price of their toil, *but one half as much as their rude ancestors did five centuries ago.*

As cure for such evil and suffering, my father found the political economists urging a reduction of taxes. But his experience taught him to regard that as a mere temporary palliative. The very reduction of government burdens might be taken as an all-sufficient plea for the further reduction of wages. Labor could be *afforded* for less. And down to the very point at which it can be afforded,—which means at that point on the road to famine at which men are not starved suddenly, but die slowly of toil inadequately sustained by scanty and unwholesome food,—down to that point of bare subsistence my father saw the laborer of Britain thrust. How? Wherefore? By what legerdemain of cruelty and injustice?

Thus the problem loomed upon him. We may imagine his reflections. Why, as the world advances in knowledge and power, do the prospects and the comforts of the mass of mankind darken and decline? How happens it that four or five centuries have passed over Britain, bringing peace where raged feuds and forays, affording protection to person and property, setting free the shackled press, spreading intelligence and liberality, reforming religion and fostering civilization,—how happens it that these centuries of improvement have left the British laborer twofold more the slave of toil than they found him? Why must mechanical inventions—inevitable even if they were mischievous, and in themselves a rich blessing as surely as they are inevitable—stand in array *against* the laborer, instead of toiling by his side?

Momentous questions these! My father pondered them, day and night. If he had tersely stated the gist of his reflections,—which he was not always able to do,—they might have assumed some such form as this: Will any man, who stands on his reputation for sanity, affirm that the *necessary* result of over-production is famine? that because labor produces more than even luxury can waste, labor shall not have bread to eat? If we can imagine a point in the progress of improvement at which all the necessaries and comforts of life shall be produced without human labor, are we to suppose that the human laborer, when that point is reached, is to be dismissed by his masters from their employment, to be told that he is now a useless incumbrance which they cannot afford to hire?

If such a result be flagrantly absurd in the extreme, it was then, and is now, in Great Britain, a terrible reality in the degree. Men *were* told that machines had filled their places and that their services were no longer required. Certain English economists scrupled not to avow the doctrine, that a man born into a world already occupied and overstocked with labor has no RIGHT to claim food; that such a one is a being superfluous on the earth, and for whom, at the great banquet of nature, there is no place to be found.*

---

* See Malthus, in his Essay on the Principle of Population. But my father believed in the axiom put forth by a French historian: "Avant toutes les lois sociales, l'homme avait le droit de subsister."—Raynal, Histoire des Indes, Vol. X. p. 322.

My father's conclusions from the data which I have here furnished were :—

1. That the enormously increased productive powers which man in modern times has acquired, involve, and in a measure necessitate, great changes in the social and industrial structure of society.

2. That the world has reached a point of progress at which co-operative industry should replace competitive labor.

3. That society, discarding large cities and solitary homes, should resolve itself into associations, each of fifteen hundred or two thousand persons, who should own land and houses in common and labor for the benefit of the community. In this way (he believed) labor-saving power would directly aid, not tend to oppress, the workman.

The first proposition is doubtless true, especially as to old countries largely engaged in manufactures ; the question remaining, however, of what character and to what extent the changes should be.

The second proposition is now on trial in England on a large scale. Through the kindness of an English friend, I have before me a report of the Fifth Annual Co-operative Congress held at Newcastle on the 12th, 13th, and 14th of last April, and which was attended by two hundred delegates from all parts of Great Britain and Ireland.* The two most prominent speakers

* Published in the Newcastle Weekly Chronicle of April 16, 1873, and covering *twenty-nine* closely printed columns. This paper is larger than the New York Tribune, and was established in 1764.

The editor speaks of this meeting as one of the most important movements he has ever been called upon to record, and winds up a long notice of the proceedings thus : " It is certain that the general adoption of the principle of co-operation will lead to an improved condition of the masses,

were members of Parliament ; namely, the well-known
Thomas Hughes, author of Tom Brown at Oxford, and
Walter Morrison.

Mr. Hughes introduced the resolution, " That this
meeting recognizes in co-operation the most effective
means of permanently raising the condition of the people." And Mr. Morrison moved the following : " That
it is of the essence of co-operation to recognize the
right of labor to a substantial share in the profits it
creates." Both resolutions were unanimously adopted.

Mr. Cowen, chairman of the Congress, said, in opening one of its meetings : " I am not an old man, yet I
recollect a meeting which was held in this room thirty
years ago. It was addressed by the father of co-operative principles in this country, Mr. Robert Owen.
(Cheers.) To the discredit of some of the inhabitants
of Newcastle, they brought the meeting to a close by
breaking the windows and dispersing the audience.
They refused to listen to the patient and, I may say,
affectionate appeals which Mr. Owen made to his hear-
ers. We have considerably advanced since then."

The experiments then commenced, in the way of co-
operative stores, failed at that time, probably because
the current of public opinion set in strongly against
them. How great the contrast is to-day appears from
the statistics, founded on Parliamentary documents,
which were laid before this Congress. One wholesale
co-operative store in Manchester has two hundred and
seventy-seven shareholding societies, and has five hundred societies doing business with it ; it has a capital of

and the abatement, if not the total extinction, of the class differences
which in the past have divided, and, unhappily, yet divide, human society
into hostile camps."—p. 4.

nearly three quarters of a million dollars, and its present annual business falls but little short of six millions. During eight years past it has done business to the amount of twenty millions, and has incurred in that period but a single thousand dollars of bad debts. Another, the North of England wholesale store, does a business varying from a hundred thousand to a hundred and forty thousand dollars a week.

There are in all, throughout England, about a thousand co-operative stores, and full returns have been made to Parliament by three-fourths of these. These three fourths had, in 1871, two hundred and sixty thousand members ; a capital of more than *twelve and a half millions;* were doing a business of more than *forty-seven millions* a year, with an annual profit of *four millions*, that is, eight and a half per cent. on the capital invested.

Besides these stores, English co-operators have engine-works employing five hundred hands ; a mining company, with twelve hundred workers ; an industrial bank at Newcastle ; linen, cotton, and other factories ; corn-mills ; a printing society ; an agricultural and horticultural association, with Thomas Hughes on its council ; and a Central Agency Society, with two members of Parliament on its committee of management.

Profiting by the experience of the past, many errors in organization and in management have been avoided. At this time, with some twenty millions of capital employed, these co-operative enterprises are, with scarcely an exception, a pecuniary success.

As to the third proposition—the resolving of society into small communities of common property—my father resolved to test it at New Harmony. I think it was a mistake to change the scene of the experiment from England to the United States. The average wages of farm labor here amount to a dollar and a quarter a day, or seven dollars and a half a week; and even if we put wheat at a dollar and eighty-five cents a bushel, which is its price only in our seaboard cities and when it is ready for shipment, a week's labor in husbandry will purchase *four* bushels of wheat, instead of *a bushel and a quarter*, as in England. The need of co-operation, or some other protection for labor, may be said to be threefold greater there than here.

My father made another and a still greater mistake. A believer in the force of circumstances and of the instinct of self-interest to reform all men, however ignorant or vicious, he admitted into his village all comers, without recommendatory introduction or any examination whatever. This error was the more fatal, because it is in the nature of any novel experiment, or any putting forth of new views which may tend to revolutionize the opinions or habits of society, to attract to itself (as the Reformation did three hundred years ago, and as Spiritualism does to-day) waifs and strays from surrounding society; men and women of crude, ill-considered, extravagant notions; nay, worse, vagrants who regard the latest heresy but as a stalking-horse for pecuniary gain, or a convenient cloak for immoral demeanor.

He did, indeed, take the precaution of establishing at New Harmony, in the first instance, a Preliminary Society only; and he did refrain from any conveyance of real estate to its members. But he allowed this motley assemblage to elect its own Committee of Management, though the constitution of the society vested in him the

appointing power.* That constitution was laid before
the inhabitants, April 27, 1825 ; Robert Owen then,
for the first time, addressing the inhabitants. It was
adopted May 1.† But my father was able to remain, to
watch its progress, little more than a month. He departed, early in June, for England, leaving a school of a
hundred and thirty children, who were boarded, educated, and clothed at the public expense. As to the
other inhabitants, they received a weekly credit on the
public store to the amount which their services were, by
the committee, deemed worth. There was a good band
of music ; and the inhabitants, on my father's recom-
mendation, resolved to meet together three evenings
each week : one to discuss all subjects connected with
the welfare of the society ; another for a concert of
vocal and instrumental music; while the third was given
up to a public ball.

My father's reception in America had been kind and
hospitable ; and he gave us, on his return to Braxfield,
a glowing account of the favor with which his plans of
social reform were regarded in the New World, and of
the condition of things, and bright promise for the future, at New Harmony. I was captivated with the picture he drew, and embarked with him toward the end
of September from Liverpool in the packet-ship New
York, exulting as an Israelite may have exulted when
Moses spoke to him of the Land of Promise.

We had a jovial set of passengers, including the
operatic troupe of the elder Garcia, together with his

---

* See New Harmony Gazette, Vol. I. page 135. My father *recommended* four of the seven persons who composed the committee ; and these
four, together with three others, were elected by the citizens.

† A copy of this constitution will be found in New Harmony Gazette.

son Manuel, twenty years old, and his two daughters—
Maria, then aged seventeen, and Pauline, then only four
years old, but who afterwards became a celebrated
singer and actress, and married a Paris journalist of
some reputation, Monsieur Viardot. She was the pet
of passengers and crew; and I have heard the child
reply, in four languages, with almost equal facility, to
remarks in French, German, Italian, and Spanish, addressed to her, in rapid succession, by the members of
her father's company.

Her elder sister, Mademoiselle Garcia, afterwards
world-renowned,—her brief career sad indeed in private, but brilliant in public to a degree hardly paralleled
in the annals of the stage—had the previous spring
made a successful *début* in London. She was a most
interesting girl, simple, frank, bright as could be,
charming in conversation, a general favorite; and I
think that during our somewhat protracted voyage, she
captivated the heart of Captain McDonald, a young and
handsome English officer, a great friend and admirer of
my father, who had accompanied us on our Trans-atlan-
tic trip. It came to nothing, perhaps because McDonald, though a noble, generous fellow, had then little
besides his commission to depend on ; but I doubt not
she would have been far happier as his wife than she
afterwards was—poor girl!—with the reputed rich but
bankrupt Malibran.

Her health seemed feeble, and this may have been
due in part to the extreme severity with which that terrible Spaniard, her father, treated his children. The
troupe had frequent rehearsals on deck when the
weather was fine, greatly to the delight of the passengers. The only drawback to our pleasure in listening

to some of the finest voices in the world, was the brutal manner in which Garcia sometimes berated the singers, but especially his son and daughter, when their performance did not please him.

One evening, after a rehearsal at which he had been so violent that his daughter seemed in mortal fear of him, she and I sat down, on a sofa on deck, to a game of chess. At first she appeared almost as lively and bright as usual; but, ere the game ended, she turned deadly pale, her head sunk on my shoulder, and had I not caught her in my arms she must have fallen to the floor. I carried her down to the cabin quite insensible; and it was some time before she recovered.

Another day, at the close of a rehearsal, the old man spoke in insulting terms to his son, I and other passengers being present. Manuel replied in a respectful, almost submissive tone; yet he earnestly vindicated himself against the charge—of wilful negligence, I think it was—which his father brought against him. This incensed Garcia to such a degree, that he suddenly struck his son a blow of his fist so violent that the youth dropped on the deck as if shot. We instantly went in search of the captain, telling him what had happened, and he came on deck at once, confronting the still enraged father.

" What is this, sir? " he said, the tone low, but with a dangerous ring in it. " Is it true that you dared to knock your son down? "

The great singer was silent and looked sullen

" It *is* true, then? " The tone rose a little and the eyes flashed; we saw there was mischief in them. " Do you know, sir," he went on, "that I am master here—ruler in my own ship—with the right to do whatever I please, if it is necessary to protect my passengers either from insult or injury. Do you know that, sir?"

Still no answer.

"Do you see these men?" pointing to some sailors who were looking on at a distance with eyes of curiosity. "A single word from me and they'll seize you on the spot! But I don't want a fuss on board my ship. This time I'll pass it by. But now attend to what I say; you had better, for your own sake. If you lay a finger again on a single passenger here,—on your son, on your daughter, or on any other soul on board,—I'll have you down below in irons, sir,—*in irons!* Do you understand that?"

He did understand, and he was fairly cowed at last. He muttered an unintelligible excuse; and the captain, turning away, issued some commonplace order to the mate, as quietly as if nothing had happened.

From that day forth, though Garcia still scolded and grumbled, he used, in our hearing, no insulting language, nor committed any other violent act. To us, when nothing crossed his will or went wrong, he was polite, and even obliging. We amused ourselves throughout the somewhat tedious voyage by getting out a weekly newspaper,—quite a creditable production it was—and in its last number appeared a song, the words by one of our party, Mr. Stedman Whitwell, a London architect, and a convert to my father's views; the music, graceful and spirited, by Garcia. It was afterwards published in New York under the title Ebor Nova, and had quite a run; for the Garcias won for themselves an enthusiastic reception.

Our pleasant voyage came to an end November 7,

1825,—the day on which I was twenty-four years old.
New York's magnificent bay, its surface just stirred by
a gentle breeze and dotted all over with white sails,—
signs of a busy and enterprising nation,—while beyond,
the city's hundred spires shot up white in the sunshine
of a fresh autumn morning,—all this, as I came upon it
after the even tenor of a long ocean voyage, outwent
whatever I had imagined of New World scenery.   I
had reached the Canaan of my hopes, and its first
glimpse was beautiful even beyond my dreams.   I
landed, as in vision of the night one enters fairy-land.

Our letters of introduction first brought us into contact with a people genial and magnetic, who seemed to
me, as to temperament, to occupy middle ground between the distant conventionality of my own countrymen, and the light vivacity of the French.   I liked them
from the first, and, with a youthful precipitancy, which,
however, I have never repented, I went at once to a
prothonotary's office, and declared my intention to become a citizen of the United States.

That was nearly forty-eight years ago.   Kindly, in-
dulgently, has my adopted country treated me since ;
and well do I love her for it.

She has her peculiarities, of course, like other nations ; and it was not long ere we came in contact with
some of these.   Martin Luther is said to have had his
latter years embittered, perhaps his life shortened, by
certain crotchety and ill-conditioned fanatics, as the
Anabaptists, Libertines, and others, who " played such
fantastic tricks before high heaven " as brought the
name of Protestant, which they had assumed, into no
little discredit for the time.   A radical reformer, if he
be of any note, commonly attracts around him erratics

The Page of Nature. 265

of this class ; and my father did not escape the common fate.

One morning he had gone out on a visit, leaving Captain McDonald and myself in a parlor of the Howard House in Broadway (where we had put up), busy writing letters home, when a waiter, entering, handed me a strange-looking visiting card, with the message, " A gentleman to see your father, sir. I told him he was out, but he would have me bring up his card." It was of green pasteboard, and bore the single word, " Page." I bade him invite Mr. Page to walk up.

" A singular fancy," said I to McDonald, " to color visiting-cards green. But, of course, in new countries we must expect new fashions."

Thereupon the door opened, and there stalked in, in a solemn way, a middle-aged personage, quite as queer-looking as his card. He was dressed, from head to foot, in light-green broadcloth ; his overcoat, cut with a plain Quaker collar, reached his ankles ; his cap and boots were of green cloth, and his gloves of green kid, all matching the rest of his costume. His long hair was divided in the centre and drooped, slightly curling, on his shoulders.

McDonald and I were so taken aback by this sudden apparition that we even forgot to offer our visitor a chair. He seemed to prefer standing, as about to declaim. His manner was dignified, and his gestures had a certain grace, as he proceeded to say : " Gentlemen, I have come, in my public capacity, to welcome a brother philanthropist. But you do not know who I am."

To this we assented, and he went on. " My name is Page. I am the page of Nature. She has enlisted me in her service. I wear her livery, as you see " (pointing

to his dress), " as a reminder of the official duty I owe
her.   She talks to me, instructs me in the way I should
go, and tells me how I can best benefit my fellow-creatures.   In the olden time I was King David's page ; and
I was a great comfort to him, as he had been to his
master, Saul, when the evil spirit from the Lord was
upon him, and when David's playing on the harp re-
freshed Saul and caused the evil spirit to depart.   David
had his dark hours also, when his sins weighed upon his
spirit ; and at those times I was able to console and
encourage him.   But Nature's service is better than that
of any king."

We were mute with amazement.   He paused, then
drew from a capacious pocket a thick roll of manuscript.
It was written on long sheets of green paper.

" Some of the words of wisdom," he pursued, "that
my gracious mistress has vouchsafed to communicate to
her votary.   They ought to have been written in green
ink ; but to human eyes the words might not have been
very intelligible.   And black cannot be said to be inappro-
priate.   In summer holiday, indeed, Nature's vestment
is green ; but she has her seasons when all is black,—
the starless midnight hour, the wintry storm's murky
darkness.   That may justify the black ink."

He unrolled and smoothed out the manuscript; but
reading in our faces, perhaps, the alarm which we certainly felt at the threatened infliction, he seemed to
change his purpose ; and with the air of a father making
allowance for his thoughtless children, he said : " Young
people have not always leisure or inclination to hear
divine truth.   Hand these leaves from the Great Book
to Robert Owen ; for he is a disciple of Nature like me,
and he will appreciate them."

With that, having bowed ceremoniously to us both, he swept slowly and majestically from the room.

McDonald sat looking intently at the fire for a minute or two after the door closed, then suddenly turned to me : " Are we *all* crazy, do you think, Robert ? Have we been poking into great subjects and thinking of a world's reform, until our brains are addled and we are fit inmates of a lunatic asylum ? "

" Well," said I, " we knew already that there are harmless bedlamites who are suffered to go at large. *We* still dress like other people. We haven't come to the conclusion yet, that the Goddess of Nature keeps a lot of pages to whom she dictates homilies, to be written out on green foolscap ; and we are not Pythagoreans, believing that our souls were once in the service of ancient kings."

" For all that," replied McDonald, " it's uncomfortable ; it gives one a shock."

The manuscript, like a hundred others which it has been my hard fortune since to glance over, was a dull tissue of sentimental commonplaces, with mad streaks through it, but with a certain method in the madness. The author had sense enough to give his address at the close, and we carefully returned it to him.

In the course of two or three weeks several pleasant and intelligent people had joined us, bound for New Harmony ; among them Thomas Say, one of the founders of the Academy of Natural Sciences in Philadelphia, who six years before had accompanied Major Long on his expedition to the Rocky Mountains as its naturalist ; Charles Lesueur, a French naturalist and designer, who had explored, with Péron, the coasts of Australia ; Gerard Troost, a native of Holland and a distinguished chemist and geologist, who was afterwards professor of chemistry in the Nashville University ; also several cultivated ladies, including Miss Sistare (afterwards the wife of Thomas Say) and two of her sisters. Whether William Maclure, president of the Philadelphia Academy of Sciences, and one of the most munificent patrons of that institution, accompanied us, or came on a few weeks later, I am not quite certain. He afterwards purchased from my father several thousand acres of the Harmony estate.

At Pittsburg, which we reached early in December, finding that steamboats had ceased to ply on the Ohio, we purchased a keel-boat and had it comfortably fitted up for the accommodation of our party, then amounting to some thirty or forty persons. About eight miles from Beaver, Pennsylvania, the ice, closing in upon us, arrested our voyage for a full month.

During that month, immensely to my satisfaction, I took my first lessons in Western country wood-craft. A dense, almost unbroken forest adjoined the spot where we had tied up our boat. I had bought in Pittsburg an excellent rifle and appurtenances, together with a good supply of ammunition. The second or third day I came upon the cabin of an old hunter of the leather-stocking school, named Rice, whose good-will I gained by the timely gift of a pound or two of excellent rifle powder. He taught me the names and qualities of the forest trees, the habits and haunts of the game then plentiful enough in that district ; but, above all, he trained me to rifle-shooting with a patience which I yet gratefully remember. Before leaving home I had read, with enthusiasm, Cooper's Pioneers, and now some of the primitive scenes I had pictured to myself were enacted before my eyes.

The eagerness with which I sought instruction, and the manner in which I profited by it, made me quite a favorite with the old man ; and, after a week or two, I was domesticated in his cabin. With his wife, also, I found favor by telling her stories of the " old country." From her, I remember, came my first reminder that I had reached a land of practical equality, in which all (white ?) adult males, rich or poor, were *men*. I had a handsome silver-mounted powder-horn which attracted the attention of one of the half-clad urchins who were running about the cabin, and I had ceded it for his amusement. He was making off with the coveted plaything out of doors when his mother recalled him, " Here, you, George Washington, give the man back his powder-horn." Later, I learned the meaning which attaches in the West (fairly enough, too) to the word *gentleman*. I was bargaining with a young fellow who had agreed to make a few thousand rails to repair a fence on one of our farms ; and, profiting by Rice's instructions, I warned him that they must be of such and such timber ; I would accept none of inferior quality ; whereupon he said, " Mister, I'm a gentleman, and I wouldn't put any man off with bad rails."

Toward the close of our ice-bound sojourn I accompanied Rice to a shooting-match. He obtained the first prize, and I, to his great delight, carried off the fourth or fifth,—a wild turkey worth twenty-five cents. I carried it home in triumph to our keel-boat.

Soon after the middle of January, 1826, we reached Harmony. In the next paper is given the recital of what I found there.

PAPER IX.

MY EXPERIENCE OF COMMUNITY LIFE.

BEFORE I left England, in 1825, the facts already stated connected with the enormously increased power to produce, coexisting with the decreased and ever-decreasing means to live, among the laboring millions in that country, had convinced me, not only that something was grievously wrong and out of adaptation to the new industrial aspect of things, but that the essential remedy for the suffering which I witnessed around me was, as my father declared it to be, the substitution of co-operative industry for competitive labor ; and I jumped to the conclusion that, under a system of co-operation, men would speedily be able, by three or four hours of easy labor each day, to supply themselves with all the necessaries and comforts of life which reasonable creatures could desire. Nay, with Utopian aspirations, I looked forward to the time when riches, because of their superfluity, would cease to be the end and aim of man's thoughts, plottings, lifelong toilings ; when the mere possession of wealth would no longer confer distinction, any more than does the possession of water, than which there is no property of greater worth.

To-day, with half a century of added experience, I think, indeed, that invaluable truths underlie these opinions ; but I think also that I much erred in judging one branch of a great social subject without sufficient reference to other collateral branches ; and that I still more gravely erred in leaving out of view a main, practical ingredient in all successful changes, namely, the element of *time*.

The human race, by some law of its being, often possesses powers in advance—sometimes ages in advance— of capacity to employ them. Alfred Wallace, in a late work on Natural Selection, reminds us that the oldest human skulls yet discovered are not materially smaller than those of our own times : a Swiss skull of the stone age corresponds to that of a Swiss youth of the present day ; the Neanderthal skull has seventy-five cubic inches of brain-space ; and the Engis skull (perhaps the oldest known) is regarded by Huxley as " a fair average skull, that might have belonged to a philosopher." Wallace's inference is that man, especially in his savage state, " possesses a brain quite disproportionate to his actual requirements,—an organ that seems prepared in advance only to be fully utilized as he progresses in civilization." *

So also I think it is in regard to man's industrial powers. He has acquired these in advance of the capacity to take advantage of them, except to a limited extent. The various departments of human progress must go forward, in a measure, side by side. Material,

---

* Contributions to the Theory of Natural Selection, by Alfred Russell Wallace, author of the Malay Archipelago, etc., London and New York, 1870, p. 343.

Mr. Wallace adds : " A brain slightly larger than that of the gorilla (which is thirty to thirty-four cubic inches) would, according to the evidence before us, have fully sufficed for the mental development of the savage."

Size of brain is the chief, though not the sole, element which determines mental power. An adult male European with less than sixty-five cubic inches of brain is invariably idiotic.

even intellectual, progress brings scanty result, unless moral and spiritual progress bear it company.

I still think it *is* true that social arrangements can be devised under which all reasonable necessaries and comforts could be secured to a nation, say by three hours' daily work of its able-bodied population. But, in the present state of moral culture, would that result, in this or any civilized country, be a benefit? Would leisure, throughout three-fourths of each day, be a blessing to uneducated or half-educated men? If such leisure were suddenly acquired by the masses, would life and property be safe? Think of the temptations of intemperance! Some of the reports even from the eight-hour experiment are discouraging.

Then, as to the popular worship of wealth,—characteristic of a period of transition or half-civilization,—that cannot be suddenly corrected. The gallants of Queen Elizabeth's day sought distinction by the help of rich velvets slashed with satin, costly laces, trussed points, coats heavy with embroidery. It would have been vain, in those days, to take them to task about their finery. It has now disappeared, even to its last lingering remnant, the lace ruffle at the wrist; but common-sense had to work for centuries, ere men were satisfied to trust, for distinction, to something better than gaudy apparel.

I still think that co-operation *is* a chief agency destined to quiet the clamorous conflicts between capital and labor; but then it must be co-operation gradually introduced, prudently managed, as now in England. I think, too, that such co-operation, aside from its healthy pecuniary results, tends to elevate character. Evidence of this, ever multiplying, comes daily to light. I have just received a paper on that subject by Thomas Hughes, published in Macmillan's Magazine, in which the writer says : " It is impossible to bring before you, in the space I have at my disposal, anything like proofs of a tithe of the good which the co-operative movement has done ; how it is steadily strengthening and purifying the daily lives of a great section of our people." From his own observation and that of a Mr. Ludlow, who, he says, " has had as much experience in this matter as any living man," Mr. Hughes states :

That the co-operative system, founded scrupulously on ready-money dealings, delivers the poor from the credit system.

That, if a co-operative workshop has elements of vitality sufficient to weather the first few years' struggles, it is found to expel drunkenness and disorder, as inconsistent with success ; to do away with the tricks and dishonesties of work, now frequent between employers and employed ; to bring about fixity of employment ; to create new ties, new forms of fellowship, even a sort of family feeling, between man and man ; and thus, after a time, to develop a new type of workingmen, characterized " not only by honesty, frankness, kindness, and true courtesy, but by a dignity, a self-respect, and a consciousness of freedom which only this phase of labor gives."

The writer met with such a type first in the *Associations Ouvrières* of Paris, and confidently regards it as " a normal result of co-operative production."

Finally, as co-operative producers and consumers have a common interest, this system shuts out adulteration in articles of food, and dishonest deterioration of goods in general, whether caused by faulty workmanship or by employing worthless materials.

A point of vast importance, this last ! The debasement of quality which, under the pressure of competition, has gradually extended of late years to almost every article used by man, is notorious. Yet as few persons except the initiated realize the immense loss to society from this source, an illustrative experience of my own may here be welcome.

When my father left me manager of the New Lanark cotton-mills, in the winter of 1824–25, a certain Mr. Bartholomew, who had long been a customer of ours to the extent of twenty-five or thirty thousand dollars a year, came to me one day, asking if I could make him a lot of yarn suitable for ordinary shirting, at such a price, naming it. " We have but one price," I said, " and you know well that we sell such yarn twenty per cent. above the rate you propose."

" I know that," he replied ; " but you *could* make it, so as to be sold at my price."

" Yes, by using waste and mixing in weak, short-stapled cotton."

" And it would look almost as well ? "

" Perhaps."

" Then I'll risk it."

" My father's instructions," I replied, " are not to lower the quality of our goods. I'm sorry ; but I can't fill your order."

He went off in a huff, but returned two days later. " See here," he said, " don't be Quixotic. I can have the yarn I asked you about spun elsewhere. What's the use of driving a good customer from you ? I shall get the stuff I want, and use it, all the same."

" It would injure the character of our mill."

" Not if you leave off your trade-mark. What do I care about the picture ? * Mark it as you will."

I hesitated ; and finally—not much to my credit—agreed to make the yarn for him. I had it marked with a large B. " It will stand either for Bartholomew or for *bad*," I said to him when he came to look at it. " I'm ashamed to turn such an article out of our mill."

But three weeks later he came again. " Just the thing ! " he said ; and he gave me a second order, thrice as large as the first.

The B yarn became a popular article in the market ; the shirting that was made from it looking smooth, and being sold at some ten per cent. less than that made from our usual quality. Yet, to my certain knowledge,—for I tried it,—it did not last half as long as the other.

That transaction sits somewhat heavily on my conscience still. Yet it helped to teach me a great lesson. It is my firm belief that, at the present time, purchasers of cotton, woollen, linen, and silk goods, of furniture, hardware, leather goods, and all other manufactured staples *lose*, on the average, because of inferior quality, *more than half of all the money they pay out.* And I doubt whether, except by co-operation, this crying evil can be remedied.

When I reached Harmony, early in 1826, these general ideas ruled in my mind, untempered by the " sober second-thoughts " which an after-life brought with it. I looked at everything with eyes of enthusiasm ; and, for a time, the life there was wonderfully pleasant and

* On each ten-pound package we were wont to paste an engraving of the mills and village ; and our yarn, in consequence, went far and near, by the name of " picture-yarn."

hopeful to me. This, I think, is the common experience of intelligent and well-disposed persons who have
joined the Brook Farm or other reputable community.
There is a great charm in the good-fellowship and in
the absence of conventionalism which characterize such
associations.

Then there was something especially taking—to me
at least—in the absolute freedom from trammels, alike
in expression of opinion, in dress, and in social converse, which I found there. The evening gatherings,
too, delighted me; the weekly meetings for discussion
of our principles, in which I took part at once; the
weekly concert, with an excellent leader, Josiah War-
ren, and a performance of music, instrumental and vocal, much beyond what I had expected in the back-
woods; last, not least, the weekly ball, where I found
crowds of young people, bright and genial if not specially cultivated, and as passionately fond of dancing
as, in those days, I myself was.

The accommodations seemed to me, indeed, of the
rudest, and the fare of the simplest; but I cared no
more for that than young folks usually care who forsake
pleasant homes to spend a summer month or two under
canvas,—their tents on the beach, perhaps, with boats
and fishing-tackle at command; or pitched in some syl-
van retreat, where youth and maiden roam the forest all
day, returning at nightfall to merry talk, improvised
music, or an impromptu dance on the greensward.

I shrank from no work that was assigned to me; and
sometimes, to the surprise of my associates, volunteered
when a hard or disagreeable job came up, as the pulling
down of sundry dreadfully dusty and dilapidated cabins
throughout the village; but, after a time, finding that

others could manage as much common labor in one
day as I in two or three, and being invited to take general charge of the school and to aid in editing the
weekly paper, I settled down to what, I confess, were
more congenial pursuits than wielding the axe or holding the plough-handles.

I had previously tried one day of sowing wheat by
hand, and held out till evening; but my right arm was
comparatively useless for forty-eight hours after. Another day, when certain young girls, who were baking
bread for one of the large boarding-houses, lacked an
additional hand, I offered to help them; but when the
result of my labors came to the table, it was suggested
that one of the loaves should be voted to me as a gift for
my diligence; the rather, as, by a little manipulation,
such as apothecaries use in making pills, it might save
me the trouble of casting bullets the next time I went
out rifle-shooting.

To atone for these and similar mishaps, I sometimes
succeeded where others had failed. When I first took
charge of the school, finding that the teachers occasionally employed corporal punishment, I strictly forbade it.
After a time the master of the eldest boys' class said to
me one day, " I find it is impossible to control these
unruly rascals. They know I am not allowed to flog
them; and when I seek to enforce rules of order, they
defy me."

I sought to show him how he might manage them
without the rod, but he persisted: " If you'd try it
yourself for a few days, Mr. Owen, you'd find out that
I'm right."

" Good," said I. " I'll take them in hand for a week
or two."

They *were* a rough, boisterous, lawless set; bright enough, quick of observation; capable of learning when they applied themselves; but accustomed to a free swing, and impatient of discipline to which they had never been subjected. I said to them, at the start, " Boys, I want you to learn; you'll be very sorry, when you come to be men, if you don't. But you can't learn anything worth knowing, without rules to go by. I must have you orderly and obedient. I won't require from you anything unreasonable; and I don't intend to be severe with you. But whatever I tell you, *has* to be done, and *shall* be done, sooner or later." Here I observed on one or two bold faces a smile that looked like incredulity; but all I added was, " You'll save time, if you do it at once."

My lessons, often oral, interested them, and things went on quietly for a few days. I knew the crisis would come. It did, in this wise. It was May, the thermometer ranging toward ninety, and I resolved to take the class to bathe in the Wabash, much to their delight. I told them, in advance, that by the doctor's advice, they were to remain in the water fifteen minutes only: that was the rule. When I called, " Time up!" they all came out, somewhat reluctantly however, except one tall fellow, named Ben, a good swimmer, who detained us ten minutes more, notwithstanding my order, several times repeated, to come on shore.

I said nothing about it till we returned to the school-room; then I asked the class, " Do you remember my saying to you that whatever I told you to do had to be done sooner or later?" They looked at Ben, and said, " Yes." Then I went on: " I am determined that if I take you to bathe again, you shall stay in fifteen minutes only. How do you think I can best manage that ?" They looked at Ben again, and seemed puzzled ; never, very surely, having been asked such a question before. "Has no one any plan ?" I said.

At length a youngster suggested, "I guess you'd better thrash him, Mr. Owen."

"I don't wish to do that," I replied ; "I think it does boys harm. Besides, I never was whipped myself, I never whipped anybody, and I know it must be a very unpleasant thing to do. Can't some of you think of a better plan ?"

One of the class suggested, "There's a closet in the garret, with a stout bolt to it. You might shut him up there till we get back."

"That's better than flogging ; but is the closet dark ?"

"It's dark as hell."

"You mustn't talk so, my child. You can't tell whether there is such a place as hell at all. You mean that the closet is quite dark, don't you ?"

"Yes."

"Then you ought to say so. But I think Ben would not like to be shut up in the dark for nearly an hour."

"No ; but then *we* don't like to be kept from bathing just for him."

Then one little fellow, with some hesitation, put in his word : "Please, Mr. Owen, wouldn't it do to leave him in the playground ?"

"If I could be sure that he would stay there ; but he might get out and go bathing, and remain in half an hour perhaps."

At this point, Ben, no longer able to restrain himself,—he had been getting more and more restless, turn-

ing first to one speaker, then to another, as we coolly
discussed the case,—burst forth : " Mr. Owen, if you
leave me in the playground when they go to bathe next
time, I'll never stir from it. I won't. You'll see I
won't."

" Well, Ben," said I, " I've never known you to tell
a falsehood, and I'll take your word for it this time. But
remember ! If you lie to me once, I shall never be able
to trust you again. We couldn't believe known liars if
we were to try."

So the next time we went bathing, I left Ben in the
playground. When we returned he met me, with eager
face, at the gate. " I never left even for a minute ; ask
them if I have," pointing to some boys at play.

" Your word is enough. I believe you."

Thereafter Ben came out of the water promptly as
soon as time was called ; and when any of his comrades
lingered, he was the first to chide them for disobeying
orders.

Once or twice afterwards I had to take a somewhat
similar stand (never against Ben), persisting each time
until I was obeyed. Then bethinking me of my Hofwyl
experience, I called in the aid of a military drill, which
the boys took to very kindly ; and when three weeks had
passed, I found that my pupils prided themselves in being—what, indeed, they were—the best disciplined and
most orderly and law-abiding class in the school.

So I carried my point against a degrading relic of
barbarism, then countenanced in England, alike in
army, navy, and some of the most accredited semi-
naries. I had witnessed an example, the year before, in
London, during a visit to the central school of Dr. Bell,
the rival of Lancaster, patronized by the Anglican

Church.   A class were standing up, for arithmetic.
" Seven times eight are fifty-six," said one boy.   " *Is*,
not *are*," sternly cried the teacher, dealing the offender
such a buffet on the ear that he staggered and finally
dropped to the ground ; then adding : " Get up ! Now
perhaps you'll remember that, another time."   But
whether it was the blow or the bit of doubtful grammar
he was bidden to remember seemed not very clear.

I still recollect how my nature revolted against this
outrage,—for such it appeared to me.   " Father," said
I, as we left the room, " I'm very sorry you gave any
money to this school."   He smiled and apologized for
the teacher, saying, " The man had probably been
treated in the same manner when he was a child, and so
knew no better."   My father had, some time before,
subscribed two thousand five hundred dollars in aid of
the Bell system ; offering to double that sum if Dr. Bell
would open his schools to the children of dissenters.
But this the ex-chaplain or his committee had refused to
do.

On the whole, my life in Harmony, for many months,
was happy and satisfying.   To this the free and simple
relation there existing between youth and maiden much
contributed.   We called each other by our Christian
names only, spoke and acted as brothers and sisters
might ; often strolled out by moonlight in groups,
sometimes in single pairs ; yet, withal, no scandal or
other harm came of it, either then or later, unless we
are to reckon as such a few improvident or unsuited
matches, that turned out poorly, as hasty love-matches
will.   What might have happened to myself amid such
familiar surroundings, if my heart had not been preoc-
cupied, I cannot tell.   I met almost daily, handsome,

interesting, warm-hearted girls ; bright, merry, and un-sophisticated ; charming partners at ball or picnic : one especially, who afterwards married a son of Oliver Evans, the celebrated inventor and machinist, to whom, I believe, we owe the high-pressure engine. But this girl, many years since dead, and others both estima-ble and attractive, were to me, engrossed by recollec-tions of Jessie, but as favorite sisters.

Naturally enough, under such circumstances, I was not haunted by doubts as to the success of the social experiment in which we were engaged. The inhabi-tants seemed to me friendly and well-disposed. There was much originality of character, and there were some curious eccentricities ; but nothing to match the Page of Nature, who had so startled Captain McDonald and myself at New York.

One example occurs to me,—an old man named Greenwood, father of Miles Greenwood, well-known afterwards to the citizens of Cincinnati as chief of their Fire Department, and still later as owner of the largest foundry and machine-shop then in the West. We had, during the summer of 1826, several terrific thunder-storms such as I had never before witnessed. The steeple of our church was shattered and one of our boarding-houses struck. It was during one of these storms, when the whole heavens seemed illuminated and the rain was falling in torrents, that I saw old Greenwood, thoroughly drenched, and carrying, up-right as a soldier does his musket, a slender iron rod, ten or twelve feet long. He was walking in the middle of the street, passed with slow step the house in which I was, and, as I afterwards learned, paraded every street in the village in the same deliberate manner. Next day

I met him and asked an explanation. "Ah, well, my young friend," said he, "I'm very old; I'm not well; I suffer much : and I thought it might be a good chance to slip off and be laid quietly in a corner of the peach orchard."*

"You hoped to be struck by lightning?"

"You see, I don't like to kill myself—seems like taking matters out of God's hands. But I thought He might perhaps send me a spare bolt when I put myself in the way. If he had only seen fit to do it, I'd then have been at rest this very minute; all my pains gone; no more trouble to any one, and no more burden to myself."

"You don't know how useful you may be yet, Mr. Greenwood."

"Under the green grass would have been better; but it wasn't to be, just yet."

In the educational department we had considerable talent, mixed with a good deal of eccentricity. We had a Frenchman, patronized by Mr. Maclure, a M. Phiquepal d'Arusmont, who became afterwards the husband of Frances Wright; a man well informed on many points, full of original ideas, some of practical value, but, withal, a wrong-headed genius, whose extravagance and wilfulness and inordinate self-conceit destroyed his usefulness. He had a small school, but it was a failure; he gained neither the good-will nor the respect of his pupils.

Another, of a very different stamp, was Professor Joseph Neef, from Pestalozzi's in Switzerland. Simple,

* Where a temporary cemetery had been opened; the Germans having reserved their graveyard, and stipulated that no one should be buried there.

straightforward, and cordial, a proficient in modern languages, a good musician, he had brought with him from Pestalozzi's institution at Iverdun an excellent mode of teaching. To his earlier life, as an officer under Napoleon, was due a blunt, off-hand manner and an abrupt style of speech, enforced, now and then, with an oath—an awkward habit for a teacher, which I think he tried ineffectually to get rid of. One day, when I was within hearing, a boy in his class used profane language. " Youngster," said Neef to him, " you mustn't swear. It's silly, and it's vulgar, and it means nothing. Don't let me hear you do so again."

" But, Mr. Neef," said the boy, hesitating, and looking half frightened, " if—if it's vulgar and wrong to swear, why—"

" Well, out with it! Never stop when you want to say anything : that's another bad habit. You wished to know why—"

" Why you swear yourself, Mr. Neef ? "

" Because I'm a d—d fool. Don't you be one, too."

With all his roughness, the good old man was a general favorite alike with children and adults. Those whose recollections of Harmony extend back thirty years preserve a genial remembrance of him walking about in the sun of July or August, in linen trousers and shirt, always bareheaded, sometimes barefooted, with a grandchild in his arms, and humming to his infant charge some martial air, in a wonderful bass voice, which, it was said, enabled him, in his younger days, when giving command to a body of troops, to be distinctly heard by ten thousand men.

We had, at this time, in the educational department, a good many persons of literary and scientific ability.

But dissensions crept in among them, and several, including Dr. Troost, finally left the place. Mr. Lesueur, however, remained many years, and Thomas Say settled in Harmony, where he spent his time in preparing his beautifully illustrated work on American Entomology, dying there in 1834.

I think my father must have been as well pleased with the condition of things at New Harmony, on his arrival there, as I myself was. At all events, some three weeks afterwards, he disclosed to me his intention to propose to the Harmonites that they should at once form themselves into a Community of Equality, based on the principle of common property. This took me by surprise, knowing, as I did, that when the preliminary society had been established, nine months before, he had recommended that this novitiate should continue two or three years, before adventuring the next and final step.

It was an experiment attended with great hazard. Until now the executive committee had estimated the value of each person's services, and given all persons employed respectively credit for the amount, to be drawn out by them in produce or store goods. But under the new constitution, all members, according to their ages, not according to the actual value of their services, were to be "furnished, as near as can be, with similar food, clothing, and education; and, as soon as practicable, to live in similar houses, and in all respects to be accommodated alike." Also the real estate of the association was to be "held in perpetual trust forever for the use of the Community;" persons leaving the society to forfeit all interest in the original land, but to have claim for "a just proportion of the

value of any real estate acquired during their member-
ship." The power of making laws was vested in the
Assembly, which consisted of all the resident adult
members of the Community. There was an Executive
Council, having superintendence and empowered to
" carry into effect all general regulations ; " but the
Council was subject at all times to any directions expressed by a majority of the Assembly, and communicated by the clerk of the Assembly to the Secretary of
the Council." * After the first formation of the Community, the assent of a majority of the Assembly was
necessary to admit a member.

Liberty, equality, and fraternity, in downright earnest! It found favor with that heterogeneous collection
of radicals, enthusiastic devotees to principle, honest
latitudinarians, and lazy theorists, with a sprinkling of
unprincipled sharpers thrown in.

A committee of seven (my brother William and myself included), elected at a town-meeting held January
26, 1826, were authorized to frame and report a Constitution. They reported on February 1 ; and, after a few
days' debate, the constitution, somewhat amended, was
adopted on February 5. Every member of the preliminary society who signed the constitution within three
days was, with his family, admitted into the Community.
All but a few, who soon after left the place, subscribed ;
and then the books were closed.

I made no opposition to all this. I had too much of
my father's all-believing disposition to anticipate results
which any shrewd, cool-headed business man might have
predicted.

How rapidly they came upon us ! Any one who still

* For a copy of the Constitution, see New Harmony Gazette, Vol. I.

owns a file of the weekly paper then published in New Harmony may readily trace them.

Two weeks after the formation of the Community we find : " On the 19th instant " (February) " a resolution was adopted by the Assembly directing the Executive Council to request the aid of Mr. Owen for one year in conducting the concerns of the Community in conformity with the principles of the constitution." * Three weeks later, in an editorial, we read : " General satisfaction and individual contentment have taken the place of suspense and uncertainty. *Under the sole direction of Mr. Owen*, the most gratifying anticipations of the future may be safely indulged." †

It was four years after the declaration, in Paris, 1848, of a Republic, before France settled down under the leadership of one man ; but, at Harmony, five weeks sufficed to bring about a somewhat similar result. The difference was, however, that Louis Napoleon, false to his oath, and resorting to a *coup d'état*, upset the Republic, while my father conscientiously adhered to the instructions given by the Assembly to conform to the principles of the constitution. This very adherence, beyond doubt, caused his failure.

For a time, however, things improved under his management. Under date March 22, an editorial tells us : " While we have been discussing abstract ideas, we have neglected practical means. Our energies have been wasted in useless efforts. . . . But by the indefatigable attention of Mr. Owen, order and system have been introduced into every branch of business. Our streets no longer exhibit groups of idle talkers ; each is busily en-

---

* New Harmony Gazette, of February 22, 1826, p. 175
† New Harmony Gazette, of March 8, 1826, p. 190.

gaged in the occupation he has chosen. Our public meetings, instead of being the arena of contending orators, are now places of business," * etc.

This is a useful lifting of the curtain, disclosing what the immediate effects of a premature step had been. Two months later appear symptoms of doubt. My father, reviewing the proceedings of the Community, May 10, says: " The great experiment in New Harmony is still going on, to ascertain whether a large, heterogeneous mass of persons, collected by chance, can be amalgamated into one community." † Up to that time, it would seem, he had delayed to make any conveyance of the land. When three months more had passed, my father, addressing the Assembly, said, in reply to a question as to having all things, land included, in common. " I shall be ready to form such a community whenever you are prepared for it. . . . But progress must be made in community education before all parties can be prepared for a community of common property." ‡ He then proposed, and the Assembly adopted, a resolution that they meet three evenings in the week for community education.

These meetings continued, with gradually lessening numbers, for a month or two. Then comes an editorial admission that " a general system of trading speculation prevails ;" together with " a want of confidence in the good intentions of each other." §

Finally, a little more than a year after the Community experiment commenced, came official acknowledgment of its failure. The editorial containing it, though with-

* New Harmony Gazette, Vol. I. p. 207.   † Same volume, p. 263.
‡ New Harmony Gazette of August 30, 1826, Vol. I. p. 391.
§ New Harmony Gazette of November 8, Vol. II. p. 46.

out signature, was written by my brother William and myself, as editors, on our own responsibility ; but it was submitted by us, for revision as to the facts, to my father. We said : " Our opinion is that Robert Owen ascribed too little influence to the early anti-social circumstances that had surrounded many of the quickly collected inhabitants of New Harmony before their arrival there ; and too much to those circumstances which his experience might enable them to create around themselves in future. . . . We are too inexperienced to hazard a judgment on the prudence and management of those who directed its execution ; and the only opinion we can express with confidence is of the perseverance with which Robert Owen pursued it at great pecuniary loss to himself. One form of government was first adopted, and when that appeared unsuitable another was tried ; until it appeared that the members were too various in their feelings and too dissimilar in their habits to govern themselves harmoniously as one community. . . . . New Harmony, therefore, is not now a community." *

Thenceforth, of course, the inhabitants had either to support themselves or to leave the town. But my father offered land on the Harmony estate to those who desired to try smaller community experiments, on an agricultural basis. Several were formed, some by honest, industrious workers, to whom land was leased at very low rates ; while other leases were obtained by unprincipled speculators who cared not a whit for co-operative principles, but sought private gain by the operation. All finally failed as social experiments. To the work-

* New Harmony Gazette, Vol. II. p. 206.

ers who had acted in good faith my father ultimately
sold, at a low price, the lands they occupied. By the
speculators he lost in the end a large amount of personal
property, of which, under false pretences, they had obtained control.

My present opinion is that, in stating the causes which
led to the failure of my father's plans of social reform at
New Harmony, my brother and I omitted the chief
error.   I do not believe that any industrial experiment
can succeed which proposes equal remuneration to all
men, the diligent and the dilatory, the skilled artisan
and the common laborer, the genius and the drudge.   I
speak of the present age ; what may happen in the distant future it is impossible to foresee and imprudent to
predict.   What may be safely predicted is, that a plan
which remunerates all alike will, in the present condition
of society, ultimately eliminate from a co-operative association the skilled, efficient, and industrious members,
leaving an ineffective and sluggish residue, in whose
hands the experiment will fail, both socially and pecu-
niarily.

The English associations which are now succeeding
were organized under a special act of Parliament, as
joint stock companies (limited) ; all heads of families
and single adults within each being at once the stock-
holders who furnish the necessary capital, and if it be a
store, the customers, or, if it be a manufacturing or
agricultural establishment, the workers who give that
capital its value.   A small executive board, its members being themselves experienced workers, and having
moderate fixed salaries, is elected by the association, and
superintends all operations.   These superintendents are
required to visit, at stated hours throughout the day,

each department of industry, and to register, on books kept for that purpose, the exact hour and duration of these visits. Each artisan or other laborer is paid wages at the rate which his services would command in the outside world ; and is entitled, at the end of each year, when the profits are declared, to a dividend on his stock, in addition.

There are other important details, for example, arrangements in the nature of benefit societies in case of sickness ; but they would be out of place here. This slight sketch may suffice to show, in a general way, how the workman, if he can once lay up in a savings' bank or elsewhere a small capital, may obtain the entire value of his labor ; may secure permanent employment which only misconduct can forfeit ; and, besides, have fair wages regularly paid, and his just proportion of profits, deducting only the necessary expense of a judicious and economical management.

Robert Owen distinguished the great principle ; but, like so many other devisers, missed the working details of his scheme. If these, when stated, seem to lie so near the surface that common sagacity ought to have detected them, let us bear in mind how wise men stumbled over Columbus's simple puzzle ; failing to balance an egg on one end till a touch from the great navigator's hand solved the petty mystery.

I have little doubt that the English co-operators are gradually furnishing a practical solution of the most important of industrial mysteries,—the great problem how increased powers to produce shall not only procure increased comforts to the producer, but at the same time, elevate him, day by day, in the moral scale, until he becomes, as the years go on, a self-respecting, up-right, intelligent man.

That these civilizing influences should result from the principle of association for mutual benefit is according to the due order of human progress.   Animals are self-dependent and individually isolated, and so are liable to grave injury from slight cause, and are daily in peril from stronger and fiercer brutes.*   Savage man is but a step in advance of this ; and scarcely more secure than he is the laborer of modern days, when segregated from his class, and fighting the life battle, single-handed, against capital and competition.   Divided, he falls lower and lower in the social scale.   United only,—but it must be judiciously united,†—can he succeed in attaining security and comfort.   Nor need he surrender whole-some liberty in associating for common good : the English co-operative workman is far more free, as well as more safe, than his isolated neighbors.

Such considerations may palliate, in my father's case, the charge of rash confidence, and what may seem reck-less self-sacrifice, in carrying out his favorite plans.   He expended in the purchase of the Harmony property, real and personal, in paying the debts of the community

* The effect upon animals of what has been called "natural selection," says Wallace, "depends mainly on their self-dependence and individual isolation.   A slight injury, a temporary illness, leaves the individual pow-erless against its enemies."—Work on Natural Selection already quoted, p. 311.

What is the effect on a laboring father of a family, with two dollars and a half a week to support them, of "slight injury or temporary illness" ? Is he not at the mercy of *his* enemies,—abject penury, starvation ?

† Trades unions are often but disguised tyrannies ; examples of an ex-cellent principle, miserably perverted.

during the year of its existence, and in meeting his ultimate losses the next year by swindlers, upwards of two hundred thousand dollars.   Had his plans succeeded, he would, beyond question, have conveyed the whole of his Indiana property in trust forever, without value received, or any compensation other than the satisfaction of success, to support co-operative associations there.   Thus, as his property did not then reach quarter of a million, he was willing to give up more than four-fifths of what he was worth to this great experiment.

The remainder, not exceeding forty thousand dollars, might have sufficed for a competence, had he been content to live quietly upon it.   But it soon melted away in a hundred expenditures for experiments, publications, and the like, connected with social and industrial reform. He seems to have felt it to be a point of honor, so long as he had means left, to avert reproach from the cause of co-operation by paying debts left standing at the close of unsuccessful experiments, whenever these had been conducted in good faith.*

One result of all this seems to me now so little like what usually happens in this world, that, if it provoke incredulity, I think the sceptics may be readily excused.   It

* In the year 1832 (for example), there was established in London, by workingmen friendly to co-operation, a Bazaar, or "Labor Exchange." At first my father was requested to act as manager, which he did without salary, merely stipulating that no expense or risk should devolve upon him; but, after a time, the parties concerned thought they could manage better themselves, and my father withdrew.   When, at a later period (says one of his biographers), the business was wound up, "there was a deficiency of upwards of twelve thousand dollars; and when it was represented to Mr. Owen that it was through confidence in him that many persons had been led to make deposits, whose distress or even ruin would ensue if the loss were not made up, he assumed and paid the whole."—Life of Robert Owen, Philadelphia, 1866, pp. 223, 224.

relates to my brother William and myself, exemplifying the effect of early habits and impressions. Soon after our return from Hofwyl, my father had made us partners in the New Lanark mills, conveying to each of us one share of fifty thousand dollars. We bought whatever we wanted ; and, as it happened, our profits amply sufficed for our wants. Yet I cannot call to mind that I ever examined my partnership account, or posted myself as to the balance.

When my father agreed to devote four-fifths of the property that would naturally have come to us, as his heirs, to the cause of reform, neither William nor I, to the best of my recollection, expressed or even felt regret that it was about to pass away from us. Several years after the purchase of Harmony, when we learned from my father that his funds were running low, we both volunteered to transfer to him, unconditionally, our New Lanark shares. He accepted the offer as frankly as it was made ; but he conveyed to us jointly land on the Harmony estate worth about thirty thousand dollars. Engrossed with the sanguine hopes of youth and the vague dreams of enthusiasm, I believe that I scarcely bestowed a second thought on the pecuniary independence for life which I was thus relinquishing. If any one had lauded my disinterestedness, it would have been unmerited praise ; it was simply indifference, not self-sacrifice. Nor do I remember ever pining after the luxuries of Braxfield, or wishing myself back again in the Old World.

My father's intention in bringing us up thus unconcerned about money and careless as to its acquisition was kind and commendable ; it was far better than to have taught us that riches are the main chance in life, and that all things else should be postponed to money-getting ; but I am of opinion now that it was a grave mistake, nevertheless. I think a father ought to say to his sons as I have said to mine : " Money is a power for good as well as for evil. It is an element of personal independence. Do not grasp after it; yet seek to acquire it fairly, honorably, without doing hard things, especially without grinding others. Do not enter public life until you shall have set apart what suffices for a reputable living, and invested your savings with reference to absolute safety rather than to high rate of interest. Thus on solid ground yourself, you can the more effectively lend a hand to the cause of reform ; and if you are elected a legislator, or to other civil service, you can act out your convictions, without fear that loss of office will reduce you to poverty."

My father took a less practical, if more Scriptural, view of things, virtually telling us : " Seek first the good of human-kind, and all other things shall be added unto you." He protected us, however, to a great extent, from suffering while following such advice. For, at a later period, he conveyed to his sons, then citizens of the United States, the New Harmony property, his only surviving daughter being already provided for. All he required of us in return was to execute a deed of trust, of some thirty thousand dollars' worth of land, burdened with an annuity to him during his life, of fifteen hundred a year ; after that a life interest to his daughters-in-law, and the fee to their children. The above annuity was his sole dependence for support during many years of his life. We, with the means he put into our hands, might have readily accumulated an assured independence by the time we reached middle age, had we known (which we did not) how to manage and improve Western property, and had we steadily followed up the pursuit of a competency, as we ought to have done. There is more power in knowledge than in gold, no matter how large the pile.

In looking back upon myself as I was in those days, I have often wondered how far my after-life might have been affected by the judicious advice of some cool-headed, dispassionate friend; one who, while sharing many of my aspirations, would have brought the chastening experience of a long life to mould and give wise direction to them ; what, for example, the result would have been if the Robert Dale Owen of seventy could have become the counsellor of the Robert Dale Owen of twenty-five ; talking over that eager youth's ideas of reform with him ; dissecting his views of life here and his doubts of life hereafter ; correcting his crudities and calling in question his hasty conclusions.

I found no such mentor, but met, instead, with a friend some ten years my senior, possessing various noble qualities, but with ideas on many subjects, social and religious, even more immature and extravagant than my own. This new acquaintance mainly shaped, for several years, the course and tenor of my life.

Frances Wright was a cultivated Englishwoman of good family, who, though left an orphan at an early age, had received a careful and finished education, was thoroughly versed in the literature of the day, well informed on all general subjects, and spoke French and Italian fluently. She had travelled and resided for years in Europe, was an intimate friend of General Lafayette, had made the acquaintance of many leading reformers,

Hungarian, Polish, and others, and was a thorough republican; indeed, an advocate of universal suffrage, without regard to color or sex,—a creed that was much more rare forty years ago than it is to-day. Refined in her manner and language, she was a radical alike in politics, morals, and religion.

She had a strong, logical mind, a courageous independence of thought, and a zealous wish to benefit her fellow-creatures; but the mind had not been submitted to early discipline, the courage was not tempered with prudence, the philanthropy had little of common-sense to give it practical form and efficiency. Her enthusiasm, eager but fitful, lacked the guiding check of sound judgment. Her abilities as an author and lecturer were of a high order; but an inordinate estimate of her own mental powers and an obstinate adherence to opinions once adopted detracted seriously from the influence which her talents and eloquence might have exerted. A redeeming point was, that to carry out her convictions she was ready to make great sacrifices, personal and pecuniary. She and a younger sister, a lady alike amiable and estimable, had always lived and journeyed together, were independent in their circumstances, and were devotedly attached to each other.

She had various personal advantages,—a tall, commanding figure, somewhat slender and graceful, though the shoulders were a little bit too high; a face the outline of which in profile, though delicately chiselled, was masculine rather than feminine, like that of an Antinous, or perhaps more nearly typifying a Mercury; the forehead broad but not high; the short, chestnut hair curling naturally all over a classic head; the large, blue eyes not soft, but clear and earnest. When I first met

her, at Harmony, in the summer of 1826, some of the
peculiarities of character above set forth had not devel-
oped themselves.   She was then known in England
and here, only as the author of a small work entitled A
Few Days in Athens, published and favorably received
in London ; and of a volume of travels in the United
States, in which she spoke in laudatory tone of our institutions and of our people.   She condemned, indeed,
in strong terms—as enlightened foreigners were wont
to do—that terrible offence against human liberty (toler-
ated, alas ! by our Constitution) which the greatest war
of modern times has since blotted out.

But she did more than to condemn the crime of slavery ; she sought, albeit, with utterly inadequate means
and knowledge, to act as pioneer in an attempt to show
how it might be gradually suppressed.   She had already
purchased a large tract of unimproved farming land,
situated in West Tennessee, about fourteen miles back
of Memphis, on both sides of a small stream called by
the Indians Nē-sho-bāh, or Wolf River ; and she had
bought and removed to that place nine negro slaves.
Her confident hope was, to prove that these people
could, in a few years, by their own labor, work out
their liberty ; and, with a strange ignorance alike of
Southern character and of the force of life-long habits,
and of the sway of selfish motive among the rich and
idle, she was credulous enough to expect that the better
intentioned among the planters of the South would
gradually follow her example.

Miss Wright's vigorous character, rare cultivation,
and hopeful enthusiasm gradually gave her great influence over me ; and I recollect her telling me, one day
when I had expressed in the New Harmony Gazette,

with more than usual fearlessness, some radical opinions
which she shared, that I was one of the few persons she
had ever met, with whom she felt that, in her reformatory efforts, she could act in unison. Thus we became
intimate friends, and in the sequel co-editors.

Friends ; but never, throughout the years we spent
together, anything more. I felt and acted toward her,
at all times, just as I would toward a brave, spirited,
elder comrade of my own sex. Affections already engaged and the difference of age may have had their
weight ; but, aside from this, while I saw much to admire in Frances Wright, I found nothing to love.

Whether I was ever Quixotic enough to believe that
her experiment at Nashoba (so she named her plantation) would, to any appreciable extent, promote negro
emancipation, I cannot now call to mind. I think that
the feature in her plan which chiefly attracted me was
her proposal there to collect, from among the cultivated
classes of England and America, a few kindred spirits
who should have their small, separate dwellings, con-
tribute to a common fund enough for their support, and
spend their time in "lettered leisure." I probably
pictured to myself a woodland cottage, with honey-
suckle-shaded porch, and with Jessie and myself as its
inmates.

We learn of one of Homer's heroes, that the gods

> "Granted half his prayer ;
> The rest the winds dispersed in empty air:"

but I was less favored. No part of my Tennessee dream
was to be realized.

PAPER X.

FRANCES WRIGHT, GENERAL LAFAYETTE, AND MARY WOLLSTONECRAFT SHELLEY.

I WAS one of ten persons to whom Frances Wright, in December of 1826, conveyed the lands of Nashoba, consisting of eighteen hundred and sixty acres, "in perpetual trust for the benefit of the negro race," my co-trustees being (besides Miss Wright's sister) General Lafayette,* William McClure, Robert Owen, Cadwallader Colden, Richeson Whitby, Robert Jennings, George Flower, and James Richardson; three of the said trustees, if resident on the lands, to constitute a quorum competent to transact business.

Cadwallader Colden was well known, in those days, as an eminent New York lawyer and statesman, who had been mayor of the city. Richeson Whitby and Robert Jennings were both members of the New Harmony Community, Whitby having formerly been a Shaker with a good knowledge of farming, and Jennings an experienced teacher. George Flower was the son of Richard Flower, already spoken of; and James Richard-

---

* It may be well, in this connection, to remind the reader that, soon after the close of our Revolutionary War, General Lafayette busied himself in promoting the abolition of slavery in the French colonies; and that he purchased a plantation in Cayenne, gave freedom to the slaves there employed, and spent a large sum in their education.

son was a Scotch physician, upright, impracticable, and an acute metaphysician of the Thomas Brown school.

Miss Wright also conveyed to us all her personal property then on these lands,—farming utensils, wagons, horses, and the like, together with five male and three female slaves ; consigning also to our care a family of female slaves (four in number, I think), entrusted to her by a certain Robert Wilson of South Carolina. The conveyance of the slaves was "on condition that, when their labor shall have paid to the Institution of Nashoba" (not to Miss Wright) " a clear capital of six thousand dollars, with six per cent. interest thereon from January 1, 1827, and also a sum sufficient to defray the expenses of colonization, all these slaves shall be emancipated, and colonized out of the limits of the United States by the trustees."

The Deed of Trust, with an appended declaration touching its objects, provided also for a society of white persons, "founded on the principle of community of property and labor ; " but it is added, " No life of idleness is proposed to the whites ; those who cannot work must give an annual equivalent." Board for non-workers was afterwards fixed at two hundred dollars a year. Members were to be admitted in the first place by the trustees ; but no one was to become a member who had not lived six months on the lands; nor then without receiving a *unanimous* vote. A member once admitted was not liable to expulsion, and was entitled, in all cases, " to attention during sickness and protection in old age ; " the children of members were to be educated, till the age of fourteen, at the expense of the institution.

Details were left to the discretion of the trustees, except that a school to include colored children was at all times to form part of the plan, and that no distinction was there to be made on account of color.

Miss Wright had radical views touching the personal independence of women, whether married or single; and these caused her to insert a provision that the admission of a husband as member should not carry with it the admission of his wife: nor the admission of a wife, the admission of her husband: each was to be voted for as an individual.

For the rest, the general tone of the paper was temperate. "In facing the subject of slavery," said the founder of Nashoba, "it is necessary to bear in mind the position of the master as well as that of the slave, bred in the prejudices of color, untaught to labor and viewing it as a degradation. We must come to the slaveholder, therefore, not in anger but in kindness; and when we ask him to change his whole mode of life, we must show him the means by which he may do so, without complete compromise of his ease and his interests."

Also, "while acknowledging with pleasure, in the members of emancipating societies, the real friends of the liberty of man," she says that she would have placed the property under their control, but for essential difference between their views and hers "respecting the moral instruction of human beings." She adds: "Emancipation based on religion has hitherto effected but little; and, generally speaking, by the tone and arguments employed, has tended rather to irritate than to convince."

Assenting to these views I accepted the trusteeship; and when, in the spring of 1827, New Harmony had

ceased to be a community, I agreed to accompany Miss
Wright on a visit to Nashoba, hoping there to find more
cultivated and congenial associates than those among
whom, for eighteen months past, I had been living.   A
week later my father left Harmony for Europe, expressing his regret that, because of his recent large expenditures, he could not prudently undertake, as he
wished, to educate the village children free of cost ; but
adding that he had paid up the debts of the community,
and had left in the hands of Mr. James Dorsey, then a
resident of New Harmony but late Treasurer of the
Miami University, three thousand dollars, as a contribution toward defraying school expenses for the coming year.

At Nashoba, where I remained ten days, I found
but three trustees, Richeson Whitby, James Richardson, and the younger Miss Wright. We consulted
daily, but even sanguine I had to admit that the outlook
was unpromising.

The land, all second-rate only, and scarcely a hundred
acres of it cleared ; three or four squared log houses,
and a few small cabins for the slaves, the only buildings ;
slaves released from fear of the lash working indolently
under the management of Whitby, whose education
in an easy-going Shaker village had not at all fitted him
for the post of plantation overseer : these were the main
facts, to which it was to be added that Miss Wright's
health, which had been feeble at New Harmony, became
so much worse ere we reached Memphis that she had
to be conveyed from that town to Nashoba in a ham-
mock swung in a covered wagon. Richardson informed
me that during the preceding year, intent on organizing
her institution, she had rashly exposed herself on horse-

back during the midday suns of July and August, sometimes even sleeping in the forest at night; had barely escaped a sunstroke, and had *not* escaped a brain fever, which prostrated her for weeks, and almost baffled his skill and her sister's unremitting care. Fearing its return, he earnestly recommended a sea-voyage and a residence during the ensuing summer in Europe. Thereupon Whitby declared that, if both the sisters left Nashoba, he despaired of being able to manage the slaves: they would obey either, as their owner and mistress, and himself only when he had their authority to back his orders.

Discouraging enough, certainly! But I was then much in the state of mind in which, more than thirty years before, Southey and Coleridge may have been when they resolved to found amid the wilds of the Susquehanna, a pantisocracy free from worldly evils and turmoils and cares, from which individual property and selfishness were to be excluded; so I adhered to my resolution, Frances Wright encouraging me to hope that in Paris and London we might find congenial associates.

Finally, a loadstar beckoning me to Braxfield, I proposed to accompany Miss Wright across the Atlantic. She found an elderly Scotchwoman as attendant. We took a Havre packet at New Orleans, and after a tedious voyage, reached France in July. I had fears even for her life, till we got fairly out to sea; but after that she gradually gathered strength, and when I left her in Paris with intimate friends, her health was, in a measure, restored.

I spent several weeks in the French metropolis. Politically, it was a period of much interest. Twelve years before, the prestige with which overshadowing talent and military glory had long invested arbitrary power in France had died out on the field of Waterloo. Louis, the corpulent and the gastronomic,—

> " That Louis whom, as king and eater,
> Some called *Dix-Huit* and some *Des Huîtres,*"—

had presented such a humiliating contrast to the great Corsican that all classes instinctively felt it. The reign of Charles X., the last of that dynasty which " forgot nothing and learned nothing," commencing three years before I reached Paris, had been but a succession of plots against human liberty. In 1824 the nation had been loaded down with a debt of a thousand millions as indemnity to emigrants ; in 1826 futile attempts had been made to restore the feudal law of primogeniture and to muzzle the press ; finally, the Jesuits had been re-established in France under the title of Fathers of the Faith,—all this during the premiership of the ultra-royalist Villèle. At a review, held three months before my arrival, by the king in person, the public discontent had broken loose, as the royal cortége approached, in loud cries of " Down with the Ministers ! Down with Villèle."

The contempt with which the common people regarded Charles was expressed without reserve. " What sort of king have you got ? " said I to the driver of a fiacre, which I had hired to take me to Versailles ; " do you like him ? "

" If I like him ? " answered the man, in a tone of disgust. " Sacre ! what is there to like ? He does nothing but hunt and pray to the good God all day."

It was a terse description of the royal occupations.

The chase and the mass made up the business of Charles's life.

Ridicule, in France the most powerful of all political weapons, was brought to bear against the imbecile monarch. At every corner one could buy weekly journals filled with pasquinades and caricatures. A trifling incident, of recent occurrence, had stirred up all Paris just then, and furnished new material for fun and jest. The Pasha of Egypt had presented to the King of France a camelopard. This animal, the first of its kind, I believe, that had ever reached Paris, seemed to be the universal theme of conversation, from the most fashionable circle down to the meanest beggar. Its picture was exhibited in every print-shop window, was printed on every stage-coach. Every new invention, every fashionable article of dress, was *à la giraffe*. Its long neck and sloping body were to be seen all over the papered walls, on the ladies' sashes, on the gentlemen's pocket-handkerchiefs, nay, the pettiest retailer of gingerbread had given his cakes the same all-fashionable form.

I went to see this most popular of quadrupeds at the Jardin des Plantes. The crowd was immense, and their exclamations of delight at the movement of the creature resembled the cries of children at sight of a new toy :—" Mais, voyez-vous, elle se couche ! Elle se couche toute seule ! Elle est couchée ! Elle reste là ! Quelle drôle de bête ! " and so on, in every varied tone of gratification and surprise.

The satirists of the press were, of course, not slow to avail themselves of the passing excitement. Before the animal arrived, they had circulated a news-item, stating that the king had issued an ordinance forbidding the entrance of the camelopard into his dominions, "parcequ'il ne voulait pas avoir une plus grande bête que lui dans son royaume." Soon after appeared a caricature representing the triumphal entry of the animal into Paris, escorted by the royal body-guards and the officers of the Cabinet; and, as it was still in every one's memory that Charles, entering Paris in triumph at the time of the Restoration, had sought to win favor by publicly declaring, "Rien n'est changé; il n'y a qu'un Français de plus,"—the artist had projected from the camelopard's mouth a scroll with the words "Rien n'est changé; il n'y a qu'une bête de plus." All this probably hit harder than even the quasi-seditious cries of the malcontent multitude at the review. When Charles, three years later, issued decrees destroying the liberty of a press which thus assailed him, and dissolving a Chamber of Deputies who stood out against these and similar acts of tyranny, it cost him his crown.

But *the* event of this visit of mine to Paris was my introduction, by Frances Wright, to General Lafayette. Of all men living he was the one I most enthusiastically admired, and the one I had the most earnestly longed to see. These feelings had gained fresh fervor in the United States. Just two months before I landed at New York, Lafayette had returned home in the Brandywine, after a year's sojourn in the land which he had aided to liberate, and by which he had been welcomed as never nation, till then, had welcomed a man.

I heard his praise on every tongue, I found love and gratitude toward him in every heart. Then, too, Frances Wright, familiar with his history, had made me acquainted with many incidents in his life not then generally known; his nice sense of honor in abstaining, during a visit to London in 1777 (just before he embarked as volunteer in the American struggle), from getting any information that might be used against England,—even declining to visit her naval station at Portsmouth ; then his noble conduct to Napoleon, first refusing all honors and office at his hands ; then voting against him as Consul for life, and telling him that he had done so ; later, when Bonaparte returned from Waterloo, urging in the Assembly his abdication ; yet finally, with a sympathy for the fallen soldier in adversity which he had never felt for the Emperor while in his pride of power, offering to procure him the means of escape to America,—an offer which Napoleon, unable to forgive old grudges, unfortunately for himself, declined.

These and a hundred other chivalrous traits of self-sacrifice and of delicate generosity had made Lafayette a hero of heroes in my eyes. And when he gave me a cordial invitation to spend a week at La Grange, adding that he would call for me with his carriage next day, I was at the summit of human felicity. The opportunity of intimacy with a man who, while yet a mere stripling, had relinquished in freedom's cause all that youth commonly most clings to and prizes ! The privilege of a talk in uninterrupted quiet, during a four or five hours' drive, with a leading spirit in two revolutions ! A chance of questioning one of the chief actors in the greatest struggles for social and political liberty which all history records ! I scarcely slept that night; and well did the morrow—a bright day in mid-August—fulfil more than all I had expected !

My admiration and sympathy were no doubt transparent, and these may have won for me, from one of the most genial of men, a hearty reception. At all events, he devoted himself to satisfy my curiosity, with an overflowing good-nature and a winning kindness and simplicity that I shall remember to my dying day.

A few items of our conversation I still most distinctly recollect. One incident, presenting the Father of his Country in a rare aspect, ever recalls to me, when I think of it, the tender eyes and the gracious, loving manner which made the grand old Frenchman the idol of all young people who were fortunate enough to share his friendship.

It was just before the unmasking of the sole traitor who loomed up during our Revolution, on one of the most eventful days in all that eventful period, and more than four years after the immortal Declaration had been read from the steps of the old Philadelphia state-house; it was the twenty-fifth of September, 1780. On the afternoon of the preceding day, Washington, after dining at Fishkill, had set out with his suite, intending to reach Arnold's head-quarters,* eighteen miles distant, that evening. What would have happened had he carried out his intention, we can now only conjecture.† What men call chance—a casual meeting near Fishkill with the French minister, De Luzerne—induced him to remain there that night. Next morning, after sending notice to Arnold that he might expect him to breakfast, he again changed his intention, turning off to visit some

* At a house belonging to Colonel Beverly Robinson, on the opposite bank of the Hudson to West Point, and about two miles below.

† Washington, writing October 13, 1780, after commenting on the providential interference which saved West Point, adds: "How far Arnold intended to involve me in the catastrophe of this place does not appear by any indubitable evidence; and I am rather inclined to think that he did not wish to hazard the more important object by attempting to combine two events."—Gordon's America, 1801; Vol. III. p. 134.

redoubts on the Hudson, opposite West Point, and sending two aides-de-camp to apologize. It was while these officers were at breakfast •with the family that Arnold received the despatch which announced André's capture, and caused his (Arnold's) instant flight, on pretence, to his visitors, of a call from West Point. Some hours later, Washington, arriving with General Knox and General Lafayette, and finding Arnold gone, followed him, as he supposed, across the river, and, learning that Arnold had not been to West Point, returned to dinner. As Washington approached the house, his aide, Colonel Hamilton, who had remained behind, came hurriedly to meet him, and placed in his hands a despatch which, as confidential staff-officer, he had already opened, and which disclosed Arnold's treachery. Washington communicated its contents, doubtless before dinner, to General Knox, and to him alone, with the brief and significant words, " Whom can we trust now ? "

The usual version is that he thus communicated the portentous news to Generals Knox *and Lafayette* jointly ; but that is an error. The statement made to me by the latter, during our journey to La Grange, surprised and interested me at the time, and has remained indelibly impressed on my memory. It was this :

When Washington sat down to dinner, no unusual emotion was visible on his countenance. He was grave and silent, but not more so than often happened when recent tidings from the army occupied his thoughts. At the close of the meal he beckoned to Lafayette to follow him, passed to an inner apartment, turned to his young friend without uttering a syllable, placed the fatal despatch in his hands, and then, giving way to an ungovernable burst of feeling, fell on his neck and sobbed aloud. The effect produced on the young French marquis, accustomed to regard his general (cold and dignified in his usual manner) as devoid of the common weaknesses of humanity, may be imagined. " I believe," said Lafayette to me in relating this anecdote, " that this was the only occasion throughout that long and sometimes hopeless struggle that Washington ever gave way, even for a moment, under a reverse of fortune ; and perhaps I am the only human being who ever witnessed in him an exhibition of feeling so foreign to his temperament. As it was, he recovered himself before I had perused the communication that had given rise to his excitement, and when we returned to his staff not a trace remained in his demeanor either of grief or despondency."

In the course of conversation, another incident from Lafayette's early life came up,—that outrage alike against international law and a decent regard for humanity—his seizure in 1792 by the same Austria that, just six hundred years before, had arrested and incarcerated the Lion-hearted king—and his confinement in the citadel of Olmütz for five years in a dark and noisome dungeon. Though his prison was shared, for the twenty-two last months, by his devoted wife, yet for more than three years previously he had been condemned to utter solitude, cut off from the world, and from all outside news, whether of events or of persons. In alluding to these terrible days, and expressing to me the opinion that a few months more of such stagnant isolation would have deprived him of reason, his characteristic thought for others rather than himself shone out. "My young friend," he said, " you will probably some day be one of the law-makers in your adopted country—"

" What I, General ?   A foreigner ? "

" Was not I a foreigner, and how have I been treated ? If you ever become a member of a legislative body, bear this in mind : that utter seclusion from one's fellow-creatures for years is a refinement of cruelty which no human being has a right to inflict upon another, no matter what the provocation.   Vote against all attempts to introduce into the criminal code of your State, as penalty for any offence, solitary confinement, at all events for more than a few months.   Prolonged beyond that term it is torture, and not reformatory punishment."

I told him I should surely conform to his advice ; and when, seven or eight years later, I served in the Indiana legislature, I kept my promise.

Of course we spoke of the French Revolution and the causes of its failure.

" Our people had not the same chance as the Americans," said Lafayette, " because the feudal wrongs under which they had suffered for ages were far more dreadful than anything that is complained of in your Declaration of Independence : and these involved a lack of education and a political ignorance which never existed in the United States.   The recollection of such wrongs maddened them, and so led to intolerable excesses.   Yet, even at such disadvantage, I believe we might have succeeded if other nations had let us alone."

" Do you think that England interfered to encourage the revolutionary excesses ? "

" I am certain that was William Pitt's policy ; and when we reach La Grange I will give you proof of this."

" But was there not lack of harmony between those who, in the first years of your Revolution, honestly sought the public good ? "

" Yes ; lack of harmony and of a correct appreciation of each other's views and motives. I have often thought, since, that if, in those early days, I had justly judged the noble character and enlightened views which, afterwards, when it was too late, I learned to ascribe to Madame Roland ; and if we two and the friends who trusted us had acted in cordial unison, it is possible that our desperate struggle for liberty might have had a happier end. Even as it is, it has left inestimable gains behind it. The king, you see, has failed to re-establish primogeniture. Villèle has been defeated in his attempts to procure a censorship of the press. Our people despise the weak sovereign who misrules them, and our Chamber of Deputies holds out against him. A very few years will see another revolution ; and our past experience will doubtless tend to give it a wiser and more peaceful character than the last."

I may add here that, in the autumn of 1830, when these predictions had been fulfilled, I received from the General a letter giving me his reasons for acceding to the measures of the party which placed an Orleans Bourbon on the throne. A monarchy limited by the surroundings of republican institutions was all that Lafayette then thought his countrymen able to sustain. The son of one whose republican preferences had won for him the title of Egalité, himself educated from infancy in the humanitarian principles of Rousseau ; an adherent, at the age of seventeen and under solemn pledges, to the revolutionary doctrines of 1790 ; a faithful soldier of the Republic up to 1793 ; finally, trained

from that time forth for twenty years in the stern school
of adversity,—it seemed as if Louis Philippe, direct de-
scendant of Louis XIV. though he was, might here be
the right man in the right place.   Yet Lafayette (so he
wrote to me) accepted him with reluctance, as a step-
ping-stone, which even then he did not fully trust, to
something better in the future.   " On the thirty-first of
July," he added, " when I presented him to the people
from a balcony of the Hôtel de Ville, as Lieutenant-
General of the kingdom, I never said, as the newspapers
made me say, 'Voilà la meilleure des républiques !'"
He did but surrender his own political preferences to
what he regarded as the necessity of the hour ; and it is
well known that a programme of government, agreed
upon between Lafayette and Louis Philippe before the
latter was elected king, embodied provisions far more
liberal than any which were ever carried into practice
during his reign.   Little wonder that the miscalled
" citizen king" rejoiced, as he notoriously did, when
the man to whom he virtually owed his throne resigned
in disgust his commission as commander of the National
Guards.

The day after we arrived, the General fulfilled his
promise by showing me various letters, intercepted
during the Reign of Terror, which afforded conclusive
evidence that the British government had, throughout
France, secret emissaries, paid to originate, or encourage, the very atrocities which brought reproach on the
republican cause.   He kindly gave me one of these letters, which I kept for many years, but finally lost
through the carelessness of a friend to whom I had lent
it.   It was addressed to the president of the revolutionary committee at St. Omer, stating that Mr. Pitt had

been well pleased with his action so far, and that he should soon have an additional remittance for his services. Among other recommendations, it contained, I remember, this, " Women and priests are the safest persons to work upon and take into your pay."

Lafayette's beautiful country-seat is too well known to justify any elaborate description here. The château struck me as a fine specimen of the old French castle, built on three sides of a quadrangle, and surrounded by a moat which modern convenience had converted into a fish-pond. The park had evidently been laid out by an English landscape gardener, and with much taste ; a beautiful lawn around the castle was dotted with clumps of trees of every variety of foliage, some of which had been planted by the General's own hand. Beyond was a farm of some four hundred acres under excellent culture. The offices, which were extensive and neatly kept, contained folds for a flock of a thousand merinos ; and in the cow-houses we found a numerous collection of the best breeds, French, Swiss, and English, the latter from the farm of Mr. Coke of Norfolk. America had contributed a flock of wild geese from the Mississippi, a flock of wild turkeys, and a variety of other curiosities.

At La Grange I found various members of the Lafayette family, including a married daughter, and a granddaughter seventeen or eighteen years old, Natalie de Lafayette, next whom at table her grandfather, much to my satisfaction, did me the honor to assign me a seat. She conversed with a knowledge of general subjects and with a freedom rarely to be met with among unmarried French girls, who are wont to reply in monosyllables if a casual acquaintance touches on any topic beyond the

commonplaces of the hour. She was strikingly handsome, too ; and when I was first introduced to her, her
beauty seemed to me strangely familiar. After puzzling over this for some time, it occurred to me that
this young lady's features recalled the female faces in
some of Ary Scheffer's best paintings, especially, if I
remember aright, his " Mignon aspirant au Ciel." When
I mentioned this casually to an English gentleman, then
a visitor at La Grange, he smiled. " Have you re-
marked it also ? " I asked.

" I, and almost every one who is acquainted with
Mademoiselle de Lafayette. Common rumor has it
that Scheffer is hopelessly in love with her ; at all
events, his ideal faces of female loveliness almost all par-
take, more or less, of her style of beauty."

I had a glimpse, during my visit, of a singular phase
of French life. Among General Lafayette's guests was
a distinguished-looking, middle-aged lady of rank and
fashion ; and, after a few days, I began to observe that
a young French noble, also a visitor, paid her assiduous
attention ; in the quietest and most unobtrusive manner, however, and with an air of marked respect. " Is
Monsieur le Marquis a relative of Madame de ―― ? "
I asked Monsieur Levasseur, the General's private
secretary, with whom I had become well acquainted.

" A relative ?   O, no.   He is—you do not know it,
then ?—her *friend*." The emphasis marked the meaning, and Levasseur added : " He is usually invited
where she happens to be."

" Did he come to La Grange with her ? "

" Ah ! " (smiling,) " one sees that you are not acquainted with our usages. It would have been a great

impropriety to accompany Madame. He arrived a day or two after her."

Next day the lady left for Paris ; and the day after I took my departure, leaving the "friend" still at La Grange.

If we are disposed to regard such a relation as an anomaly in refined society, we may, at least, readily detect its cause. An English lady, whose acquaintance I had made soon after I arrived in Paris, told me that a few weeks before, during an afternoon visit, she was conversing in a fashionable drawing-room with the eldest daughter of the house, when the mother, who was standing at a front window, called out, "Tiens, ma fille ; voilà ton futur ! Don't you want to see your intended ? "

" But without doubt, dear mamma. Which is he ? "

" You see these three gentlemen who are coming up arm in arm ? "

" Yes, yes."

" Well, it is the middle one of the three ; he who wears the blue coat."

As a general rule marriage is a negotiation between two families ; and, " if there be no repugnance " (that is deemed the sole necessary inquiry), the young people ratify the bargain, and the ceremony follows. Position in society, but still more frequently the relative wealth of the parties, stamps the suitability of the match. Quarter of a million livres ought to win and marry quarter of a million livres ; and, if there be birth and beauty, ought to attract and subdue *half* a million. Purses are mated. What wonder that poor hearts, thus cheated, take their after revenge ?

Young men are somewhat more at liberty than their

marriageable sisters ; but even they seldom choose for
themselves.   It is not said of a young gentleman, " He
is about to marry," but " His father is about to marry
him."   My experience, then and later, of French life in
the upper classes is, that if a young bachelor, by a rare
chance, should ever happen to originate an attachment,
it is, as a general rule, lightly felt and soon passed over.
Ere I left Paris I met at a small evening party a young
Frenchman, who, having just returned from a visit to
the United States, sought my acquaintance, and confided to me in the first half hour what he seemed to
consider a love adventure.   " It was in Philadelphia.
Two months ago I loved her much, for she was, indeed,
very well ; one might say, quite charming.   It was what
is called there a good family ; rich too ; and the parents
allowed me to see her alone several times.   I think she
did not regard me with indifference, and sometimes she
looked quite pretty.   But what would you have ?   My
father was not there, and who can tell in what light he
might have regarded it ?   He had always warned me
against a mésalliance.   Then, after a time, I drifted into
another circle and did not see her for several weeks
—de manière que la chose se passait.   But I think
of her still sometimes.   She was très gentille, and really
carried herself with a grace which one does not expect
out of Paris."

All said in the easiest tone, just as he might have
related to me a visit to the theatre, and made a confession that he was struck with a pretty little actress whom
he met there ; to a stranger, too, whom he saw then for
the first time, and never expected to see again !   It
amazed me.

These ideas touching marriage based on mercenary

motives, were by no means confined to the upper classes. Of this, an anecdote which I heard about this time may afford proof.

A certain Lady of the Manor residing in one of the provinces, more wealthy than liberal of her money, said to her favorite femme de chambre one day : " Lisette, you have served me faithfully many years. If you wish to marry, I will give you a dôte of a hundred francs."

The girl expressed her obligation for the offer, and her mistress added : " When you have made a selection, bring your intended to the château. I am curious to see what sort of a choice you will make."

Some ten days afterward Lisette brought the young man for inspection ; and her mistress spoke to him kindly and encouragingly : but after he had taken his leave, " My good Lisette," she said, " your choice may be an excellent one ; that youth may be worthy and all that ; but assuredly he is not handsome."

"Ah, mon Dieu," replied the girl, "what could Madame expect for a hundred francs ? "

Although at that time half a century had passed since America had declared her independence, and made good her declaration, some of the inhabitants of Paris had evidently not yet awakened to the fact. Soon after reaching the city I went to have my hair cut. When I sat down, the barber, stepping back a pace or two, seemed to take a survey of his visitor.

" Apparently," he said at last, " Monsieur's hair was not cut the last time in Paris."

I confessed that it was not.

" May I ask," he then added, " where Monsieur's hair was last cut ? "

"It was at some distance from here,—in the United States."

"Pardon! Where did Monsieur say that his hair was cut?"

"In the United States—in America."

"Ah! in the colonies? Are there, then, already hair-dressers in the colonies?" *

I assured him that in the United States of America many of his profession were to be found; and I hope that thenceforth he regarded us, if not as an independent, at least as a civilized, nation.

I had heard, as every one has, of the politeness for which the French of all classes are famous; and I resolved strictly to test it.

On one of the crowded boulevards I saw, one day, a woman, who might be of any age from sixty to eighty, sitting, bowed as with infirmity, over a stall loaded with apples and oranges; her wrinkled face the color of time-stained parchment, her eyes half closed, and her whole expression betokening stolid sadness and habitual suffering. I made no offer to buy, but doffed my hat to her, as one instinctively does in France when addressing any woman, told her I was a stranger, that I desired to reach such a street, naming it, and begged that she would have the goodness to direct me thither.

I shall never forget the transformation that took place while I was speaking. The crouched figure erected itself; the face awoke, its stolid look and half its wrinkles, as it seemed, gone; the apparent sullenness replaced by a gentle and kindly air; while the voice was

---

* "Y a-t-il donc déjà des friseurs dans les colonies?" were, I recollect well, the very words.

pitched in a pleasant and courteous tone. It said, " Monsieur will be so good as to cross the boulevard just here, then to pass on, leaving two cross streets behind him ; at the third cross street he will please turn to the right, and then he will be so kind as to descend that street, until he shall have passed a cathedral on the left ; Monsieur will be careful not to leave this street until he shall have passed the cathedral and another cross street ; then he will turn to the left and continue until he reaches a fountain, after which—" and so on through sundry other turnings and windings.

I thanked the good woman, but begged she would have the kindness to repeat her directions, as I feared to forget them. This she did, word for word, with the utmost patience and *bonhomie*, accompanying her speech, as she had done before, with little, appropriate gestures. I was sorely tempted to offer her a piece of money. But something restrained me, and I am satisfied that she did not expect it. So I merely took off my hat a second time, bowed, and bade her farewell. She dismissed me as gracefully as a *grande dame* of the Faubourg St. Germain might some visitor to her gorgeous boudoir.

From France I crossed over to Scotland. My readers already know how I fared there. I took leave of the family at Braxfield, and of Jessie, in the middle of October, and proceeded directly to London.

The most interesting person I met there was Mrs. Shelley, daughter of Godwin and Mary Wollstonecraft, and widow since Percy Bysshe Shelley's death in 1822 of that poet :—interesting, not only because of the celebrity of her parents and of her husband, but far more for her own sake ; interesting, too, because of the remarkable discrepancy which I discovered that there was between her actual character and all her antecedents and surroundings.

I expected to find Mrs. Shelley a radical reformer, probably self-asserting, somewhat aggressive, and at war with the world; more decidedly heterodox in religion and morals than I myself was; endorsing and enforcing the extreme opinions of her father and mother, and (as I then understood them) of her husband. I found her very different from my preconceptions.

Genial, gentle, sympathetic, thoughtful and matured in opinion beyond her years, for she was then but twenty-nine; essentially liberal in politics, ethics, and theology, indeed, yet devoid alike of stiff prejudice against the old or ill-considered prepossession in favor of the new; and, above all, womanly, in the best sense, in every sentiment and instinct; she impressed me also as a person with warm social feelings, dependent for happiness on loving encouragement; needing a guiding and sustaining hand.

I felt all this, rather than reasoned it out, during our too brief acquaintance; and few women have ever attracted me so much in so short a time. Had I remained in London I am sure we should have been dear friends. She wrote me several charming letters to America.

In person, she was of middle height and graceful figure. Her face, though not regularly beautiful, was comely and spiritual, of winning expression, and with a look of inborn refinement as well as culture. It had a touch of sadness when at rest; yet when it woke up in animated conversation, one could see that underneath there was a bright, cheerful, even playful nature, at variance, I thought, with depressing circumstances and isolated position.

Looking back on those days, I feel assured that if fate had thrown Mary Shelley and myself together at that period of my life, instead of bringing me in contact with Frances Wright, the influence would have been much more salutary. I required to be restrained, not urged; needed not the spur, but the guiding-rein. Mrs. Shelley shared many of my opinions and respected them all; and as well on that account as because I liked her and sympathized with her from the first, I should have taken kindly, and weighed favorably, advice or remonstrance from her lips, which when it came later, in aggressive form, from the pens of religious or political opponents, carried little weight and no conviction. I am confirmed in these opinions by having read, only a few years since, an extract from this excellent lady's private journal, written eleven years after I made her acquaintance, and which vividly recalls the pleasant and profitable hours I spent with her.

It is dated October 21st, 1838. She writes, " I have often been abused for my lukewarmness in ' the good cause,' and shall put down here a few thoughts on the subject. . . . Some have a passion for reforming the world, others do not cling to particular opinions. That my parents and Shelley were of the former class makes me respect it. For myself I earnestly desire the good and enlightenment of my fellow-creatures; I see all, in the present course, tending to this, and I rejoice; but I am not for violent extremes, which only bring injurious reaction. I have never written a word in disfavor of liberalism, but neither have I openly supported it: first, because I have not argumentative power; I see things pretty clearly, but cannot demonstrate them : next, because I feel the counter arguments too strongly. On some topics (especially with regard to my own sex), I am far from having made up my own mind."

Then, farther on, she adds, " I like society ; I believe all persons in sound health, and who have any talent, do. Books do much ; but the living intercourse is the vital heat. Debarred from that, how have I pined and died ! Yet I never crouched to society,—never sought it unworthily. If I have never written to vindicate the rights of women, I have, at every risk, befriended women, when oppressed. God grant a happier and better day is near ! " *

She did not live to see it. Ere the clouds of detraction which then obscured Shelley's fame had fully cleared away, and the world had learned to recognize, despite extravagance of sentiment and immaturity of opinion, the upright, unselfish man, and the true poet,† his widow, weary of heart solitude, had passed away, to join in a better world the husband whose early loss had darkened her life in this. She died in about twelve years after the above extracts were written.

Mrs. Shelley told me that her husband, toward the close of his too short life, saw cause to modify the religious opinions which, in his earlier works, he had expressed, especially his estimate of the character of

---

* Shelley Memorials, from authentic sources, edited by Lady Shelley (wife of Mrs. Shelley's only son, who became, at his grandfather's death, Sir Percy Shelley): Boston reprint, 1859; pp. 258-268.

† Macaulay, writing of Shelley, declared that the words " bard " and " inspiration," meaningless when applied to most modern poets, had a special significance when applied to him.

Christ, and of the ethical and spiritual system which Jesus gave to the world. With this strikingly accords the tenor of a document first printed in the volume from which I have extracted above. Lady Shelley entitles it, " An Essay on Christianity ; " yet it is, in fact, but notes, fragmentary and suddenly interrupted by death, toward such an essay,—very interesting and significant notes, however, as the following extracts, picked out here and there, but in which the original wording is preserved, may serve to show :

" The Being," thus he begins, " who has influenced in the most remarkable manner the opinions and the fortunes of the human race, is Jesus Christ. At this day his name is connected with the devotional feelings of two hundred millions of men. His extraordinary genius, the wide and rapid effect of his unexampled doctrines, his invincible gentleness and benignity, suggested a persuasion to his followers that he was something divine. The supernatural events which the historians of this wonderful man subsequently asserted to have been connected with his career, established the opinion."

Further on he says : " With respect to the miracles which these biographers have related, I decline to enter into any discussion on their nature or their existence. To judge truly the moral and philosophical character of Socrates, it is not necessary to determine the question of his alleged familiar Spirit. The power of the human mind as to intercourse with the invisible world, or dominion over it, is doubtless an interesting theme."

We may connect with this what Captain Kennedy, who met Shelley when but twenty-one years old, says of him : " He disclosed no fixed views of spiritual things ; all seemed wild and fanciful. He said that he once thought the surrounding atmosphere was peopled with the spirits of the departed." *

As to the Gospel record, Shelley's opinion was : " It cannot be precisely ascertained in what degree Jesus Christ really said all that he is related to have said. But it is not difficult to distinguish the inventions by which his historians have filled up the interstices of tradition, or corrupted the simplicity of truth. They have left sufficiently clear indications of the genuine character of Jesus Christ, to rescue it forever from the imputations cast upon it by their ignorance and fanaticism. We discover that he is the enemy of oppression and falsehood ; that he is the advocate of equal justice ; that he is neither disposed to sanction bloodshed nor deceit, under whatever pretences. We discover that he was a man of meek and majestic demeanor, calm in danger ; of natural and simple thoughts and habits ; beloved to adoration by his adherents ; unmoved, solemn, and severe." . . . ." Jesus Christ opposed, with earnest eloquence, the panic fears, and hateful superstitions which have enslaved mankind for ages."

Then, speaking of him as a reformer believing in human progress, he says : " The wisest and most sublime of the ancient poets taught that mankind had gradually degenerated from the virtue which enabled them to enjoy or maintain a happy state. Their doctrine was philosophically false. Jesus Christ foresaw what the poets retrospectively imagined."

In these notes touching Christianity, Shelley may be considered to have embodied his latest conceptions of a

---

* Shelley Memorials, p. 74.

God. These have a certain poetic vagueness about them. He says, " There is a Power by which we are surrounded, as by the atmosphere, in which some motionless lyre is suspended which visits with its breath our silent chords at will. Our most imperial and stupendous qualities,—those on which the majesty and the power of humanity is erected,—are, relatively to the inferior portion of its mechanism, active and supreme ; but they are the passive slaves of some higher and more omnipotent Power. This Power is God, and those who have seen God, have, in the period of their purer and more perfect nature, been harmonized by their own will to so exquisite a consentaneity of power, as to give forth divinest melody when the breath of universal being sweeps over their frame."

Elsewhere, after quoting the words of Jesus : " Blessed are the pure in heart, for they shall see God," he says that Christ used " the venerable word God to express the overruling Spirit of the collective energy of the moral and material world ; " and that when he speaks of man seeing God he but " affirms that a being of pure and gentle habits will not fail, in every thought, to be aware of benignant visitings from the invisible energies by which he is surrounded."

This has a certain pantheistical flavor about it ; yet not much more, perhaps, than the primitive Quaker idea of the light within, and the waiting until the Spirit moves. Shelley and George Fox, have *they* a point of resemblance ?

As to the next world, Shelley says, "Jesus Christ asserts that another and more extensive state of being will follow from that mysterious change which we call Death. When we awaken from the languor of disease the glories and happiness of Paradise are around us: evil and pain have ceased forever. Our happiness is adapted to the nature of what is most perfect in our being. How magnificent the conception suggested by this bold theory, even if it be no more than the imagination of some sublimest and most holy poet ! "

Shelley admired and hoped, rather than asserted. But the spiritual tendencies of that delicate nature cannot be mistaken. We have seen that he did not deny the " signs and wonders " of the first century ; that he declared the power of communing with the invisible world to be an interesting theme, and conceived the same idea that was expressed a few years later by Isaac Taylor, namely, that " within the field occupied by the visible and ponderable universe, and on all sides of us, there is existing and moving another element fraught with another species of life." * What he needed,—what so many strong and earnest souls have needed—was experimental proof (if, as I believe, it is to be had) of man's continued existence, and of the reality of a better life to come.

Lacking this, he still made encouraging progress toward " that tranquillity " (to use his own words) " which is the attribute and accompaniment of power ; " †
and the chief cause of such advance is not hard to find. After some stormy years of mistake and disappointment, though he never attained entire peace, though the tempest of prejudice still raged without, yet by his

* Physical Theory of Another Life ; London, 1839 ; p. 232.
† In a letter of Shelley's to Godwin, under date December 11, 1817, the words occur, in connection with a confession, on Shelley's part, that he was conscious of being deficient in the equanimity which he admired. Shelley Memorials, p. 96.

hearth, at least, were sympathy, and encouragement, and love. " Mrs. Shelley's influence over him," says her daughter-in-law, " was of an important kind. His mind, by gradually bending to milder influences, divested itself of much of that hostile bitterness of thought and feeling with which he had hitherto attacked political and social abuses." *

He knew and acknowledged this. In the whole range of poetry I call to mind no tribute from husband to wife that can match, in sweetness and power, his dedication to her to whom he ever looked as his " own heart's home," of his " Revolt of Islam." Uncertain as to its success even while conscious of its merit, he lays his poem at her feet :—

> " Its doubtful promise thus I would unite
> With thy beloved name, thou Child of love and light."

And again, a few stanzas farther on, occurs this testimony to her benign influence :—

> " Thou Friend, whose presence on my wintry heart
> Fell, like bright Spring upon some herbless plain,
> How beautiful, and calm, and free thou wert
> In thy young wisdom!"

If the Mediterranean had spared him, and if, instead of perishing at thirty, he had lived, cherished and piloted by his noble wife, to twice that age, I believe he might have borne comparison with any of the poets of our century, even though Goethe and Byron are of the number. At all events, he would, I feel assured, have

* Shelley Memorials, p. 82.

gloriously carried out what he has confided to us as his youthful aspiration :—

> " I will be wise,
> And just, and free, and mild, if in me lies
> Such power ; for I grow weary to behold
> The selfish and the strong still tyrannize
> Without reproach or check."

The heart stamps the man ; and no one ever better merited than Shelley the brief, tender epitaph which loving friends, depositing his ashes in a Roman cemetery, inscribed on his tomb—*Cor Cordium.*

PAPER XI.

THERE have been, in all ages, men destined to be
celebrated who have been called upon to bear up, for
long years—fortunate when it was not for life—under
professional contempt and popular ridicule. Among
the number are Drs. Gall and Spurzheim. Half a century ago phrenology, claiming to be a science, was refused admission as such into accredited scientific circles.

I have had occasion elsewhere to express the opinion
that the growth of a new-born hypothesis resembles
that of a human being. During its infancy its suggestions carry small weight. It is listened to with a slight
smile, and set aside with little ceremony. Throughout
its years of nonage it may be said to have no rights of
property, no privilege of appropriation. Proofs in its
favor may present themselves from time to time, but
they are not deemed entitled to a judgment by the common rules of evidence. They are listened to as fresh
and amusing, but they have no legal virtue ; they obtain no official record ; they are not placed to the credit
of the minor. An infant hypothesis is held to be outside the limits of human justice.

Thus, as late as the year 1827, had phrenology been
treated. But its very novelty had an attraction for me ;
and when, in the autumn of that year, I met Dr. Spurzheim at the house of Mr. Martineau (father of Harriet),

I listened to him with eager attention, and expressed to him, in strong terms, ere we parted, the deep interest I had felt in his conversation. He smiled, and cordially invited me to visit him in his studio. When I called he gave up to me an entire forenoon, and seemed to take good-natured pleasure in showing his collection of casts and skulls, and in explaining the first principles of his system. His candor, modesty, and simple methods of illustration impressed me at once in his favor. How devoid of pretension, how free from all dogmatic assertion, was the Master, compared to some of his half-fledged disciples whom I have since met !

He brought me the cast of a head, having taken the precaution to cover up the features with a cloth, and asked me what character I should assign to the original. I answered readily that I should suppose him to be a wise and intelligent man. Then, with similar precaution, he produced another bust, which, at a glance, I pronounced to be that of an idiot.

" You are right in both cases," he said. " You see, then, that, without any previous research, you instinctively detect the extremes. I pretend to nothing more, after years of careful study and the examination and comparison of many thousand skulls, than to be able to detect, in detail, some of the minuter indications of human character."

But, though his mode and manner won me ; though I perceived also that he was anything but a man of one idea ; though I knew it was admitted, on all hands, not only that he was an excellent anatomist and physiologist, but that his analysis of the mind—the division of its powers and attributes into the various propensities, sentiments, perceptive and reasoning faculties—evinced a careful study of mental philosophy ; yet in that first interview I was able to assent only to a few general deductions : as that the frontal organs correspond to the intellectual powers ; the sincipital, to the moral sentiments ; the basilar, to the lower propensities. I could follow him when he went on to affirm that when the mass of brain contained in the basilar and occipital regions is less than that contained in the frontal and sincipital, the man, as a general rule, is superior to the average of his fellows ; though it is to be conceded that too great a disparity indicates a lack of animal energy —often a serious deficiency. Nor did I dissent from his opinion, that, take the average heads of mankind, savage and civilized, in our day, the basilar and occipital masses of brain exceed the frontal and sincipital : a fact, it seemed to me, to which my good father was not wont to give sufficient heed.

The theory of craniology, however, in its details, struck me, on this first presentation, as vague and fanciful ; and when Dr. Spurzheim, as I took leave of him, said that if I would call on him again he would give me a chart of my head, I resolved, in partial satisfaction of my doubts, to try an experiment ; and since one purpose of an autobiography is to furnish to its readers materials for a thorough acquaintance with the autobiographer, I shall here chronicle the result of that experiment, at expense, it may be, of incurring the charge of egotism.

There was at that time in London a Mr. De Ville, a lecturer on phrenology, a man of limited literary and scientific knowledge as compared to Spurzheim, but an industrious and critical observer, who had made the best collection of casts and skulls in England, larger even than that of Dr. Spurzheim himself. To him I went;

and finding that he furnished to visitors, for a moderate compensation, a written statement of their cranial developments, I asked for mine. As soon as I received it, I went straight to Dr. Spurzheim to pay him my second visit; obtained the promised chart from him also, without showing him De Ville's, and brought both home to compare them. They coincided much more nearly than I imagined they would.

The degrees of comparison indicated were five: 1. Predominant; 2. Large; 3. Rather large; 4. Full; 5. Small. I have before me Spurzheim's estimation, with De Ville's added in parentheses whenever there was a variation of opinion, which I here copy :—

1. ORGANS PREDOMINANT.

Benevolence.
Conscientiousness.
Adhesiveness.
Causality.
Comparison. (D. V., 2.)
Firmness. (D. V., 2.)
Love of Offspring. (D. V., 2.)
Love of Approbation. (D. V., 2.)
Locality. (D. V., 2.)
Eventuality. (D. V., 4.)

2. ORGANS LARGE.

Ideality. (D. V., 1.)
Constructiveness. (D. V., 1.)
Individuality. (D. V., 1.)
Form. (D. V., 1.)
Destructiveness. (D. V., 3.)
Amativeness.
Self-esteem.
Language.

Size.
Imitation. (D. V., 3.)

3. ORGANS FULL.

Acquisitiveness.
Melody.
Secretiveness. (D. V., 5.)

4. ORGANS MODERATE.

Caution.
Hope. (D. V., 2.)
Veneration. (D. V., 2.)
Calculation. (D. V., 3.)
Combativeness. (D. V., 3.)
Time. (D. V., 3.)

5. ORGANS SMALL.

Inhabitiveness.
Marvellousness.
Color.
Wit. (D. V., 4.)

Thus, with a range of five figures indicating size of organs, it will be observed—

That thirteen out of the thirty organs examined correspond to a single figure.

That thirteen more differ a single figure only.

Therefore that there are four organs only, out of thirty, as to which the variation is more than one degree out of five, while only one of these differs more than two figures.

Four organs were set down by both examiners as dominant; namely, Benevolence, Conscientiousness, Adhesiveness, Causality.

Five were set down as very large by Spurzheim, but as large only by De Ville; namely, Firmness, Love of Offspring, Love of Approbation, Comparison, Locality.

Three were set down as very large by De Ville, but as large only by Spurzheim; namely, Ideality, Constructiveness, and Individuality.

At home, before visiting De Ville, I had questioned my conscience and set down, as honestly and accurately as I was able, my own estimate. It corresponded, in a general way, to the above; except that I had not felt justified in naming more than one organ (Adhesiveness) as predominant, and had rated the others which were esteemed predominant by Spurzheim and De Ville as large only.

I incline to the opinion that Spurzheim was right in giving me somewhat more Firmness and Comparison, and somewhat less Ideality and Constructiveness than De Ville; and that, on the other hand, De Ville was right in giving me somewhat more Hope, Veneration, and Form (especially Hope), and somewhat less Imitation and Locality, than Spurzheim. As to Eventuality (the only organ in which there was a variation of three figures), I think the truth lies between the two.

The substantial accordance between these two charts of character gave me somewhat increased confidence in the phrenological mapping of the skull.   The fact that the character thus ascribed to me was a good one may very likely have tended to influence my judgment in the same direction.   The readers of this Autobiography, if I live to complete it, will have the means of judging, to a certain extent, how far the two best phrenologists then in England succeeded, or failed, in deciding correctly in my case.

I am afraid that if the above should fall into the hands of some good people with conservative tendencies who know me by report only, it will weaken their faith in Spurzheim and De Ville's sagacity as phrenologists.   I speak of those who may have thought of Robert Dale Owen as a visionary dreamer, led away by fancy into the region of the marvellous, there to become an advocate of the wild belief that occasional intervention from another world in this is not a superstitious delusion, but a grand reality.   To such persons the assertion in which both these observers unite—namely, that Causality, or the reasoning power, is a predominating faculty in my brain, while Marvellousness is one of its smallest organs —will appear incredible.

When I come to relate, as I propose to do, the origin and progress of my connection, many years later in life, with the Spiritual movement, there will be means of judging whether my opinion touching intercommunion between two phases of human existence is based on logical premises, or is due to a love of the marvellous, outrunning practical experience and sound discretion.

Here I am reminded that, some thirty years before I myself held this opinion, I came in contact with a noted

person who suffered severely, a few years after I saw
him, for entertaining somewhat similar views. I am not
sure whether it was during the visit to London of which
I am now writing or during a previous visit in 1823, that
I accompanied my father to hear a remarkable sermon
from a very remarkable man.

Few of the present generation think of the Rev.
Edward Irving except, perhaps, as a superstitious en-
thusiast ; yet, with all his eccentricities, he was a man
eminently worth knowing and listening to. Educated to
the Scottish Church, his powers as a public teacher,
brilliant at once and logical, were first discovered by Dr.
Chalmers, whose assistant he was for three years.
Within a few months after he was called to the Caledo-
nian Church, Hatton Garden, London, he became the
most popular preacher of his day. Tickets of admission, by which alone outsiders could have a chance to
hear him, were eagerly sought after ; and the two which
admitted my father and myself were obtained as a
special favor. The highest nobility, the most eminent
men of science, literary and fashionable celebrities,
famous beauties, judges, distinguished barristers, noted
members of Parliament, all pressed in crowds to his
weekly services. We found every street that led to his
church literally encumbered with stylish equipages ; and
though we had gone early, it was with great exertions
that we penetrated the excited throng, barely in time to
get seats.

But we were rewarded. The personal appearance of
the speaker at once arrested my attention. Over six
feet high, limbs and body finely proportioned, the ample forehead surmounted by a mass of jet-black hair,
parted in the centre and dropping in curls on his shoul-

ders : the features regular and expressive, especially the
piercing dark eyes (their effect somewhat marred, however, by a squint) ; a stately bearing, and a majestic
style of eloquence, such as might befit an apostle, conscious of a mission from on high ; gestures sometimes,
indeed, *outré*, even fantastic, yet often startlingly em-
phatic,*—everything about him was strange, strong,
telling. The man himself and his weird aspect at first
engrossed one's thoughts ; yet when he fairly warmed
to his subject, and the stirring tones of a voice at
once persuasive and commanding gradually asserted
their magnetic power, one forgot the speaker and all his
peculiarities, listening, not to the words, but to the
thoughts, fiery and earnest,—thoughts, one instinctively
felt, that had their origin down in the depths of conscientious conviction.

Wedlock was the theme ; and it was treated by com-
paring with the true marriage of soul and spirit the
fashionable espousals, based on mercenary motive and
worldly calculation.

First he portrayed, in terms which lost none of their
force by quaint old turns of expression, the self-forget-
ting devotion of two faithful hearts.—"They see
through a sweet glamour," he said, "yet what they
see is more real than all other sublunary things. How
fair and pleasant are they to each other, yea, altogether
lovely ! All that is blithe and beautiful upon earth is

* The story ran that, ere he left Edinburgh, he was wont to rise in the
night, pluck the blanket from his bed, cast it around his person after the
fashion of a Spanish mantle, and study gestures and declamation by the
hour before a large mirror. Who knows what ambitious visions of future
distinction may then have been passing through the young Scotchman's
mind ?

the interpreter of their love. The voice of birds echoes
it. The flowers, fresh with heaven's dew, are its ex-
pounders. 'I am my beloved's' (the virgin saith),
'and my beloved is mine.' Her desire is unto him by
day and night ; in dream her soul waketh to his image.
He counts his life as nothing for her sake : the world of
happiness is where she is ; he has none other. Everything about her has an unutterable charm. Her eyes
are doves' eyes and they overcome him ; her breath is
like the zephyr that has swept the spices of Araby. Yet
there is between them a mutual enchantment far deeper,
more holy, than any idolatry of person. When they
stand up at God's altar, invoking on their young affection ecclesiastical blessing, the inner cry is, 'O thou
whom my soul loveth !' It is a mating of the spiritual
and the eternal. The Church but records vows long
since plighted in the heart of hearts ; and there is a
transcript of the record in Heaven's chancery. God
looks down, well pleased ; for his children have fulfilled
his law."

Much more in the same strain he said, and then he
paused. I awoke from the spell which his words had
cast over me, to a consciousness of the breathless silence that had settled down on that vast, dense audience. Every eye was strained on the speaker, and for
the moment I realized, what I had heard said, that
Irving's face, in some of his moods of benignant majesty, recalled certain ideals of Christ, as rendered by the
old masters. But, the moment after the likeness had
vanished. The benignity was gone, replaced by a
glance of scorn and reprobation. When he first resumed, his tones were passionless and stern, kindling,
however, as he went on :—

" Sometimes God has to look down on feelings and doings far other than these. I see two men, hard-eyed, parchment-faced, seated over a table, in a large, dingy office, amid dusty tomes and time-stained documents. They are doctors of the law. I hear them debating of moneys, stocks, securities, estates in tail, messuages, settlements. Each is driving a hard bargain with the other. They dispute, they wrangle, they recriminate. Of a surety their clients must be adversaries, disposed to sue each other at the law and take coat and cloak and whatever else they can clutch. Nay, I am deceived! They seem to be gambling agents, adventuring heavy stakes; for I hear the advocate of one party casting birth and station into the scale as weighty considerations; while the counsel for the other offsets these with cash in bank and great expectations contingent on a life that has already stretched out to threescore years and ten.

" What is it all about? Ah! it is a terrible desecration of sacred things. It is a laying of sacrilegious hands on that which is holy as the ark of the covenant, even upon human love,—love, brighter than hope, greater than faith; love that is more precious than rubies, fairer, in its purity, than the rose of Sharon or the lily of the valley. Two immortal souls are waiting, ere they decide the greatest of all life-questions, the issue of that miserable squabble over earthly hoards. If the hagglers who represent them can only agree, two young hearts may be allowed to set about trying whether they can manage to take a fancy for each other; or whether, dispensing with fancy as a vain thing, they will suffer to be uttered the solemn declaration that God himself has joined them together until death.   Have they forgotten that He hears and sees them ?

" Let rank and fashion take thought, ere it is too late ! Is not the heart of every creature God has made a little temple dedicate to him, consecrate to his worship ? But what shall be done unto those who profane the dwelling of the Most High,—money-changers in the Holy of Holies ? When God's Son walked the earth, what was the fate of such, at His hands ? They were cast out,—*cast out!*   Christ drove forth, as malefactors, those who bought and sold in the Temple, saying : ' It is written, My house shall be made the house of prayer, but ye have made it a den of thieves.' "

Some of the words, as they linger in my memory, I have given ; but the voice, the gesture, the ardent, fearless bearing, as of one having authority, cannot be transferred to paper. I heard, through the death-like stillness with which the closing denunciation was received, the rustle of rich silks, as if their owners stirred uneasily on their seats.

Irving's hold on the public mind was afterwards lost almost as suddenly as it had been won. Certain remarkable phenomena, purporting to be words spoken under supernatural influence, sometimes in English, sometimes in forms of language unknown, appeared in his congregation, were accepted as real and reported by Irving himself to Frazer's Magazine. They were, doubtless, similar in character to what are now termed spiritual manifestations.

Thereupon this once celebrated preacher not only forfeited his popularity, but was deposed, on a charge of heresy, by the Presbytery of Annan, his native place. Yet so sound a thinker as Baden Powell expresses, in his paper among the Oxford Essays, his conviction that the phenomena in question, though not miraculous, were genuine.*

I met, in London, several members of a very remarkable family, possessing, I think, more practical ability, administrative and deliberative, than I have ever since found united in any one household ; a family deserving well of their country, and every member of which has since made his mark, in one department or other ; the Hills, formerly of Hazelwood, Birmingham.

At that time Rowland Hill, afterwards to become one of the benefactors of his race, had removed from Birmingham and was engaged, with one or two of his brothers, in an educational enterprise at Bruce Castle, a handsome country-seat six miles from London, with extensive pleasure-grounds. There I visited them, and found some seventy students. The institution was admirably conducted, as indeed everything was which they undertook ; and I remember wishing that more of England's aristocratic mansions might be similarly transformed. A few days afterwards I met the barrister of the family (Matthew) at the Strand Club, a debating society to which he belonged ; and listened to an admirable and thoroughly practical speech by him in favor of " The Co-operative System of Political Economy ; " that being the subject of the evening's debate. No allusion was made to my father, nor to any of his peculiar opinions on theology or ethics ; and, young as I was, I saw

* " The matter," he says, " was closely scrutinized and inquired into *at the time*, and unprejudiced and even sceptical persons were fully convinced that *certain extraordinary manifestations did occur.*" (Italics in original.) He thinks "they were, in some way to be ascribed to natural causes as yet, perhaps, little understood."—Recent Inquiries in Theology, p. 122.

how wisely Mr. Hill managed his case ; refraining from
mixing up a great industrial question with any extrane-
ous matter ; thus evading prejudices and evoking a decision on the simple issue he presented.

It was ten years later that Rowland Hill brought before the public that scheme of cheap postage with which
his name is indissolubly connected, and for his services
in connection with which he was created a knight ; a
distinction often bestowed for trivial merit, or no merit
at all, but never more worthily conferred than on him :
—a paltry reward it was for eminent desert.

Some great inventions have two aspects : they speedily influence móral and social, as well as physical advancement : others, for the time, affect only the material progress of the world.   Of this latter class was Arkwright's (spoken of in a former paper), which revolutionized the mode of producing all the textile fabrics in the
world.   Of the former class is the steam-engine.   While
it drives the vast cotton-mill, or drains the deep mine,
it is a physical agent only ; but as locomotive on the
railway track, it becomes a civilizing agency of wonderful power, bringing human hearts and minds nearer to
each other.   So of Morse's invention, which tends to
knit and unite the social fabric.   Steam and the electric
wires probably saved to us our Pacific possessions as an
integral part of the Union, at a time when there was
serious risk of disruption, not between North and South
only, but between East and distant West.

But, aside from local effects, the influence of rapid
intercommunication is ever wholesome and beneficent.
It has been said, and I incline to believe, that, in the next
world, our wishes will correspond to locomotion ; we
shall be where we desire to be.   While the earth-clog

of the body clings to us, it must always be an element of isolation ; but an element that weighs upon us less and less, as the ages pass.   In modes of transit we have outgone the race-horse at his utmost speed ; we may be approaching the fleetness of the carrier-pigeon.   In the transmission of thought, bird and racer are already left behind at illimitable distance.

Similar in character was the reform brought about by the clear brain and untiring persistence of Rowland Hill. Whether, when I met him at Bruce Castle, he had conceived the idea of postal reform, I cannot say ; so far as I remember, he did not broach it to me ; but I know he communicated the details of his plan to Robert Owen before the public had an inkling of it, and that my father gave him, not only encouragement in words, but essential aid.

It created an entire revolution in the English post-office system ; relieving letter-writers, on the average, from more than nine-tenths of the cost of correspondence. Its success was marvellous, far exceeding the sanguine expectations of its author ; and that success was even greater in its social than in its economical aspect. Sir Rowland told me, I think in 1860, that the number of letters then yearly posted in the twelve miles square which then constituted the London postal district, and addressed to persons living within that district, was equal to the entire number of letters that had been posted and delivered annually, only twenty years earlier, throughout the whole of Great Britain and Ireland.   The practical result, in a social aspect, was that friends and acquaintances had been induced to converse by letter at least ten times as often as before.

One can say of Hill's postal system, what cannot be

said of a hundred other advances, that it resulted in
even greater benefit to the poor than to the rich.   A
shilling, formerly the common postage for a single letter, was the sacrifice of nearly a day's wages for a common laborer; but Hill enabled him to send twelve
letters for the same amount.   And in this case the gain
was secured without any attendant injury or risk.
Railroads and telegraphs fall into the hands of gigantic
corporations, with much power, indeed, for good, but
with possibilities for grave evil, both financial and political.   Then, too, a factory system, which brings
hundreds of young children together, in one vast, over-
heated building, offers us, it is true, cottons and wool-
lens at a low rate; but, in the Old World especially,
holds childhood's health and well-being at rate as
cheap.   The children, in many manufacturing districts,
like the young nomadic swarms in the courts and alleys
of our great cities, have no child's life; neither fresh
air, nor bright sun, nor joyous game, nor any of the
gay fancies or exuberant spirits or vaguely blissful life-
dreams that haunt happy youngsters who can roam
field or forest at free will.   I remember well how my
father mourned the change which, after forty years' absence, he found in his native place, Newtown.   It lived
in his recollection humble and homely in its ways, but
cheerful and care-free also.   No factory bell calling
little children from their beds at daybreak.   Village
ways and village freedom.   In those days they had
taken all things easily.   Saturday was, by common
usage, a holiday, when half the population, young and
old, had been wont to gather on the public green, to
watch the good old game of fives (now crowded out by
more ambitious novelties), played against the high and

wide blank wall of some public building hard by. But with the lapse of years there had come a shadow over the place. He found it a busy, bustling, manufacturing town, producing beautifully figured Welsh flannels; but no holidays, no village games, no childhood life of glee : wealthier, no doubt, by statistical returns; for census-takers do not register content, nor freedom, nor rural mirth.

Goldsmith's lines have a wider range of truth in England to-day than when he wrote them :—

> " Those homely joys that plenty bade to bloom,
> Those calm desires that asked but little room,
> Those healthful sports that graced the peaceful scene,—
> Lived in each look, and brightened all the green,—
> These, far departing, seek a kinder shore,
> And rural mirth, and manners are no more."

Thus, if Rowland Hill's postal reform has done less extended good throughout the world than the agencies of steam and electricity, it has, at least, been good unmixed with evil ; no drawback of overgrown wealth or power, often abused ; no oppression of children ; no gain for the rich at expense of the poor : and all that goes for much in a world where evil hangs on the skirts of good ; and where we have ever to ask ourselves, each time that the tree of knowledge, shaken, drops its fruit, whether mankind, for the time being, have been the gainers or the losers thereby.

I made the acquaintance, during this visit to London, of one of those celebrities, appearing from time to time, who are a riddle even to their best friends, Letitia Elizabeth Landon, author of the Improvatrice, the Troubadour, and many minor pieces which appeared occasionally (under the signature of L. E. L.) in the (London) Literary Gazette, then edited by Jerdan. Her poetry was usually characterized by deep feeling, sad and romantic ; and it had won her for the time a brilliant reputation, albeit it has scarcely outlasted the age in which she wrote. She and Thomas Moore were, in my early youth, my favorite poets ; and I had read, I think, almost every line she ever published. Great was my amazement when I met the writer ! Pretty, careless, it seemed, lively, with just a touch of flippancy in her manner, she took pains to disclaim all tender or profound emotion ; speaking jestingly of everything that savored of enthusiasm, and declaring that whatever of sentimental appeared in her poetry was but a dressed-up copy of what others had felt and expressed, and had never actually come from her own heart. The real things, she was wont to say, were good dinners, nice suppers, handsome apartments in busy London, (far preferable to the dull country !) an equipage, and all the appointments of distinguished society. I was reminded of her many years after, by a stylish young lady to whom I was introduced one evening during supper, at the La Pierre House in Philadelphia (famed for its larder), who said little until she had tasted a smoking dish which the waiter had just set before her ; but then she thawed out, exclaiming enthusiastically, " Well, this world *is* worth living in after all, as long as such tenderloin steak as this is to be had in it."

But though Miss Landon thus sought to make herself out a mere worldly character, I do not think that she really was so. She remained to the last the cherished favorite of a circle of warm and devoted friends ; but selfishness does not win and retain for itself the love and devotion of those who see it and feel it for years in daily life. She gave me the impression of a dejected woman, whose heart had been wronged, and who thought to face it out, by deriding the dreams she had failed to realize. I do not believe that she was devoid of the devoted affection she had so often and so charmingly portrayed. As Maria Edgeworth has somewhere said, genuine feeling is seldom successfully counterfeited ; the tone of simulated emotion is pitched either too high or too low, as deaf persons bawl or speak in a whisper.

I think Miss Landon's mocking spirit was the result of some bitter, unacknowledged disappointment in early life. Here and there, in her writings, the same spirit crops out, as in some lines, the concluding stanzas of which, as I remember them, read :—

> " The neck of the peacock,
>   The iris's dyes,
>   The light in the opal,
>   The April-day skies,—
>   Would they be lovely,
>   As all of them are,
>   But for the chance
>   And the change that are there ?
>
> " Breathe no vow to me,
>   I will give none of mine ;
>   Love should light in an instant,
>   As quickly decline.
>   His blushes, his sighs,
>   Are bewildering things ;
>   Then away with his fetters,
>   And give me his wings ! "

Miss Landon was but twenty-five when I met her. Her after-story was a sad one. At the age of thirty-six she married a Mr. Maclean, who had been appointed

governor of a British settlement on the coast of Africa.
Bulwer (not then Lord Lytton) gave her away.   At the
wedding breakfast a large number of literary celebrities
were present, and more than one of these took occasion
to express, in flattering terms, their high appreciation
of the amiable and talented lady from whom they were
now, alas! about to part, perhaps for long years.   In
reply the bridegroom rose, and, in the coolest tone, said
" he hoped Mrs. Maclean would deserve these encomi-
ums."   Years afterwards, Bulwer, relating the circumstance to an intimate friend,* added : " Imagine what a
shock it must have been to us!   The poor bride turned
pale as a sheet ; and not a guest at the table but deplored
her fate."

It is inconceivable how any man, with the slightest
pretension, one need not say to conjugal affection, but
to the common amenities of social life, could have
uttered the coarse, unfeeling words.   When one reads
that, after the lapse of a single year, the wife died at
Cape Coast Castle and was buried on a rude African
shore, one need not credit a vague rumor which had a
certain currency at the time, that she hastened her
escape from a wedded lot too hard to bear.   Grief,
isolation, and an unhealthy climate, acting on a frail
body and a sensitive nature, sufficiently account for
premature death.

A shudder went through the literary circles of London
when her fate was announced,—a shudder, and probably a sigh of relief and an application (one word
changed) of a well-known line,

" After life's fitful fever, she sleeps well ! "

* From whom I had this anecdote.

I spent some very pleasant weeks in London ; making the acquaintance of George Combe, whose work on the Constitution of Man had recently been published, and with whom I remember I had a long argument on what I deemed his unqualified optimism, as there set forth. I should agree with him now better than I did then.   I had previously made the acquaintance of his elder brother, Abram, a man not inferior in talent to the rest of that remarkable family, and whose early death was a loss to the world.   Pickersgill, the artist, then at the height of his reputation, I met several times ; and his daughters, at that time from fifteen to twenty years of age and equally intelligent and amiable, interested me exceedingly.   Pickersgill expressed to me his intention to paint a full-length portrait of my father ; but this intention was never, I believe, carried out.   James Mill, the political economist, I saw once or twice ; he seemed to me equally cold and logical.   I regretted much not to be able further to cultivate the acquaintance of these and of many others whose names have escaped me.

Despite their shortcomings, I like the English. Theirs is not the highest character, but it has noble elements, —energy, earnestness, hardihood, directness, great power, intellectual and practical.

It is not the highest.   It falls sadly short of Christ's standard, as set forth, in a moment of inspiration, by converted Paul.   We cannot say of the typical Englishman, that he suffereth long and is kind ; that he vaunteth not himself, is not puffed up, seeketh not his own, is not easily provoked, thinketh no evil ; nor yet that he beareth all things, believeth all things, hopeth all things, endureth all things.

Like us, their legitimate descendants, the English exhibit a self-sufficiency somewhat of the Pharisaical stamp, which thanks God that it is not as other men, or even as these French, Spaniards, Italians. They overlook the fact that less sturdy races have their compensating qualities, and that they themselves would have been vastly improved if a portion of the geniality and light-heartedness of the Southern temperament had fallen to their lot. As it is, they are estimable rather than amiable, and their perceptions of justice are quicker than their emotions of mercy.

Yet; withal, there is a ring in the metal of the English character, like that in some verses of Charles Kingsley,—verses which indicate one of the influences that may have tended to make the writer's countrymen the *plucky* race they are :—

> " Let the luscious south-wind
>   Breathe in lovers' sighs,
> While the lazy gallants
>   Bask in ladies' eyes.
> What does he but soften
>   Heart alike and pen ?
> 'Tis the hard gray weather
>   Breeds hard English men.

>   .   .   .   .

> " Come, as came our fathers,
>   Heralded by thee,
> Conquering from the eastward,
>   Lords by land and sea.
> Come ; and strong within us
>   Stir the Viking's blood,
> Bracing bone and sinew ;
>   Blow, thou wind of God !"

There is a bluff good-humor about them, too.; and even an English mob, if the Viking blood be not too savagely stirred, has a rude sense of fair play. It is to be admitted, also, that, though the aristocratic classes, with traditional haughtiness, deem the world and its chief seats their own by divine right,—or, as a witty Frenchman * has phrased it, because they had taken the trouble of being born,—yet a certain nobility of character often shines through the exclusive cloud. The *noblesse oblige*—elsewhere too often a dead letter—shows as a reality among the better portion of them. George III. introduced General Arnold to Lord Balcarras. "What, Sire, the traitor Arnold?" exclaimed the indignant noble, turning away, and rejecting, even at the bidding of royalty, the fellowship of dishonor.

The English have not the dash, the *élan*, of the French. They do not rush impetuously to reform, as did the French revolutionists of 1789. But when they do make a step in advance, they have the solid habit of *belaying*, as sailors say,—of holding on to all they have got. They would have made more rapid progress in practical reforms than they have but for their stiff persistence, especially as regards the training of the influential classes, in the old ruts. It is Dugald Stewart, I think, who says (I quote from memory) : "The learned foundations of Europe are not without their use to the historian of the human mind. Immovably moored to the same station by the strength of their cables and the weight of their anchors, they serve to indicate the

---

* " Noblesse, fortune, un rang, des places : tout cela rend si fier ! Qu'avez vous fait pour tant de biens? Vous vous êtes donné la peine de naitre, et rien de plus."—BEAUMARCHAIS, *Le Marriage de Figaro*, Acte V., Scene 3.

velocity with which the rest of the world is borne past them."

Oxford and Cambridge turn out thorough classical scholars, excellent mathematicians ; yet that goes but a little way toward qualifying a man for public service, legislative or executive. Still, for all, we would ourselves be obliged, perhaps, to go back a generation or two to find, save in exceptional cases, statesmen to match the best among England's leaders, in sound judgment, breadth of view, and yet more in probity above suspicion. The well-known pamphlet put forth by Alexander Hamilton, in which that statesman frankly confesses a grave transgression, to rebut the false imputation of dishonest meanness in his public capacity, has its bright as well as its dark side. Without extenuating his fault, we may admire his high sense of pecuniary integrity,—a sense that is lacking—alas ! in how many —among our politicians of the present day.

In alluding to the English universities, I am reminded of a story that was related to me in London, at the time of which I am writing, by a gentleman who assured me that the incident happened, substantially as I give it, a few years before. I hope it may amuse some of my readers as much as it did me.

A TALE OF ENGLISH MAIL-COACH DAYS.

An English gentleman of true John Bull proportions —weighing some eighteen or twenty stone—had occasion to travel in summer by stage-coach from Oxford to London. The stage carried six inside; and our hero engaged two places (as, in consideration of his size, he usually did) for himself. The other four seats were taken by Oxford students.

These youths, being lighter than our modern Lambert, reached the stage before he did, and each snugly possessed himself of a corner seat, leaving a centre seat on each side vacant. The round, good-tempered face of John Bull soon after appeared at the carriage door; and, peering into the vehicle and observing the local arrangements, its owner said, with a smile, "You see, I am of a pretty comfortable size, gentlemen; so I have taken two seats. It will greatly oblige me if one of you will kindly move into the opposite seat, so that I may be able to enter."

"My good sir," said a pert young law-student, "possession is nine-tenths of the law. You engaged two seats. There they are, one on each side. We engaged one each, entered regularly into possession, and our titles to the seats we occupy are indisputable."

"I do not dispute your titles," said the other, "but I trust to your politeness, seeing how the case stands, to enable me to pursue my journey."

"O, hang politeness!" said a hopeful young scion of some noble house, "I have a horror of a middle seat, and would not take one to oblige my grandmother; it's ungraceful as well as uncomfortable; and, besides, one has no chance of looking at the pretty girls along the road. Good old gentleman, arrange your concerns as you please; I stick to my corner." And he leaned back, yawned, and settled himself with hopeless composure in his place.

Our corpulent friend, though a man not easily discomposed, was somewhat put out by this unmannerly obstinacy. He turned to a smart-looking youth with a simper on his face—a clerical student who had hitherto sat in reverie, possibly thinking over his chances of a rich benefice in the future. "Will you accommodate me?" he asked; "this is the last stage that starts for London to-day, and business of urgent importance calls me to town."

"Some temporal affair, no doubt," said the graceless youth, with mock gravity; "some speculation with filthy lucre for its object. Good father, at your age your thoughts should turn heavenward, instead of being confined to the dull, heavy tabernacle of clay that chains us to earth." And his companions roared with laughter at the "d—d clever joke."

A glow of indignation just colored the stranger's cheek; but he mastered the feeling in a moment, and said, with much composure, to the fourth, "Are you also determined that I shall lose my place; or will you oblige me by taking a centre seat?"

"Ay, do, Tom," said his lordship to the person addressed; "he's something in the way of your profession, quite a physiological curiosity. You ought to accommodate him."

"May I be poisoned if I do," replied the student of medicine; "in a dissecting-room he'd make an excellent subject; but in a coach, and this warm weather, too! Old gentleman, if you'll put yourself under my care, I'll engage in the course of six weeks, by a judicious course of depletives, to save you hereafter the expense of a double seat. But really, to take a middle seat in the month of July is contrary to all the rules of hygiene, and a practice to which I have a professional objection."

And the laugh was renewed at the old gentleman's expense.

By this time the patience of coachee, who had listened to the latter part of the dialogue, was exhausted. "Harkee, gemmen," said he, "settle the business as you like ; but it wants just three quarters of a minute of twelve, and with the first stroke of the University clock my horses must be off.   I would not wait three seconds longer for the king, God bless him."   And with that he mounted his box, took up the reins, bid the hostler shut the door, and sat with upraised whip, listening for the expected stroke.

As it sounded from the venerable belfry the horses, as if they recognized the signal, shot off at a gallop with the four young rogues, to whom their own rudeness and our fat friend's dilemma afforded a prolific theme for merriment during the whole stage.

Meanwhile the subject of their mirth hired a postchaise, followed and overtook them at the second change of horses, where the passengers got out ten minutes for lunch.   As the postchaise drove up to the inn door, two young chimney-sweeps passed with their bags and brooms and their well-known cry.

"Come hither, my lads," said the corpulent gentleman, "what say you to a ride ? "

The whites of their eyes enlarged into still more striking contrast with the dark shades of the sooty cheeks.   "Will you have a ride, my boys, in the stage-coach ? "

"Ees zur," said the elder, scarcely daring to trust the evidence of his ears.

"Well, then, hostler, open the stage-door.   In with you !   And d'ye hear? be sure to take the two middle seats ; so, one on each side."

The guard's horn sounded, and coachee's voice was

heard : " Only one minute and a half more, gen'lemen ;
come on ! "

They came, bowed laughingly to our friend of the
corporation, and passed on to the coach. The young
lord was the first to put his foot on the steps. "Why,
how now, coachee ? What confounded joke is this !
Get out, you rascals, or I'll teach you how to play gentlemen such a trick again."

" Sit still, my lads ; you're entitled to your places.
My lord, the two middle seats, through your action
and that of your young friends, are mine ; they were
regularly taken and duly paid for. I choose that two
protégés of mine shall occupy them. An English stage-
coach is free to every one who behaves quietly, and I
am answerable for their good conduct ; so mind you be-
have, boys ! Your lordship has a horror of a middle
seat; pray take the corner one."

" Overreached us, by Jove ! " said the law student.
" We give up the cause, and cry you mercy, Mr. Bull."

" You forget that possession is nine-tenths of the
law, my good sir, and that the title of these lads to
their seats is indisputable. I have installed them as my
locum tenentes, if that be good law Latin. It would
be highly unjust to dislodge the poor youths, and I cannot permit it. You have your corner."

" Heaven preserve us ! " cried the clerical student.

" You are surely not afraid of a black coat," retorted
the other. " Besides, we ought not to suffer our
thoughts to dwell on petty earthly concerns, but to turn
them heavenward."

" I'd rather go through my examination a second
time than to sit by these dirty devils," groaned the
medical student.

" Soot is perfectly wholesome, my young friend ; and you will not be compelled to violate a single hygienic rule. The corner you selected is vacant. Pray get in."

At these words, coachee, who had stood grinning behind, cheated into forgetfulness of time by the excellence of the joke, came forward. " Gentlemen, you have lost me a minute and a quarter already. I must drive on without ye, if so be ye don't like your company."

The students cast rueful glances at each other, and then crept warily into their respective corners. As the hostler shut the door he found it impossible to control his features. " I'll give you something to change your cheer, you grinning rascal," said the disciple of Æsculapius, stretching out of the window ; but the hostler nimbly evaded the blow.

" My white pantaloons ! " cried the lord.

" My beautiful drab surtout ! " exclaimed the lawyer expectant. " The filthy rascals ! "

The noise of the carriage-wheels and the unrestrained laughter of the spectators drowned the sequel of their lamentations.

At the next stage a bargain was struck. The sweeps were liberated and dismissed with a gratuity ; the seats shaken and brushed ; the worthy sons of the university made up, among themselves, the expenses of the post-chaise ; the young doctor violated, for once, the rules of hygiene, by taking a middle seat ; and all journeyed on together, without further quarrel or grumbling, except from coachee, who declared that " to be kept over time a minute and a quarter at one stage and only three seconds less than three minutes at the next was enough to try the patience of a saint ; that it was ! "

PAPER XII.

CLOSE OF THE TENTATIVE YEARS.

I LEFT England in November, 1827, to take up my permanent residence in the United States, accompanying my father, who sailed for New Orleans. Ascending the Mississippi, I spent several weeks at Nashoba; satisfied myself that Frances Wright's experiment there was a pecuniary failure; received a letter from my father, urging me to come to his aid in settling matters at New Harmony; obeyed the summons, and succeeded in enabling him to get rid of certain swindlers to whom he had given unmerited confidence; spent the summer of 1828 chiefly in editing the New Harmony Gazette, and toward the close of that year engaged in an enterprise which many may deem Quixotic,—reasonably enough too, perhaps.

In those days I had not before my eyes the fear of that French dramatist, who, looking to comfort and an easy life, and thinking these to be best assured by letting other people alone, declared,

> " Que c'est une folie à nulle autre seconde
> De vouloir se mêler de corriger le monde."

I saw what seemed to me grievous errors and abuses, and must needs intermeddle, hoping to set things right. Up to what point I succeeded, and how far, for lack of experience, I failed, or fell short of my views, some of those who have followed me thus far may wish to know.

But here ends the first portion of my life, during which my home was in the Old World and in my native land. These were the tentative years, the years throughout which I was proving all things and seeking for that which is good. Up to that time I seem to myself to have been but THREADING MY WAY; and I thought I had found it. I had energy, moral courage, eagerness to render service in the cause of truth, and a most overweening opinion of the good which I imagined that I could do, in the way of enlightening my fellow-creatures. It needed quarter of a century more to teach me how much that intimately regards man's welfare and advancement, moral and spiritual, had till then been to me a sealed book ; to bring home the conviction that I stood but on the very threshold of the most important knowledge that underlies the civilization of our race.

Dating from the period which this Autobiography has reached, guided by such experience as I then had, my life was to be in the main a public one, active and stirring. Hereafter I may be able, life and health permitting, to relate the more interesting of its varied experiences ; the scene being chiefly in our own country, but sometimes on the continent of Europe.

If these shall be received with the same kindness with which I gratefully acknowledge that the press has already accepted the preceding chapters as they appeared in serial form, I shall not regret having undertaken what is a somewhat perilous task,—the writing of a book chiefly filled with talk about one's self.

THE END.